ERNEST THOMPSON-SETON

Collected Novels

CASTLE

Ernest Thompson Seton

Manufactured in the United States of America

ISBN 0-89009-936-7

The Castle logo is registered in the United States Patent and Trademark Office

85 86 87 88   9 8 7 6 5 4 3 2 1

Contents

WILD ANIMALS
I HAVE
KNOWN

CONTENTS

LOBO

The King of Currumpaw

Currumpaw is a vast cattle range in northern New Mexico. It is a land of rich pastures and teeming flocks and herds, a land of rolling mesas and precious running waters that at length unite in the Currumpaw River, from which the whole region is named. And the king whose despotic power was felt over its entire extent was an old gray wolf.

Old Lobo, or the king, as the Mexicans called him, was the gigantic leader of a remarkable pack of gray wolves, that had ravaged the Currumpaw Valley for a number of years. All the shepherds and ranchmen knew him well, and, wherever he appeared with his trusty band, terror reigned supreme among the cattle, and wrath and despair among their owners. Old Lobo was a giant among wolves, and was cunning and strong in proportion to his size. His voice at night was well-known and easily distinguished from that of any of his fellows. An ordinary wolf might howl half the night about the herdsman's bivouac without attracting more than a passing notice, but when the deep roar of the old king came booming down the cañon, the watcher bestirred himself and prepared to learn in the morning that fresh and serious inroads had been made among the herds.

Old Lobo's band was but a small one. This I never quite understood, for usually, when a wolf rises to the position and power that he had, he attracts a numerous following. It may be that he had as many as he desired, or perhaps his ferocious temper prevented the increase of his pack. Certain is it that Lobo had only five followers during the latter part of his reign. Each of these, however, was a wolf of renown, most of them were above the ordinary size, one in particular, the second in command, was a veritable giant, but even he was far below the leader in size and prowess. Several of the band, besides the two leaders, were especially noted. One of those was a beautiful white wolf, that the Mexicans called Blanca; this was supposed to be a female, possibly Lobo's mate. Another was a yellow wolf of remarkable swiftness, which, according to current stories had, on several occasions, captured an antelope for the pack.

5

It will be seen, then, that these wolves were thoroughly well-known to the cowboys and shepherds. They were frequently seen and oftener heard, and their lives were intimately associated with those of the cattlemen, who would so gladly have destroyed them. There was not a stockman on the Currumpaw who would not readily have given the value of many steers for the scalp of any one of Lobo's band, but they seemed to possess charmed lives, and defied all manner of devices to kill them. They scorned all hunters, derided all poisons, and continued, for at least five years, to exact their tribute from the Currumpaw ranchers to the extent, many said, of a cow each day. According to this estimate, therefore, the band had killed more than two thousand of the finest stock, for, as was only too well-known, they selected the best in every instance.

The old idea that a wolf was constantly in a starving state, and therefore ready to eat anything, was as far as possible from the truth in this case, for these freebooters were always sleek and well-conditioned, and were in fact most fastidious about what they ate. Any animal that had died from natural causes, or that was diseased or tainted, they would not touch, and they even rejected anything that had been killed by the stockmen. Their choice and daily food was the tenderer part of a freshly killed yearling heifer. An old bull or cow they disdained, and though they occasionally took a young calf or colt, it was quite clear that veal or horseflesh was not their favorite diet. It was also known that they were not fond of mutton, although they often amused themselves by killing sheep. One night in November, 1893, Blanca and the yellow wolf killed two hundred and fifty sheep, apparently for the fun of it, and did not eat an ounce of their flesh.

These are examples of many stories which I might repeat, to show the ravages of this destructive band. Many new devices for their extinction were tried each year, but still they lived and throve in spite of all the efforts of their foes. A great price was set on Lobo's head, and in consequence poison in a score of subtle forms was put out for him, but he never failed to detect and avoid it. One thing only he feared—that was firearms, and knowing full well that all men in this region carried them, he never was known to attack or face a human being. Indeed, the set policy of his band was to take refuge in flight whenever, in the day-

time, a man was descried, no matter at what distance. Lobo's habit of permitting the pack to eat only that which they themselves had killed, was in numerous cases their salvation, and the keenness of his scent to detect the taint of human hands or the poison itself, completed their immunity.

On one occasion, one of the cowboys heard the too familiar rally-ing-cry of Old Lobo, and stealthily approaching, he found the Currum-paw pack in a hollow, where they had 'rounded up' a small herd of cat-tle. Lobo sat apart on a knoll, while Blanca with the rest was endeavor-ing to 'cut out' a young cow, which they had selected; but the cattle were standing in a compact mass with their heads outward, and pre-sented to the foe a line of horns, unbroken save when some cow, frightened by a fresh onset of the wolves, tried to retreat into the middle of the herd. It was only by taking advantage of these breaks that the wolves had succeeded at all in wounding the selected cow, but she was far from being disabled, and it seemed that Lobo at length lost patience with his followers, for he left his position on the hill, and, uttering a deep roar, dashed toward the herd. The terrified rank broke at his charge, and he sprang in among them. Then the cattle scattered like the pieces of a bursting bomb. Away went the chosen victim, but ere she had gone twenty-five yards Lobo was upon her. Seizing her by the neck he suddenly held back with all his force and so threw her heavily to the ground. The shock must have been tremendous, for the heifer was thrown heels over head. Lobo also turned a somersault, but imme-diately recovered himself, and his followers falling on the poor cow, killed her in a few seconds. Lobo took no part in the killing—after hav-ing thrown the victim, he seemed to say, "Now, why could not some of you have done that at once without wasting so much time?"

The man now rode up shouting, the wolves as usual retired, and he, having a bottle of strychnine, quickly poisoned the carcass in three places, then went away, knowing they would return to feed, as they had killed the animal themselves. But next morning, on going to look for his expected victims, he found that, although the wolves had eaten the heifer, they had carefully cut out and thrown aside all those parts that had been poisoned.

The dread of this great wolf spread yearly among the ranchmen, and each year a larger price was set on his head, until at last it reached $1,000, an unparalleled wolf-bounty, surely; many a good man has been hunted down for less. Tempted by the promised reward, a Texan ranger named Tannerey came one day galloping up the cañon of the Currumpaw. He had a superb outfit for wolf-hunting—the best of guns and horses, and a pack of enormous wolf-hounds. Far out on the plains of the Pan-handle, he and his dogs had killed many a wolf, and now he never doubted that, within a few days, old Lobo's scalp would dangle at his saddle-bow.

Away they went bravely on their hunt in the gray dawn of a sum-mer morning, and soon the great dogs gave joyous tongue to say that they were already on the track of their quarry. Within two miles, the grizzly band of Currumpaw leaped into view, and the chase grew fast and furious. The part of the wolf-hounds was merely to hold the wolves at bay till the hunter could ride up and shoot them, and this usually was easy on the open plains of Texas; but here a new feature of the country came into play, and showed how well Lobo had chosen his range; for the rocky cañons of the Currumpaw and its tributaries inter-

Tannerey, with his dogs, came galloping up the cañon

sect the prairies in every direction. The old wolf at once made for the nearest of these and by crossing it got rid of the horsemen. His band then scattered and thereby scattered the dogs, and when they reunited at a distant point of course all of the dogs did not turn up, and the wolves no longer outnumbered, turned on their pursuers and killed or desperately wounded them all. That night when Tannerey mustered his dogs, only six of them returned, and of these, two were terribly lacerated. This hunter made two other attempts to capture the royal scalp, but neither of them was more successful than the first, and on the last occasion his best horse met its death by a fall; so he gave up the chase in disgust and went back to Texas, leaving Lobo more than ever the despot of the region.

Next year, two other hunters appeared, determined to win the promised bounty. Each believed he could destroy this noted wolf, the first by means of a newly devised poison, which was to be laid out in an entirely new manner; the other a French Canadian, by poison assisted with certain spells and charms, for he firmly believed that Lobo was a veritable 'loup-garou,' and could not be killed by ordinary means. But cunningly compounded poisons, charms, and incantations were all of no avail against this grizzly devastator. He made his weekly rounds and daily banquets as aforetime, and before many weeks had passed, Calone and Laloche gave up in despair and went elsewhere to hunt.

In the spring of 1893, after his unsuccessful attempt to capture Lobo, Joe Calone had a humiliating experience, which seems to show that the big wolf simply scorned his enemies, and had absolute confidence in himself. Calone's farm was on a small tributary of the Currumpaw, in a picturesque cañon, and among the rocks of this very cañon, within a thousand yards of the house, old Lobo and his mate selected their den and raised their family that season. There they lived all summer, and killed Joe's cattle, sheep, and dogs, but laughed at all his poisons and traps, and rested securely among the recesses of the cavernous cliffs, while Joe vainly racked his brain for some method of smoking them out, or of reaching them with dynamite. But they escaped entirely unscathed, and continued their ravages as before. "There's where he lived all last summer," said Joe, pointing to the face of the cliff, "and I couldn't do a thing with him. I was like a fool to him."

* * *

This history, gathered so far from the cowboys, I found hard to believe until in the fall of 1893, I made the acquaintance of the wily marauder, and at length came to know him more thoroughly than anyone else. Some years before, in the Bingo days, I had been a wolf-hunter, but my occupations since then had been of another sort, chaining me to stool and desk. I was much in need of a change, and when a friend, who was also a ranch-owner on the Currumpaw, asked me to come to New Mexico and try if I could do anything with this predatory pack, I accepted the invitation and, eager to make the acquaintance of its king, was as soon as possible among the mesas of that region. I spent some time riding about to learn the country, and at intervals, my guide would point to the skeleton of a cow to which the hide still adhered, and remark, "That's some of his work."

It became quite clear to me that, in this rough country, it was useless to think of pursuing Lobo with hounds and horses, so that poison or traps were the only available expedients. At present we had no traps large enough, so I set to work with poison.

I need not enter into the details of a hundred devices that I

employed to circumvent this 'loup-garou'; there was no combination of strychnine, arsenic, cyanide, or prussic acid, that I did not essay; there was no manner of flesh that I did not try as bait; but morning after morning, as I rode forth to learn the result, I found that all my efforts had been useless. The old king was too cunning for me. A single instance will show his wonderful sagacity. Acting on the hint of an old trapper, I melted some cheese together with the kidney fat of a freshly killed heifer, stewing it in a china dish, and cutting it with a bone knife to avoid the taint of metal. When the mixture was cool, I cut it into lumps, and making a hole in one side of each lump, I inserted a large dose of strychnine and cyanide, contained in a capsule that was impermeable by any odor; finally I sealed the holes up with pieces of the cheese itself. During the whole process, I wore a pair of gloves steeped in the hot blood of the heifer, and even avoided breathing on the baits. When all was ready, I put them in a raw-hide bag rubbed all over with blood, and rode forth dragging the liver and kidneys of the beef at the end of a rope. With this I made a ten-mile circuit, dropping a bait at each quarter of a mile, and taking the utmost care, always, not to touch any with my hands.

Lobo, generally, came into this part of the range in the early part of each week, and passed the latter part, it was supposed, around the base of Sierra Grande. This was Monday, and that same evening, as we were about to retire, I heard the deep bass howl of his majesty. On hearing it one of the boys briefly remarked, "There he is, we'll see."

The next morning I went forth, eager to know the result. I soon came on the fresh trail of the robbers, with Lobo in the lead—his track was always easily distinguished. An ordinary wolf's forefoot is $4\frac{1}{2}$ inches long, that of a large wolf $4\frac{3}{4}$ inches, but Lobo's, as measured a number of times, was $5\frac{1}{2}$ inches from claw to heel; I afterward found that his other proportions were commensurate, for he stood three feet high at the shoulder, and weighed 150 pounds. His trail, therefore, though obscured by those of his followers, was never difficult to trace. The pack had soon found the track of my drag, and as usual followed it.

I could see that Lobo had come to the first bait, sniffed about it, and finally had picked it up.

Then I could not conceal my delight. "I've got him at last," I exclaimed; "I shall find him stark within a mile," and I galloped on with eager eyes fixed on the great broad track in the dust. It led me to the second bait and that also was gone. How I exulted—I surely have him now and perhaps several of his band. But there was the broad paw-mark still on the drag; and though I stood in the stirrup and scanned the plain I saw nothing that looked like a dead wolf. Again I followed—to find now that the third bait was gone—and the king-wolf's track led on to the fourth, there to learn that he had not really taken a bait at all, but had merely carried them in his mouth. Then having piled the three on the fourth, he scattered filth over them to express his utter contempt for my devices. After this he left my drag and went about his business with the pack he guarded so effectively.

This is only one of the many similar experiences which convinced me that poison would never avail to destroy this robber, and though I continued to use it while awaiting the arrival of the traps, it was only because it was meanwhile a sure means of killing many prairie wolves and other destructive vermin.

About this time there came under my observation an incident that will illustrate Lobo's diabolic cunning. These wolves had at least one pursuit which was merely an amusement, it was stampeding and killing sheep, though they rarely ate them. The sheep are usually kept in flocks from one thousand to three thousand under one or more shepherds. At night they are gathered in the most sheltered place available, and a herdsman sleeps on each side of the flock to give additional protection. Sheep are such senseless creatures that they are liable to be stampeded by the veriest trifle, but they have deeply ingrained in their nature one, and perhaps only one, strong weakness, namely, to follow their leader. And this the shepherds turn to good account by putting half a dozen  goats in the flock of sheep. The latter recognize the superior intelligence of their bearded cousins, and when a night alarm occurs they crowd around them, and usually are thus saved from a stampede and are easily protected. But it was not always so. One night late in last November, two Perico shepherds were aroused by an onset of wolves. Their flocks huddled around the goats, which being neither fools nor cowards, stood their ground and were bravely defiant; but alas for them, no common wolf was heading this attack. Old Lobo, the weir-wolf, knew as well as the shepherds that the goats were the moral force of the flock, so hastily running over the backs of the densely packed sheep, he fell on these leaders, slew them all in a few minutes, and soon had the luckless sheep stampeding in a thousand different directions. For weeks afterward I was almost daily accosted by some anxious shepherd, who asked, "Have you seen any stray OTO sheep lately?" and usually I was obliged to say I had; one day it was, "Yes, I came on some five or six carcasses by Diamond Springs;" or another, it was to the effect that I had seen a small 'bunch' running on the Malpai Mesa; or again, "No, but Juan Meira saw about twenty, freshly killed, on the

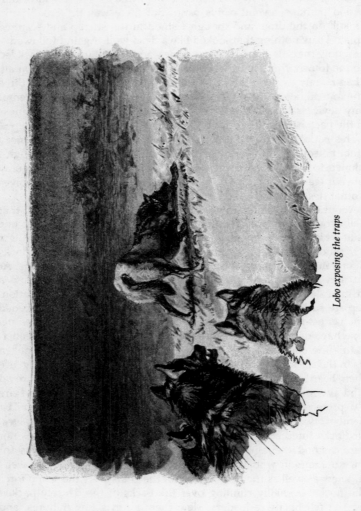

Lobo exposing the traps

Cedra Monte two days ago."

At length the wolf traps arrived, and with two men I worked a whole week to get them properly set out. We spared no labor or pains, I adopted every device I could think of that might help to insure success. The second day after the traps arrived, I rode around to inspect, and soon came upon Lobo's trail running from trap to trap. In the dust I could read the whole story of his doings that night. He had trotted along in the darkness, and although the traps were so carefully concealed, he had instantly detected the first one. Stopping the onward march of the pack, he had cautiously scratched around it until he had disclosed the trap, the chain, and the log, then left them wholly exposed to view with the trap still unsprung, and passing on he treated over a dozen traps in the same fashion. Very soon I noticed that he stopped and turned aside as soon as he detected suspicious signs on the trail and a new plan to outwit him at once suggested itself. I set the traps in the form of an H; that is, with a row of traps on each side of the trail, and one on the trail for the cross-bar of the H. Before long, I had an opportunity to count another failure. Lobo came trotting along the trail, and was fairly between the parellel lines before he detected the single trap in the trail, but he stopped in time, and why or how he knew enough I cannot tell, the Angel of the wild things must have been with him, but without turning an inch to the right or left, he slowly and cautiously backed on his own tracks, putting each paw exactly in its old track until he was off the dangerous ground. Then returning at one side he scratched clods and stones with his hind feet till he had sprung every trap. This he did on many other occasions, and although I varied my methods and redoubled my precautions, he was never deceived, his sagacity seemed never at fault, and he might have been pursuing his career of rapine to-day, but for an unfortunate alliance that proved his ruin and added his name to the long list of heroes who, unassailable when alone, have fallen through the indiscretion of a trusted ally.

* * *

Once or twice, I had found indications that everything was not quite right in the Currumpaw pack. There were signs of irregularity, I thought; for instance there was clearly the trail of a smaller wolf running ahead of the leader, at times, and this I could not understand until a cowboy made a remark which explained the matter.

"I saw them to-day," he said, "and the wild one that breaks away is Blanca." Then the truth dawned upon me, and I added, "Now, I know that Blanca is a she-wolf, because were a he-wolf to act thus, Lobo would kill him at once."

This suggested a new plan. I killed a heifer, and set one or two rather obvious traps about the carcass. Then cutting off the head, which is considered useless offal, and quite beneath the notice of a wolf, I set it a little apart and around it placed six powerful steel traps properly deodorized and concealed with the utmost care. During my operations I

Lobo and Blanca

kept my hands, boots, and implements smeared with fresh blood, and afterward sprinkled the ground with the same, as though it had flowed from the head; and when the traps were buried in the dust I brushed the place over with the skin of a coyote, and with a foot of the same animal made a number of tracks over the traps. The head was so placed that there was a narrow passage between it and some tussocks, and in this passage I buried two of my best traps, fastening them to the head itself.

Wolves have a habit of approaching every carcass they get the wind of, in order to examine it, even when they have no intention of eating of it, and I hoped that this habit would bring the Currumpaw pack within reach of my latest stratagem. I did not doubt that Lobo would detect my handiwork about the meat, and prevent the pack approaching it, but I did build some hopes on the head, for it looked as though it had been thrown aside as useless.

Next morning, I sallied forth to inspect the traps, and there, oh, joy! were the tracks of the pack, and the place where the beef-head and its traps had been was empty. A hasty study of the trail showed that Lobo had kept the pack from approaching the meat, but one, a small wolf, had evidently gone on to examine the head as it lay apart and had walked right into one of the traps.

We set out on the trail, and within a mile discovered that the hapless wolf was Blanca. Away she went, however, at a gallop, and although encumbered by the beef-head, which weighed over fifty pounds, she speedily distanced my companion who was on foot. But we overtook her when she reached the rocks, for the horns of the cow's head became caught and held her fast. She was the handsomest wolf I had ever seen. Her coat was in perfect condition and nearly white.

She turned to fight, and raising her voice in the rallying cry of her race, sent a long howl rolling over the cañon. From far away upon the mesa came a deep response, the cry of Old Lobo. That was her last call, for now we had closed in on her, and all her energy and breath were devoted to combat.

Then followed the inevitable tragedy, the idea of which I shrank from afterward more than at the time. We each threw a lasso over the neck of the doomed wolf, and strained our horses in opposite directions until the blood burst from her mouth, her eyes glazed, her limbs stiffened and then fell limp. Homeward then we rode, carrying the dead wolf, and exulting over this, the first death-blow we had been able to inflict in the Currumpaw pack.

At intervals during the tragedy, and afterward as we rode homeward, we heard the roar of Lobo as he wandered about on the distant mesas, where he seemed to be searching for Blanca. He had never really deserted her, but knowing that he could not save her, his deeprooted dread of firearms had been too much for him when he saw us approaching. All that day we heard him wailing as he roamed in his quest, and I remarked at length to one of the boys, "Now, indeed, I truly know that Blanca was his mate."

As evening fell he seemed to be coming toward the home cañon, for his voice sounded continually nearer. There was an unmistakable note of sorrow in it now. It was no longer the loud, defiant howl, but a long, plaintive wail; "Blanca! Blanca!" he seemed to call. And as night came down, I noticed that he was not far from the place where we had overtaken her. At length he seemed to find the trail, and when he came to the spot where we had killed her, his heart-broken wailing was piteous to hear. It was sadder than I could possibly have believed. Even the stolid cowboys noticed it, and said they had "never heard a wolf carry on like that before." He seemed to know exactly what had taken place, for her blood had stained the place of her death.

Then he took up the trail of the horses and followed it to the ranchhouse. Whether in hopes of finding her there, or in quest of revenge, I know not, but the latter was what he found, for he surprised our unfortunate watchdog outside and tore him to little bits within fifty yards of the door. He evidently came alone this time, for I found but one trail next morning, and he had galloped about in a reckless manner that was very unusual with him. I had half expected this, and had set a number of additional traps about the pasture. Afterward I found that he had indeed fallen into one of these, but such was his strength, he had torn himself loose and cast it aside.

I believed that he would continue in the neighborhood until he found her body at least, so I concentrated all my energies on this one enterprise of catching him before he left the region, and while yet in this reckless mood. Then I realized what a mistake I had made in killing Blanca, for by using her as a decoy I might have secured him the next night.

I gathered in all the traps I could command, one hundred and thirty strong steel wolf-traps, and set them in fours in every trail that led into the cañon; each trap was separately fastened to a log, and each log was separately buried. In burying them, I carefully removed the sod and every particle of earth that was lifted we put in blankets, so that after the sod was replaced and all was finished the eye could detect no trace of human handiwork. When the traps were concealed I trailed the body of poor Blanca over each place, and made of it a drag that circled all about the ranch, and finally I took off one of her paws and made with it a line of tracks over each trap. Every precaution and device known to me I used, and retired at a late hour to await the result.

Once during the night I thought I heard Old Lobo, but was not sure of it. Next day I rode around, but darkness came on before I completed the circuit of the north cañon, and I had nothing to report. At supper one of the cowboys said, "There was a great row among the cattle in the north cañon this morning, maybe there is something in the traps there." It was afternoon of the next day before I got to the place referred to, and as I drew near a great grizzly form arose from the ground, vainly endeavoring to escape, and there revealed before me stood Lobo, King of the Currumpaw, firmly held in the traps. Poor old hero, he had never ceased to search for his darling, and when he found the trail her body had made he followed it recklessly, and so fell into the snare prepared for him. There he lay in the iron grasp of all four traps, perfectly helpless, and all around him were numerous tracks showing how the cattle had gathered about him to insult the fallen despot, without daring to approach within his reach. For two days and two nights he had lain there, and now was worn out with struggling. Yet, when I went near him, he rose up with bristling mane and raised his voice, and for the last time made the cañon reverberate with his deep bass roar, a call for help, the muster call of his band. But there was none to answer him, and, left alone in his extremity, he whirled about with all his strength and made a desperate effort to get at me. All in vain, each trap was a dead drag of over three hundred pounds, and in their relentless fourfold grasp, with great steel jaws on every foot, and the heavy logs and chains all entangled together, he was absolutely powerless. How his huge ivory tusks did grind on those cruel chains, and when I ventured to touch him with my rifle-barrel he left grooves on it which are there to this day. His eyes glared green with hate and fury, and his jaws snapped with a hollow 'chop,' as he vainly endeavored to reach me and my trembling horse. But he was worn out with hunger and struggling and loss of blood, and he soon sank exhausted to the ground.

Something like compunction came over me, as I prepared to deal out to him that which so many had suffered at his hands.

"Grand old outlaw, hero of a thousand lawless raids, in a few minutes you will be but a great load of carrion. It cannot be otherwise." Then I swung my lasso and sent it whistling over his head. But not so fast; he was yet far from being subdued, and, before the supple coils had fallen on his neck he seized the noose and, with one fierce chop, cut through its hard thick strands, and dropped it in two pieces at his feet.

Of course I had my rifle as a last resource, but I did not wish to spoil his royal hide, so I galloped back to the camp and returned with a cowboy and a fresh lasso. We threw to our victim a stick of wood which he seized in his teeth, and before he could relinquish it our lassoes whistled through the air and tightened on his neck.

Yet before the light had died from his fierce eyes, I cried, "Stay, we will not kill him; let us take him alive to the camp." He was so completely powerless now that it was easy to put a stout stick through his mouth, behind his tusks, and then lash his jaws with a heavy cord which was also fastened to the stick. The stick kept the cord in, and the cord kept the stick in so he was harmless. As soon as he felt his jaws were tied he made no further resistance, and uttered no sound, but looked calmly at us and seemed to say, "Well, you have got me at last, do as you please with me." And from that time he took no more notice of us.

We tied his feet securely, but he never groaned, nor growled, nor turned his head. Then with our united strength were just able to put him on my horse. His breath came evenly as though sleeping, and his eyes were bright and clear again, but did not rest on us. Afar on the great rolling mesas they were fixed, his passing kingdom, where his famous band was now scattered. And he gazed till the pony descended the pathway into the cañon, and the rocks cut off the view.

By travelling slowly we reached the ranch in safety, and after securing him with a collar and a strong chain, we staked him out in the pasture and removed the cords. Then for the first time I could examine him closely, and proved how unreliable is vulgar report when a living hero or tyrant is concerned. He had *not* a collar of gold about his neck, nor was there on his shoulders an inverted cross to denote that he had leagued hmself with Satan. But I did find on one haunch a great broad scar, that tradition says was the fang-mark of Juno, the leader of Tannerey's wolf-hounds—a mark which she gave him the moment before he stretched her lifeless on the sand of the cañon.

I set meat and water beside him, but he paid no heed. He lay calmly on his breast, and gazed with those steadfast yellow eyes away past me down through the gateway of the cañon, over the open plains—his plains—nor moved a muscle when I touched him. When the sun went down he was still gazing fixedly across the prairie. I expected he would call up his band when night came, and prepared for them, but he had called once in his extremity, and none had come; he would never call again.

A lion shorn of his strength, an eagle robbed of his freedom, or a dove bereft of his mate, all die, it is said, of a broken heart; and who will aver that this grim bandit could bear the threefold brunt, heart-whole? This only I know, that when the morning dawned, he was lying there still in his position of calm repose, but his spirit was gone—the old king-wolf was dead.

I took the chain from his neck, a cowboy helped me to carry him to the shed where lay the remains of Blanca, and as we laid him beside her, the cattle-man exclaimed: "There, you *would* come to her, now you are together again."

SILVERSPOT

The Story of a Crow

How many of us have ever got to know a wild animal? I do not mean merely to meet with one once or twice, or to have one in a cage, but to really know it for a long time while it is wild, and to get an insight into its life and history. The trouble usually is to know one creature from his fellow. One fox or crow is so much like another that we cannot be sure that it really is the same next time we meet. But once in awhile there arises an animal who is stronger or wiser than his fellow, who becomes a great leader, who is, as we would say, a genius, and if he is bigger, or has some mark by which men can know him, he soon becomes famous in his country, and shows us that the life of a wild animal may be far more interesting and exciting than that of many human beings.

Of this class were Courtrand, the bob-tailed wolf that terrorized the whole city of Paris for about ten years in the beginning of the fourteenth century; Clubfoot, the lame grizzly bear that in two years ruined all the hog-raisers, and drove half the farmers out of business in the upper Sacramento Valley; Lobo, the king-wolf of New Mexico, that killed a cow every day for five years, and the Soehnee panther that in less than two years killed nearly three hundred human beings—and such also was Silverspot, whose history, as far as I could learn it, I shall now briefly tell.

Silverspot was simply a wise old crow; his name was given because of the silvery white spot that was like a nickel, stuck on his right side, between the eye and the bill, and it was owing to this spot that I was able to know him from the other crows, and put together the parts of his history that came to my knowledge.

Crows are, as you must know, our most intelligent birds—'Wise as an old crow' did not become a saying without good reason. Crows know the value of organization, and are as well drilled as soldiers—very much better than some soldiers, in fact, for crows are always on duty, always at war, and always dependent on each other for life and safety. Their leaders not only are the oldest and wisest of the band, but also the strongest and bravest, for they must be ready at any time with sheer force to put down an upstart or a rebel. The rank and file are the youngsters and the crows without special gifts.

Silverspot

Old Silverspot was the leader of a large band of crows that made their headquarters near Toronto, Canada, in Castle Frank, which is a pine-clad hill on the northeast edge of the city. This band numbered about two hundred, and for reasons that I never understood did not increase. In mild winters they stayed along the Niagara River; in cold winters they went much farther south. But each year in the last week of February Old Silverspot would muster his followers and boldly cross the forty miles of open water that lies between Toronto and Niagara; not, however, in a straight line would he go, but always in a curve to the west, whereby he kept in sight of the familiar landmark of Dundas Mountain, until the pine-clad hill itself came in view. Each year he came with his troop, and for about six weeks took up his abode on the hill. Each morning thereafter the crows set out in three bands to forage. One band went southeast to Ashbridge's Bay. One went north up the Don, and one, the largest, went northwestward up the ravine. The last Silverspot led in person. Who led the others I never found out.

On calm mornings they flew high and straight away. But when it was windy the band flew low, and followed the ravine for shelter. My windows overlooked the ravine, and it was thus that in 1885 I first noticed this old crow. I was a new-comer in the neighborhood, but an

old resident said to me then "that there old crow has been a-flying up and down this ravine for more than twenty years." My chances to watch were in the ravine, and Silverspot doggedly clinging to the old route, though now it was edged with houses and spanned by bridges, became a very familiar acquaintance. Twice each day in March and part of April, then again in the later summer and the fall, he passed and repassed, and gave me chances to see his movements, and hear his orders to his bands, and so, little by little, opened my eyes to the fact that the crows, though a little people, are of great wit, a race of birds with a language and a social system that is wonderfully human in many of its chief points, and in some is better carried out than our own.

One windy day I stood on the high bridge across the ravine, as the old crow, heading his long, straggling troop, came flying down homeward. Half a mile away I could hear the contented '*All's well, come right*

along!' as we should say, or as he put it, and as also his lieutenant echoed it at the rear of the band. They were flying very low to be out of the wind, and would have to rise a little to clear the bridge on which I was. Silverspot saw me standing there, and as I was closely watching him he didn't like it. He checked his flight and called out, '*Be on your guard,*' or

and rose much higher in the air. Then seeing that I was not armed he flew over my head about twenty feet, and his followers in turn did the same, dipping again to the old level when past the bridge.

Next day I was at the same place, and as the crows came near I raised my walking stick and pointed it at them. The old fellow at once cried out '*Danger,* and rose fifty feet higher than before.

Seeing that it was not a gun, he ventured to fly over. But on the third day I took with me a gun, and at once he cried out, '*Great danger—a gun.*'

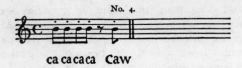

ca ca ca ca **Caw**

His lieutenant repeated the cry, and every crow in the troop began to tower and scatter from the rest, till they were far above gun shot, and so passed safely over, coming down again to the shelter of the valley when well beyond reach. Another time, as the long, straggling troop came down the valley, a red-tailed hawk alighted on a tree close by their intended route. The leader cried out, '*Hawk, hawk,*', and stayed his

Caw   Caw

flight, as did each crow on nearing him, until all were massed in a solid body. Then, no longer fearing the hawk, they passed on. But a quarter of a mile farther on a man with a gun appeared below, and the cry, '*Great danger—a gun, a gun; scatter for your lives,*''

ca ca ca ca **Caw**

at once caused them to scatter widely and tower till far beyond range. Many others of his words of command I learned in the course of my long acquaintance, and found that sometimes a very little difference in the sound makes a very great difference in meaning. Thus while No. 5 means hawk, or any large, dangerous bird, this means '*wheel around,*'

Caw   Caw   ca ca ca ca

evidently a combination of No. 5, whose root idea is danger, and of No. 4, whose root idea is retreat, and this again is a mere '*good day,*'

Caw   Caw

to a far away comrade. This is usually addressed to the ranks and means '*attention.*'

No. 9.

Early in April there began to be great doings among the crows. Some new cause of excitement seemed to have come on them. They spent half the day among the pines, instead of foraging from dawn to dark. Pairs and trios might be seen chasing each other, and from time to time they showed off in various feats of flight. A favorite sport was to dart down suddenly from a great height toward some perching crow, and just before touching it to turn at a hairbreadth and rebound in the air so fast that the wings of the swooper whirred with a sound like distant thunder. Sometimes one crow would lower his head, raise every feather, and coming close to another would gurgle out a long note like

No. 10.

C - r - r - r - a — w

What did it all mean? I soon learned. They were making love and pairing off. The males were showing off their wing powers and their voices to the lady crows. And they must have been highly appreciated, for by the middle of April all had mated and had scattered over the country for their honeymoon, leaving the sombre old pines of Castle Frank deserted and silent.

* * *

The Sugar Loaf hill stands alone in the Don Valley. It is still covered with woods that join with those of Castle Frank, a quarter of a mile off. In the woods, between the two hills, is a pine-tree in whose top is a deserted hawk's nest. Every Toronto school-boy knows the nest, and, excepting that I had once shot a black squirrel on its edge, no one had ever seen a sign of life about it. There it was year after year, ragged and old, and falling to pieces. Yet, strange to tell, in all that time it never did drop to pieces, like other old nests.

One morning in May I was out at gray dawn, and stealing gently through the woods, whose dead leaves were so wet that no rustle was made. I chanced to pass under the old nest, and was surprised to see a black tail sticking over the edge. I struck the tree a smart blow, off flew a crow, and the secret was out. I had long suspected that a pair of crows nested each year about the pines, but now I realized that it was

Silverspot and his wife. The old nest was theirs, and they were too wise to give it an air of spring-cleaning and housekeeping each year. Here they had nested for long, though guns in the hands of men and boys hungry to shoot crows were carried under their home every day. I never surprised the old fellow again, though I several times saw him through my telescope.

One day while watching I saw a crow crossing the Don Valley with something white in his beak. He flew to the mouth of the Rosedale Brook, then took a short flight to the Beaver Elm. There he dropped the white object, and looking about gave me a chance to recognize my old friend Silverspot. After a minute he picked up the white thing—a shell—and walked over past the spring, and here, among the docks and the skunk-cabbages, he unearthed a pile of shells and other white, shiny things. He spread them out in the sun, turned them over, lifted them one by one in his beak, dropped them, nestled on them as though they were eggs, toyed with them and gloated over them like a miser. This was his hobby, his weakness. He could not have explained *why* he enjoyed them, any more than a boy can explain why he collects postage-stamps, or a girl why she prefers pearls to rubies; but his pleasure in them was very real, and after half an hour he covered them all, including the new one, with earth and leaves, and flew off. I went at once to the spot and examined the hoard; there was about a hatful in all, chiefly white pebbles, clam-shells, and some bits of tin, but there was also the handle of a china cup, which must have been the gem of the collection. That was the last time I saw them. Silverspot knew that I had found his treasures, and he removed them at once; where I never knew.

During the space that I watched him so closely he had many little adventures and escapes. He was once severely handled by a sparrow-hawk, and often he was chased and worried by kingbirds. Not that these did him much harm, but they were such noisy pests that he avoided their company as quickly as possible, just as a grown man avoids a conflict with a noisy and impudent small boy. He had some cruel tricks, too. He had a way of going the round of the small birds' nests each morning to eat the new laid eggs, as regularly as a doctor visiting his patients. But we must not judge him for that, as it is just what we ourselves do to the hens in the barnyard.

His quickness of wit was often shown. One day I saw him flying down the ravine with a large piece of bread in his bill. The stream below him was at this time being bricked over as a sewer. There was one part of two hundred yards quite finished, and, as he flew over the open water just above this, the bread fell from his bill, and was swept by the current out of sight into the tunnel. He flew down and peered vainly into the dark cavern, then, acting upon a happy thought, he flew to the downstream end of the tunnel, and awaiting the reappearance of the floating bread, as it was swept onward by the current, he seized and bore it off in triumph.

Silverspot was a crow of the world. He was truly a successful crow. He lived in a region that, though full of dangers, abounded with food. In the old, unrepaired nest he raised a brood each year with his wife,

The handle of a china cup, the gem of the collection

whom, by the way, I never could distinguish, and when the crows again gathered together he was their acknowledged chief.

The reassembling takes place about the end of June—the young crows with their bob-tails, soft wings, and falsetto voices are brought by their parents, whom they nearly equal in size, and introduced to society at the old pine woods, a woods that is at once their fortress and college. Here they find security in numbers and in lofty yet sheltered

Roost in a row, like big folks

perches, and here they begin their schooling and are taught all the secrets of success in crow life, and in crow life the least failure does not simply mean begin again. It means *death*.

The first week or two after their arrival is spent by the young ones in getting acquainted, for each crow must know personally all the others in the band. Their parents meanwhile have time to rest a little after the work of raising them, for now the youngsters are able to feed themselves and roost on a branch in a row, just like big folks.

In a week or two the moulting season comes. At this time the old crows are usually irritable and nervous, but it does not stop them from beginning to drill the youngsters, who, of course, do not much enjoy the punishment and nagging they get so soon after they have been mamma's own darlings. But it is all for their good, as the old lady said when she skinned the eels, and old Silverspot is an excellent teacher. Sometimes he seems to make a speech to them. What he says I cannot guess, but, judging by the way they receive it, it must be extremely witty. Each morning there is a company drill, for the young ones naturally drop into two or three squads according to their age and strength. The rest of the day they forage with their parents.

When at length September comes we find a great change. The rabble of silly little crows have begun to learn sense. The delicate blue iris of their eyes, the sign of a fool-crow, has given place to the dark brown eye of the old stager. They know their drill now and have learned sentry duty. They have been taught guns and traps and taken a special course in wire-worms and greencorn. They know that a fat old farmer's wife is much less dangerous, though so much larger, than her fifteen-year-old son, and they can tell the boy from his sister. They know that an umbrella is not a gun, and they can count up to six, which is fair for young crows, though Silverspot can go up nearly to thirty. They know the smell of gunpowder and the south side of a hemlock-tree, and begin to plume themselves upon being crows of the world. They always fold their wings three times after alighting, to be sure that it is neatly done. They know how to worry a fox into giving up half his dinner, and also that when the kingbird or the purple martin assails them they must dash into a bush, for it is as impossible to fight the little pests as it is for the fat apple-woman to catch the small boys who have raided her basket. All these things do the young crows know; but they have taken no lessons in egg-hunting yet, for it is not the season. They are unacquainted with clams, and have never tasted horses' eyes, or seen sprouted corn, and they don't know a thing about travel, the greatest educator of all. They did not think of that two months ago, and since then they have thought of it, but have learned to wait till their betters are ready.

September sees a great change in the old crows, too. Their moulting is over. They are now in full feather again and proud of their handsome coats. Their health is again good, and with it their tempers are improved. Even old Silverspot, the strict teacher, becomes quite jolly, and the youngsters, who have long ago learned to respect him, begin really to love him.

He has hammered away at drill, teaching them all the signals and words of command in use, and now it is a pleasure to see them in the early morning.

'*Company I!*' the old chieftan would cry in crow, and Company I would answer with a great clamor.

'*Fly!*' and himself leading them, they would all fly straight forward.

'*Mount!*' and straight upward they turned in a moment.

'*Bunch!*' and they all massed into a dense black flock.

'*Scatter!*' and they spread out like leaves before the wind.

'*Form line!*' and they strung out into the long line of ordinary flight.

'*Descend!*' and they all dropped neatly to the ground.

'*Forage!*' and they alighted and scattered about to feed, while two of the permanent sentries mounted duty—one on a tree to the right, the other on a mound to the far left. A minute or two later Silverspot would cry out, '*A man with a gun!*' The sentries repeated the cry and the company flew at once in open order as quickly as possible toward the trees. Once behind these, they formed line again in safety and returned to the home pines.

Sentry duty is not taken in turn by all the crows, but a certain number whose watchfulness has been often proved are the perpetual sentries, and are expected to watch and forage at the same time. Rather hard on them it seems to us, but it works well and the crow organization is admitted by all birds to be the very best in existence.

Finally, each November sees the troop sail away southward to learn new modes of life, new landmarks and new kinds of food, under the guidance of the ever-wise Silverspot.

* * *

There is only one time when a crow is a fool, and that is at night. There is only one bird that terrifies the crow, and that is the owl. When, therefore, these come together it is a woful thing for the sable birds. The distant hoot of an owl after dark is enough to make them withdraw their heads from under their wings, and sit trembling and miserable till morning. In very cold weather the exposure of their faces thus has often resulted in a crow having one or both of his eyes frozen, so that blindness followed and therefore death. There are no hospitals for sick crows.

But with the morning their courage comes again, and arousing themselves they ransack the woods for a mile around till they find that owl, and if they do not kill him they at least worry him half to death and drive him twenty miles away.

In 1893 the crows had come as usual to Castle Frank. I was walking in these woods a few days afterward when I chanced upon the track of a rabbit that had been running at full speed over the snow and dodging about among the trees as though pursued. Strange to tell, I could see no track of the pursuer. I followed the trail and presently saw a drop of blood on the snow, and a little farther on found the partly devoured

The track of the murderer

The death of Silverspot

remains of a little brown bunny. What had killed him was a mystery until a careful search showed in the snow a great double-toed track and a beautifully pencilled brown feather. Then all was clear—*a horned owl.* Half an hour later, in passing again by the place, there, in a tree, within ten feet of the bones of his victim, was the fierce-eyed owl himself. The murderer still hung about the scene of his crime. For once circumstantial evidence had not lied. At my approach he gave a guttural '*grrr-oo*' and flew off with low flagging flight to haunt the distant sombre woods.

Two days afterward, at dawn, there was a great uproar among the crows. I went out early to see, and found some black feathers drifting over the snow. I followed up the wind in the direction from which they came and soon saw the bloody remains of a crow and the great double-toed track which again told me that the murderer was the owl. All around were signs of the struggle, but the fell destroyer was too strong. The poor crow had been dragged from his perch at night, when the darkness had put him at a hopeless disadvantage.

I turned over the remains, and by chance unburied the head—then started with an exclamation of sorrow. Alas! It was the head of old Silverspot. His long life of usefulness to his tribe was over—slain at last by the owl that he had taught so many hundreds of young crows to beware of.

The old nest on the Sugar Loaf is abandoned now. The crows still come in spring-time to Castle Frank, but without their famous leader their numbers are dwindling, and soon they will be seen no more about the old pine-grove in which they and their forefathers had lived and learned for ages.

RAGGYLUG

The Story of a Cottontail Rabbit

Raggylug, or Rag, was the name of a young cottontail rabbit. It was given him from his torn and ragged ear, a life-mark that he got in his first adventure. He lived with his mother in Olifant's swamp, where I made their acquaintance and gathered, in a hundred different ways, the little bits of proof and scraps of truth that at length enabled me to write this history.

Those who do not know the animals well may think I have humanized them, but those who have lived so near them as to know somewhat of their ways and their minds will not think so.

Truly rabbits have no speech as we understand it, but they have a way of conveying ideas by a system of sounds, signs, scents, whisker-touches, movements, and example that answers the purpose of speech; and it must be remembered that though in telling this story I freely translate from rabbit into English, *I repeat nothing that they did not say.*

* * *

The rank swamp grass bent over and concealed the snug nest where Raggylug's mother had hidden him. She had partly covered him with some of the bedding, and, as always, her last warning was to 'lay low and say nothing, whatever happens.' Though tucked in bed, he was

32

wide awake and his bright eyes were taking in that part of his little green world that was straight above. A bluejay and a red-squirrel, two notorious thieves, were loudly berating each other for stealing, and at one time Rag's home bush was the centre of their fight; a yellow warbler caught a blue butterfly but six inches from his nose, and a scarlet and black ladybug, serenely waving her knobbled feelers, took a long walk up one grassblade, down another, and across the nest and over Rag's face—and yet he never moved nor even winked.

After a while he heard a strange rustling of the leaves in the near thicket. It was an odd, continuous sound, and though it went this way and that way and came ever nearer, there was no patter of feet with it. Rag had lived his whole life in the Swamp (he was three weeks old) and yet had never heard anything like this. Of course his curiosity was

'Mammy, Mammy!' he screamed, in mortal terror

greatly aroused. His mother had cautioned him to lay low, but that was understood to be in case of danger, and this strange sound without footfalls could not be anything to fear.

The low rasping went past close at hand, then to the right, then back, and seemed going away. Rag felt he knew what he was about; he wasn't a baby; it was his duty to learn what it was. He slowly raised his roly-poly body on his short fluffy legs, lifted his little round head above the covering of his nest and peeped out into the woods. The sound had ceased as soon as he moved. He saw nothing, so took one step forward to a clear view, and instantly found himself face to face with an enormous Black Serpent.

"Mammy," he screamed in mortal terror as the monster darted at him. With all the strength of his tiny limbs he tried to run. But in a flash the Snake had him by one ear and whipped around him with his coils to gloat over the helpless little baby bunny he had secured for dinner.

"Mam-my—Mam-my," gasped poor little Raggylug as the cruel monster began slowly choking him to death. Very soon the little one's cry would have ceased, but bounding through the woods straight as an arrow came Mammy. No longer a shy, helpless little Molly Cottontail, ready to fly from a shadow: the mother's love was strong in her. The cry of her baby had filled her with the courage of a hero, and—hop, she went over that horrible reptile. Whack, she struck down at him with her sharp hind claws as she passed, giving him such a stinging blow that he squirmed with pain and hissed with anger.

"M-a-m-m-y," came feebly from the little one. And Mammy came leaping again and again and struck harder and fiercer until the loathsome reptile let go the little one's ear and tried to bite the old one as she leaped over. But all he got was a mouthful of wool each time, and Molly's fierce blows began to tell, as long bloody rips were torn in the Black Snake's scaly armor.

Things were now looking bad for the Snake; and bracing himself for the next charge, he lost his tight hold on Baby Bunny, who at once wriggled out of the coils and away into the underbrush, breathless and terribly frightened, but unhurt save that his left ear was much torn by the teeth of that dreadful Serpent.

Molly now had gained all she wanted. She had no notion of fighting for glory or revenge. Away she went into the woods and the little one followed the shining beacon of her snow-white tail until she led him to the safe corner of the Swamp.

* * *

Old Olifant's Swamp was a rough, brambly tract of second-growth woods, with a marshy pond and a stream through the middle. A few ragged remnants of the old forest still stood in it and a few of the still older trunks were lying about as dead logs in the brushwood. The land about the pond was of that willow-grown sedgy kind that cats and horses avoid, but that cattle do not fear. The drier zones were overgrown with briars and young trees. The outermost belt of all, that next the fields, was of thrifty, gummy-trunked young pines whose living needles in air and dead ones on earth offer so delicious an odor to the nostrils of the passer-by, and so deadly a breath to those seedlings that would compete with them for the worthless waste they grow on.

All around for a long way were smooth fields, and the only wild tracks that ever crossed these fields were those of a thoroughly bad and unscrupulous fox that lived only too near.

The chief indwellers of the swamp were Molly and Rag. Their nearest neighbors were far away, and their nearest kin were dead. This was their home, and here they lived together, and here Rag received the training that made his success in life.

Molly was a good little mother and gave him a careful bringing up. The first thing he learned was 'to lay low and say nothing.' His adventure with the snake taught him the wisdom of this. Rag never forgot that lesson; afterward he did as he was told, and it made the other things come more easily.

The second lesson he learned was 'freeze.' It grows out of the first, and Rag was taught it as soon as he could run.

'Freezing' is simply doing nothing, turning into a statue. As soon as he finds a foe near, no matter what he is doing, a well-trained Cottontail keeps just as he is and stops all movement, for the creatures of the woods are of the same color as the things in the woods and catch the eye only while moving. So when enemies chance together, the one who first sees the other can keep himself unseen by 'freezing' and thus have all the advantages of choosing the time for attack or escape. Only those who live in the woods know the importance of this; every wild creature and every hunter must learn it; all learn to do it well, but not one of them can beat Molly Cottontail in the doing. Rag's mother taught him this trick by example. When the white cotton cushion that she always carried to sit on went bobbing away through the woods, of course Rag ran his hardest to keep up. But when Molly stopped and 'froze,' the natural wish to copy made him do the same.

But the best lesson of all that Rag learned from his mother was the secret of the Brierbush. It is a very old secret now, and to make it plain you must first hear why the Brierbush quarrelled with the beasts.

Long ago the Roses used to grow on bushes that had no thorns. But the Squirrels and Mice used to climb after them, the Cattle used to knock them off with their horns, the Possum would twitch them off with his long tail, and the Deer, with his sharp hoofs, would break them down. So the Brierbush armed itself with spikes to protect its roses and declared eternal war on all creatures that climbed trees, or had horns, or hoofs, or long tails. This left the Brierbush at peace with none but Molly Cottontail, who could not climb, was hornless, hoofless, and had scarcely any tail at all.

In truth the Cottontail had never harmed a Brierrose, and having now so many enemies the Rose took the Rabbit into especial friendship, and when dangers are threatening poor Bunny he flies to the nearest Brierbush, certain that it is ready with a million keen and poisoned daggers to defend him.

So the secret that Rag learned from his mother was, 'The Brierbush is your best friend.'

Much of the time that season was spent in learning the lay of the land, and the bramble and brier mazes. And Rag learned them so well that he could go all around the swamp by two different ways and never leave the friendly briers at any place for more than five hops.

It is not long since the foes of the Cottontails were disgusted to find that man had brought a new kind of bramble and planted it in long lines throughout the country. It was so strong that no creatures could break it down, and so sharp that the toughest skin was torn by it. Each year there was more of it and each year it became a more serious matter to the wild creatures. But Molly Cottontail had no fear of it. She was not brought up in the briers for nothing. Dogs and foxes, cattle and sheep, and even man himself might be torn by those fearful spikes; but Molly understands it and lives and thrives under it. And the further it spreads the more safe country there is for the Cottontail. And the name of this new and dreaded bramble is—*the barbed-wire fence.*

* * *

Molly had no other children to look after now, so Rag had all her care. He was unusually quick and bright as well as strong, and he had uncommonly good chances; so he got on remarkably well.

All the season she kept him busy learning the tricks of the trail, and what to eat and drink and what not to touch. Day by day she worked to train him; little by little she taught him, putting into his mind hundreds of ideas that her own life or early training had stored in hers, and so equipped him with the knowledge that makes life possible to their kind.

Close by her side in the clover-field or the thicket he would sit and copy her when she wobbled her nose 'to keep her smeller clear,' and pull the bite from her mouth or taste her lips to make sure he was getting the same kind of fodder. Still copying her, he learned to comb his ears with his claws and to dress his coat and to bite the burrs out of his vest and socks. He learned, too, that nothing but clear dewdrops from the briers were fit for a rabbit to drink, as water which has once touched the earth must surely bear some taint. Thus he began the study of woodcraft, the oldest of all sciences.

As soon as Rag was big enough to go out alone, his mother taught him the signal code. Rabbits telegraph each other by thumping on the ground with their hind feet. Along the ground sound carries far; a thump that at six feet from the earth is not heard at twenty yards will, near the ground, be heard at least one hundred yards. Rabbits have very keen hearing, and so might hear this same thump at two hundred yards, and that would reach from end to end of Olifant's Swamp. A single *thump* means 'look out' or 'freeze.' A slow *thump thump* means 'come.' A fast *thump thump* means 'danger;' and a very fast *thump thump thump* means 'run for dear life.'

At another time, when the weather was fine and the bluejays were quarrelling among themselves, a sure sign that no dangerous foe was about, Rag began a new study. Molly, by flattening her ears, gave the sign to squat. Then she ran far away in the thicket and gave the thumping signal for 'come.' Rag set out at a run to the place but could not find Molly. He thumped, but got no reply. Setting carefully about his search he found her foot-scent and following this strange guide, that the beasts all know so well and man does not know at all, he worked out the trail and found her where she was hidden. Thus he got his first lesson in trailing, and thus it was that the games of hide and seek they played became the schooling for the serious chase of which there was so much in his after life.

Before that first season of schooling was over he had learnt all the principal tricks by which a rabbit lives and in not a few problems showed himself a veritable genius.

He was an adept at 'tree,' 'dodge,' and 'squat,' he could play 'log-lump,' with 'wind' and 'baulk' with 'back-track' so well that he scarcely needed any other tricks. He had not yet tried it, but he knew just how to play 'barb-wire,' which is a new trick of the brilliant order; he had made a special study of 'sand,' which burns up all scent, and he was deeply versed in 'change-off,' 'fence,' and 'double' as well as 'hole-up,' which is a trick requiring longer notice, and yet he never forgot that 'lay-low' is the beginning of all wisdom and 'brierbush' the only trick that is always safe.

He was taught the signs by which to know all his foes and then the way to baffle them. For hawks, owls, foxes, hounds, curs, minks, weasels, cats, skunks, coons, and men, each have a different plan of pursuit, and for each and all of these evils he was taught a remedy.

And for knowledge of the enemy's approach he learnt to depend first on himself and his mother, and then on the bluejay. "Never neglect the bluejay's warning," said Molly; "he is a mischief-maker, a marplot, and a thief all the time, but nothing escapes him. He wouldn't mind harming us, but he cannot, thanks to the briers, and his enemies are ours, so it is well to heed him. If the woodpecker cries a warning you can trust him, he his honest; but he is a fool beside the bluejay, and though the bluejay often tells lies for mischief you are safe to believe him when he brings ill news."

The barb-wire trick takes a deal of nerve and the best of legs. It was long before Rag ventured to play it, but as he came to his full powers it became one of his favorites.

"It's fine play for those who can do it," said Molly. "First you lead off your dog on a straightaway and warm him up a bit by nearly letting him catch you. Then keeping just one hop ahead, you lead him at a long slant full tilt into a breast-high barb-wire. I've seen many a dog and fox crippled, and one big hound killed outright this way. But I've also seen more than one rabbit lose his life in trying it."

Rag early learnt what some rabbits never learn at all, that 'hole-up' is not such a fine ruse as it seems; it may be the certain safety of a wise rabbit, but soon or late is a sure deathtrap to a fool. A young rabbit always thinks of it first, an old rabbit never tries it till all others fail. It means escape from a man or dog, a fox or a bird or prey, but it means sudden death if the foe is a ferret, mink, skunk, or weasel.

There were but two ground-holes in the Swamp. One on the Sunning Bank, which was a dry sheltered knoll in the South-end. It was open and sloping to the sun, and here on fine days the Cottontails took their sunbaths. They stretched out among the fragrant pine needles and winter-green in odd cat-like positions, and turned slowly over as though roasting and wishing all sides well done. And they blinked and panted, and squirmed as if in dreadful pain; yet this was one of the keenest enjoyments they knew.

In odd cat-like positions

Just over the brow of the knoll was a large pine stump. Its grotesque roots wriggled out above the yellow sand-bank like dragons, and under their protecting claws a sulky old woodchuck had digged a den long ago. He became more sour and ill-tempered as weeks went by, and one day waited to quarrel with Olifant's dog instead of going in so that Molly Cottontail was able to take possession of the den an hour later.

This, the pine-root hole, was afterward very coolly taken by a self-sufficient young skunk who with less valor might have enjoyed greater longevity, for he imagined that even man with a gun would fly from him. Instead of keeping Molly from the den for good, therefore, his reign, like that of a certain Hebrew king, was over in four days.

The other, the fern-hole, was in a fern thicket next the clover field. It was small and damp, and useless except as a last retreat. It also was the work of a woodchuck, a well-meaning friendly neighbor, but a hare-brained youngster whose skin in the form of a whip-lash was now developing higher horse-power in the Olifant working team.

"Simple justice," said the old man, "for that hide was raised on stolen feed that the team would a' turned into horse-power anyway."

The Cottontails were now sole owners of the holes, and did not go near them when they could help it, lest anything like a path should be made that might betray these last retreats to an enemy.

There was also the hollow hickory, which, though nearly fallen, was still green, and had the great advantage of being open at both ends. This had long been the residence of one Lotor, a solitary old coon whose ostensible calling was frog-hunting, and who, like the monks of old, was supposed to abstain from all flesh food. But it was shrewdly suspected that he needed but a chance to indulge in a diet of rabbit. When at last one dark night he was killed while raiding Olifant's hen-house, Molly, so far from feeling a pang of regret, took possession of his cosy nest with a sense of unbounded relief.

* * *

Bright August sunlight was flooding the Swamp in the morning. Everything seemed soaking in the warm radiance. A little brown swamp-sparrow was teetering on a long rush in the pond. Beneath him there were open spaces of dirty water that brought down a few scraps of the blue sky, and worked it and the yellow duckweed into an exquisite mosaic, with a little wrong-side picture of the bird in the middle. On the bank behind was a great vigorous growth of golden green skunk-cabbage, that cast dense shadow over the brown swamp tussocks.

The eyes of the swamp-sparrow were not trained to take in the color glories, but he saw what we might have missed; that two of the numberless leafy brown bumps under the broad cabbage-leaves were furry living things, with noses that never ceased to move up and down whatever else was still.

It was Molly and Rag. They were stretched under the skunk-cabbage, not because they liked its rank smell, but because the winged ticks could not stand it at all and so left them in peace.

Rabbits have no set time for lessons, they are always learning; but what the lesson is depends on the present stress, and that must arrive before it is known. They went to this place for a quiet rest, but had not been long there when suddenly a warning note from the ever-watchful bluejay caused Molly's nose and ears to go up and her tail to tighten to her back. Away across the Swamp was Olifant's big black and white dog, coming straight toward them.

"Now," said Molly, "squat while I go and keep that fool out of mischief." Away she went to meet him and she fearlessly dashed across the dog's path.

"Bow-ow-ow," he fairly yelled as he bounded after Molly, but she kept just beyond his reach and led him where the million daggers struck fast and deep, till his tender ears were scratched raw, and guided him at last plump into a hidden barbed-wire fence, where he got such a gashing that he went homeward howling with pain. After making a short double, a loop and a baulk in case the dog should come back, Molly returned to find that Rag in his eagerness was standing bolt upright and craning his neck to see the sport.

This disobedience made her so angry that she struck him with her hind foot and knocked him over in the mud.

One day as they fed on the near clover field a red-tailed hawk came swooping after them. Molly kicked up her hind legs to make fun of him and skipped into the briers along one of their old pathways, where of course the hawk could not follow. It was the main path from the Creek-side Thicket to the Stove-pipe brush-pile. Several creepers had grown across it, and Molly, keeping one eye on the hawk, set to work and cut the creepers off. Rag watched her, then ran on ahead, and cut some more that were across the path. "That's right," said Molly, "always keep the runways clear, you will need them often enough. Not wide, but clear. Cut everything like a creeper across them and some day you will find you have cut a snare. "A what?" asked Rag, as he scratched his right ear with his left hind foot.

"A snare is something that looks like a creeper, but it doesn't grow and it's worse than all the hawks in the world," said Molly, glancing at the now far-away red-tail, "for there it hides night and day in the runway till the chance to catch you comes."

"I don't believe it could catch me," said Rag, with the pride of youth as he rose on his heels to rub his chin and whiskers high up on a smooth sapling. Rag did not know he was doing this, but his mother saw and knew it was a sign, like the changing of a boy's voice, that her little one was no longer a baby but would soon be a grown-up Cottontail.

* * *

There is magic in running water. Who does not know it and feel it? The railroad builder fearlessly throws his bank across the wide bog or lake, or the sea itself, but the tiniest rill of running water he treats with great respect, studies its wish and its way and gives it all it seems to ask. The thirst-parched traveller in the poisonous alkali deserts holds back in deadly fear from the sedgy ponds till he finds one down whose centre is a thin, clear line, and a faint flow, the sign of running, living water, and joyfully he drinks.

There is magic in running water, no evil spell can cross it. Tam O'Shanter proved its potency in time of sorest need. The wild-wood creature with its deadly foe following tireless on the trail scent, realizes its nearing doom and feels an awful spell. Its strength is spent, its every trick is tried in vain till the good Angel leads it to the water, the running, living water, and dashing in it follows the cooling stream, and then with force renewed takes to the woods again.

There is magic in running water. The hounds come to the very spot and halt and cast about; and halt and cast in vain. Their spell is broken by the merry stream, and the wild thing lives its life.

And this was one of the great secrets that Raggylug learned from his mother—"after the Brierrose, the Water is your friend."

One hot, muggy night in August, Molly led Rag through the woods. The cotton-white cushion she wore under her tail twinkled ahead and was his guiding lantern, though it went out as soon as she stopped and sat on it. After a few runs and stops to listen, they came to the edge of the pond. The hylas in the trees above them were singing '*sleep, sleep*,' and away out on a sunken log in the deep water, up to his chin in the cooling bath, a bloated bullfrog was singing the praises of a '*jug o' rum*.'

"Follow me still," said Molly, in rabbit, and 'flop' she went into the pond and struck out for the sunken log in the middle. Rag flinched but plunged with a little 'ouch,' gasping and wobbling his nose very fast but still copying his mother. The same movements as on land sent him through the water, and thus he found he could swim. On he went till he reached the sunken log and scrambled up by his dripping mother on the high dry end, with a rushy screen around them and the Water that tells no tales. After this in warm black nights when that old fox from

Rag followed the snow-white beacon

Springfield came prowling through the Swamp, Rag would note the place of the bullfrog's voice, for in case of direst need it might be a guide to safety. And thenceforth the words of the song that the bullfrog sang were, '*Come, come, in danger come.*'

This was the latest study that Rag took up with his mother—it was really a post-graduate course, for many little rabbits never learn it at all.

* * *

No wild animal dies of old age. Its life has soon or late a tragic end. It is only a question of how long it can hold out against its foes. But Rag's life was proof that once a rabbit passes out of his youth he is likely to outlive his prime and be killed only in the last third of life, the downhill third we call old age.

The Cottontails had enemies on every side. Their daily life was a series of escapes. For dogs, foxes, cats, skunks, coons, weasels, minks, snakes, hawks, owls, and men, and even insects were all plotting to kill them. They had hundreds of adventures, and at least once a day they had to fly for their lives and save themselves by their legs and wits.

More than once that hateful fox from Springfield drove them to taking refuge under the wreck of a barbed-wire hog-pen by the spring. But once there they could look calmly at him while he spiked his legs in vain attempts to reach them.

Once or twice Rag when hunted had played off the hound against a skunk that had seemed likely to be quite as dangerous as the dog.

Once he was caught alive by a hunter who had a hound and a ferret to help him. But Rag had the luck to escape next day, with a yet deeper distrust of ground holes. He was several times run into the water by the cat, and many times was chased by hawks and owls, but for each kind of danger there was a safeguard. His mother taught him the principal dodges, and he improved on them and made many new ones as he grew older. And the older and wiser he grew the less he trusted to his legs, and the more to his wits for safety.

Ranger was the name of a young hound in the neighborhood. To train him his master used to put him on the trail of one of the Cottontails. It was nearly always Rag that they ran, for the young buck enjoyed the runs as much as they did, the spice of danger in them being just enough for zest. He would say:

"Oh, mother! here comes the dog again, I must have a run to-day."

"You are too bold, Raggy, my son!" she might reply. "I fear you will run once too often."

"But, mother, it is such glorious fun to tease that fool dog, and it's all good training. I'll thump if I am too hard pressed, then you can come and change off while I get my second wind."

On he would come, and Ranger would take the trail and follow till Rag got tired of it. Then he either sent a thumping telegram for help, which brought Molly to take charge of the dog, or he got rid of the dog by some clever trick. A description of one of these shows how well Rag had learned the arts of the woods.

He knew that his scent lay best near the ground, and was strongest when he was warm. So if he could get off the ground, and be left in peace for half an hour to cool off, and for the trail to stale, he knew he would be safe. When, therefore, he tired of the chase, he made for the Creekside brier-patch, where he 'wound'—that is, zigzagged—till he left a course so crooked that the dog was sure to be greatly delayed in working it out. He then went straight to D in the woods, passing one hop to windward of the high log E. Stopping at D, he followed his back trail to F, here he leaped aside and ran toward G. Then, returning on his trail to J, he waited till the hound passed on his trail at I. Rag then got back on his old trail at H, and followed it to E, where, with a scent-baulk or great leap aside, he reached the high log, and running to its higher end, he sat like a bump.

Ranger lost much time in the bramble maze, and the scent was very poor when he got it straightened out, and came to D. Here he began to circle to pick it up, and after losing much time, struck the trail

The hound came sniffing along the log

which ended suddenly at G. Again he was at fault, and had to circle to find the trail. Wider and wider the circles, until at last, he passed right under the log Rag was on. But a cold scent, on a cold day, does not go downward much. Rag never budged nor winked, and the hound passed.

Again the dog came round. This time he crossed the low part of the log, and stopped to smell it. 'Yes, clearly it was rabbity,' but it was a stale scent now; still he mounted the log.

It was a trying moment for Rag, as the great hound came sniff-sniffing along the log. But his nerve did not forsake him; the wind was right; he had his mind made up to bolt as soon as Ranger came half way up. But he didn't come. A yellow cur would have seen the rabbit sitting there, but the hound did not, and the scent seemed stale, so he leaped off the log, and Rag had won.

* * *

Rag had never seen any other rabbit than his mother. Indeed he had scarcely thought about there being any other. He was more and more away from her now, and yet he never felt lonely, for rabbits do not hanker for company. But one day in December, while he was among the red dogwood brush, cutting a new path to the great Creekside thicket, he saw all at once against the sky over the Sunning Bank the head and ears of a strange rabbit. The newcomer had the air of a well-pleased discoverer and soon came hopping Rag's way along one of *his* paths into *his* Swamp. A new feeling rushed over him, that boiling mixture of anger and hatred called jealousy.

The stranger stopped at one of Rag's rubbing-trees—that is, a tree against which he used to stand on his heels and rub his chin as far up as he could reach. He thought he did this simply because he liked it; but all buck-rabbits do so, and several ends are served. It makes the tree rabbity, so that other rabbits know that this swamp already belongs to a rabbit family and is not open for settlement. It also lets the next one know by the scent if the last caller was an acquaintance, and the height from the ground of the rubbing-places shows how tall the rabbit is.

Now to his disgust Rag noticed that the newcomer was a head taller than himself, and a big, stout, buck at that. This was a wholly new experience and filled Rag with a wholly new feeling. The spirit of murder entered his heart; he chewed very hard with nothing in his mouth, and hopping forward onto a smooth piece of hard ground he struck slowly:

'Thump—thump—thump,' which is a rabbit telegram for, 'Get out of my swamp, or fight.'

The new-comer made a big V with his ears, sat upright for a few seconds, then, dropping on his fore-feet, sent along the ground a louder, stronger, 'Thump—thump—thump.'

And so war was declared.

They came together by short runs side-wise, each one trying to get the wind of the other and watching for a chance advantage. The stranger was a big, heavy buck with plenty of muscle, but one or two trifles such as treading on a turnover and failing to close when Rag was on low ground showed that he had not much cunning and counted on winning his battles by his weight. On he came at last and Rag met him like a little fury. As they came together they leaped up and struck out with their hind feet. *Thud, thud* they came, and down went poor little Rag. In a moment the stranger was on him with his teeth and Rag was bitten, and lost several tufts of hair before he could get up. But he was swift of foot and got out of reach. Again he charged and again he was knocked down and bitten severely. He was no match for his foe, and it soon became a question of saving his own life.

Hurt as he was he sprang away, with the stranger in full chase, and bound to kill him as well as to oust him from the Swamp where he was born. Rag's legs were good and so was his wind. The stranger was big and so heavy that he soon gave up the chase, and it was well for poor Rag that he did, for he was getting stiff from his wounds as well as tired. From that day began a reign of terror for Rag. His training had been against owls, dogs, weasels, men, and so on, but what to do when chased by another rabbit, he did not know. All he knew was to lay low till he was found, then run.

Poor little Molly was completely terrorized; she could not help Rag and sought only to hide. But the big buck soon found her out. She tried to run from him, but she was not now so swift as Rag. The stranger made no attempt to kill her, but he made love to her, and because she hated him and tried to get away, he treated her shamefully. Day after day he worried her by following her about, and often, furious at her lasting hatred, he would knock her down and tear out mouthfuls of her soft fur till his rage cooled somewhat, when he would let her go for a while. But his fixed purpose was to kill Rag, whose escape seemed hopeless. There was no other swamp he could go to, and whenever he took a nap now he had to be ready at any moment to dash for his life. A dozen times a day the big stranger came creeping up to where he slept, but each time the watchful Rag awoke in time to escape. To escape yet not to escape. He saved his life indeed, but oh! what a miserable life it had become. How maddening to be thus helpless, to see his little mother daily beaten and torn, as well as to see all his favorite feeding-grounds, the cosy nooks, and the pathways he had made with so much labor, forced from him by this hateful brute. Unhappy Rag realized that to the victor belong the spoils, and he hated him more than ever he did fox or ferret.

How was it to end? He was wearing out with running and watching and bad food, and little Molly's strength and spirit were breaking down under the long persecution. The stranger was ready to go to all lengths to destroy poor Rag, and at last stooped to the worst crime known among rabbits. However much they may hate each other, all good rabbits forget their feuds when their common enemy appears. Yet one day when a great goshawk came swooping over the Swamp, the stranger, keeping well under cover himself, tried again and again to drive Rag into the open.

Once or twice the hawk nearly had him, but still the briers saved him, and it was only when the big buck himself came near being caught that he gave it up. And again Rag escaped, but was no better off. He made up his mind to leave, with his mother, if possible, next night and go into the world in quest of some new home when he heard old Thunder, the hound, sniffing and searching about the outskirts of the swamp, and he resolved on playing a desperate game. He deliberately crossed the hound's view, and the chase that then began was fast and furious. Thrice around the Swamp they went till Rag had made sure that his mother was hidden safely and that his hated foe was in his usual nest. Then right into that nest and plump over him he jumped, giving him a rap with one hind foot as he passed over his head.

"You miserable fool, I kill you yet," cried the stranger, and up he jumped only to find himself between Rag and the dog and heir to all the peril of the chase.

On came the hound baying hotly on the straight-away scent. The buck's weight and size were great advantages in a rabbit fight, but now they were fatal. He did not know many tricks. Just the simple ones like 'double,' 'wind,' and 'hole-up,' that every baby Bunny knows. But the chase was too close for doubling and winding, and he didn't know where the holes were.

It was a straight race. The brier-rose, kind to all rabbits alike, did its best, but it was no use. The baying of the hound was fast and steady. The crashing of the brush and the yelping of the hound each time the briers tore his tender ears were borne to the two rabbits where they crouched in hiding. But suddenly these sounds stopped, there was a scuffle, then loud and terrible screaming.

Rag knew what it meant and it sent a shiver through him, but he soon forgot that when all was over and rejoiced to be once more the master of the dear old Swamp.

* * *

Old Olifant had doubtless a right to burn all those brush-piles in the east and south of the Swamp and to clear up the wreck of the old barbed-wire hog-pen just below the spring. But it was none the less hard on Rag and his mother. The first were their various residences and out-posts, and the second their grand fastness and safe retreat.

They had so long held the Swamp and felt it to be their very own in every part and suburb—including Olifant's grounds and buildings—that they would have resented the appearance of another rabbit even about the adjoining barnyard.

Their claim, that of long, successful occupancy, was exactly the same as that by which most nations hold their land, and it would be hard to find a better right.

During the time of the January thaw the Olifants had cut the rest of the large wood about the pond and curtailed the Cottontails' domain on all sides. But they still clung to the dwindling Swamp, for it was their home and they were loath to move to foreign parts. Their life of daily perils went on, but they were still fleet of foot, long of wind, and bright of wit. Of late they had been somewhat troubled by a mink that had wandered up-stream to their quiet nook. A little judicious guidance had transferred the uncomfortable visitor to Olifant's hen-house. But they were not yet quite sure that he had been properly looked after. So for the present they gave up using the ground-holes, which were, of course, dangerous blind-alleys, and stuck closer than ever to the briers and the brush-piles that were left.

That first snow had quite gone and the weather was bright and warm until now. Molly, feeling a touch of rheumatism, was somewhere in the lower thicket seeking a teaberry tonic. Rag was sitting in the weak sunlight on a bank in the east side. The smoke from the familiar gable chimney of Olifant's house come fitfully drifting a pale blue haze through the underwoods and showing as a dull brown against the brightness of the sky. The sun-gilt gable was cut off midway by the banks of brierbrush, that purple in shadow shone like rods of blazing crimson and gold in the light. Beyond the house the barn with its gable and roof, new gilt as the house, stood up like a Noah's ark.

The sounds that came from it, and yet more the delicious smell that mingled with the smoke, told Rag that the animals were being fed cabbage in the yard. Rag's mouth watered at the idea of the feast. He blinked and blinked as he snuffed its odorous promises, for he loved cabbage dearly. But then he had been to the barnyard the night before after a few paltry clover-tops, and no wise rabbit would go two nights running to the same place.

Therefore he did the wise thing. He moved across where he could not smell the cabbage and made his supper of a bundle of hay that had been blown from the stack. Later, when about to settle for the night, he was joined by Molly, who had taken her teaberry and then eaten her frugal meal of sweet birch near the Sunning Bank.

Meanwhile the sun had gone about his business elsewhere, taking all his gold and glory with him. Off in the east a big black shutter came pushing up and rising higher and higher; it spread over the whole sky, shut out all light and left the world a very gloomy place indeed. Then another mischief-maker, the wind, taking advantage of the sun's absence, came on the scene and set about brewing trouble. The weather turned colder and colder; it seemed worse than when the ground had been covered with snow.

"Isn't this terribly cold? How I wish we had our stove-pipe brush-pile," said Rag.

"A good night for the pine-root hole," replied Molly, "but we have not yet seen the pelt of that mink on the end of the barn, and it is not safe till we do."

The hollow hickory was gone—in fact at this very moment its trunk, lying in the wood-yard, was harboring the mink they feared. So the Cottontails hopped to the south side of the pond and, choosing a brush-pile, they crept under and snuggled down for the night, facing the wind but with their noses in different directions so as to go out different ways in case of alarm. The wind blew harder and colder as the hours went by, and about midnight a fine icy snow came ticking down on the dead leaves and hissing through the brush heap. It might seem a poor night for hunting, but that old fox from Springfield was out. He came pointing up the wind in the shelter of the Swamp and chanced in the lee of the brush-pile, where he scented the sleeping Cottontails. He halted for a moment, then came stealthily sneaking up toward the brush under which his nose told him the rabbits were crouching. The noise of the wind and the sleet enabled him to come quite close before Molly heard the faint crunch of a dry leaf under his paw. She touched Rag's whiskers, and both were fully awake just as the fox sprang on them; but they always slept with their legs ready for a jump. Molly darted out into the blinding storm. The fox missed his spring but followed like a racer, while Rag dashed off to one side.

There was only one road for Molly; that was straight up the wind, and bounding for her life she gained a little over the unfrozen mud that would not carry the fox, till she reached the margin of the pond. No chance to turn now, on she must go.

Splash! splash! through the weeds she went, then plunge into the deep water.

And plunge went the fox close behind. But it was too much for Reynard on such a night. He turned back, and Molly, seeing only one course, struggled through the reeds into the deep water and struck out for the other shore. But there was a strong headwind. The little waves, icy cold, broke over her head as she swam, and the water was full of snow that blocked her way like soft ice, or floating mud. The dark line of the other shore seemed far, far away, with perhaps the fox waiting for her there.

But she laid her ears flat to be out of the gale, and bravely put forth all her strength with wind and tide against her. After a long, weary swim in the cold water, she had nearly reached the farther reeds when a great mass of floating snow barred her road; then the wind on the bank made strange, fox-like sounds that robbed her of all force, and she was drifted far backward before she could get free from the floating bar.

Again she struck out, but slowly—oh so slowly now. And when at last she reached the lee of the tall reeds, her limbs were numbed, her strength spent, her brave little heart was sinking, and she cared no more whether the fox were there or not. Through the reeds she did indeed pass, but once in the weeds her course wavered and slowed, her feeble strokes no longer sent her landward, the ice forming around her, stopped her altogether. In a little while the cold, weak limbs ceased to move, the furry nosetip of the little mother Cottontail wobbled no more, and the soft brown eyes were closed in death.

But there was no fox waiting to tear her with ravenous jaws. Rag had escaped the first onset of the foe, and as soon as he regained his wits he came running back to change-off and so help his mother. He met the old fox going round the pond to meet Molly and led him far

No chance to turn now

and away, then dismissed him with a barbed-wire gash on his head, and came to the bank and sought about and trailed and thumped, but all his searching was in vain; he could not find his little mother. He never saw her again, and he never knew whither she went, for she slept her never-waking sleep in the ice-arms of her friend the Water that tells no tales.

Poor little Molly Cottontail! She was a true heroine, yet only one of unnumbered millions that without a thought of heroism have lived and done their best in their little world, and died. She fought a good fight in the battle of life. She was good stuff; the stuff that never dies. For flesh of her flesh and brain of her brain was Rag. She lives in him, and through him transmits a finer fibre to her race.

And Rag still lives in the Swamp. Old Olifant died that winter, and the unthrifty sons ceased to clear the Swamp or mend the wire fences. Within a single year it was a wilder place than ever; fresh trees and brambles grew, and falling wires made many Cottontail castles and last retreats that dogs and foxes dared not storm. And there to this day lives Rag. He is a big strong buck now and fears no rivals. He has a large family of his own, and a pretty brown wife that he got no one knows where. There, no doubt, he and his children's children will flourish for many years to come, and there you may see them any sunny evening if you have learnt their signal code, and choosing a good spot on the ground, know just how and when to thump it.

BINGO

The Story of My Dog

It was early in November, 1882, and the Manitoba winter had just set in. I was tilting back in my chair for a few lazy moments after breakfast idly alternating my gaze from the one window-pane of our shanty, through which was framed a bit of the prairie and the end of our cowshed, to the old rhyme of the 'Franckelyn's dogge' pinned on the logs near by. But the dreamy mixture of rhyme and view was quickly dispelled by the sight of a large gray animal dashing across the prairie into the cowshed, with a smaller black and white animal in hot pursuit.

"A wolf," I exclaimed, and seizing a rifle dashed out to help the dog. But before I could get there they had left the stable, and after a short run over the snow the wolf again turned at bay, and the dog, our neighbor's collie, circled about watching his chance to snap.

I fired a couple of long shots, which had the effect only of setting them off again over the prairie. After another run this matchless dog closed and seized the wolf by the haunch, but again retreated to avoid the fierce return chop. Then there was another stand at bay, and again a race over the snow. Every few hundred yards this scene was repeated. The dog managing so that each fresh rush should be toward the settlement, while the wolf vainly tried to break back toward the dark belt of trees in the east. At last after a mile of this fighting and running I overtook them, and the dog, seeing that he now had good backing, closed in for the finish.

After a few seconds the whirl of struggling animals resolved itself into a wolf, on his back, with a bleeding collie gripping his throat, and it was now easy for me to step up and end the fight by putting a ball through the wolf's head.

Frank retreated each time the wolf turned

Then, when this dog of marvellous wind saw that his foe was dead, he gave him no second glance, but set out at a lope for a farm four miles across the snow where he had left his master when first the wolf was started. He was a wonderful dog, and even if I had not come he undoubtedly would have killed the wolf alone, as I learned he had already done with others of the kind, in spite of the fact that the wolf, though of the smaller or prairie race, was much larger than himself.

I was filled with admiration for the dog's prowess and at once sought to buy him at any price. The scornful reply of his owner was, "Why don't you try to buy one of the children?"

Since Frank was not in the market I was obliged to content myself with the next best thing, one of his alleged progeny. That is, a son of his wife. This probable offspring of an illustrious sire was a roly-poly ball of black fur that looked more like a long-tailed bear-cub than a puppy. But he had some tan markings like those on Frank's coat, that were, I hoped, guarantees of future greatness, and also a very characteristic ring of white that he always wore on his muzzle.

Having got possession of his person, the next thing was to find him a name. Surely this puzzle was already solved. The rhyme of the 'Franckelyn's dogge' was inbuilt with the foundation of our acquaintance, so with adequate pomp we 'yclept him little Bingo.'

* * *

The rest of that winter Bingo spent in our shanty, living the life of a lubberly, fat, well-meaning, ill-doing puppy; gorging himself with food and growing bigger and clumsier each day. Even sad experience failed to teach him that he must keep his nose out of the rat-trap. His most friendly overtures to the cat were wholly misunderstood and resulted only in an armed neutrality that, varied by occasional reigns of terror, continued to the end; which came when Bingo, who early showed a mind of his own, got a notion for sleeping at the barn and avoiding the shanty altogether.

When the spring came I set about his serious education. After much pains on my behalf and many pains on his, he learned to go at the word in quest of our old yellow cow, that pastured at will on the unfenced prairie.

Once he had learned his business, he became very fond of it and nothing pleased him more than an order to go and fetch the cow. Away he would dash, barking with pleasure and leaping high in the air that he might better scan the plain for his victim. In a short time he would return driving her at full gallop before him, and gave her no peace until, puffing and blowing, she was safely driven into the farthest corner of her stable.

Less energy on his part would have been more satisfactory, but we bore with him until he grew so fond of this semi-daily hunt that he began to bring 'old Dunne' without being told. And at length not once or twice but a dozen times a day this energetic cowherd would sally forth on his own responsibility and drive the cow home to the stable.

At last things came to such a pass that whenever he felt like taking a little exercise, or had a few minutes of spare time, or even happened to think of it, Bingo would sally forth at racing speed over the plain and a few minutes later return, driving the unhappy yellow cow at full gallop before him.

At first this did not seem very bad, as it kept the cow from straying too far; but soon it was seen that it hindered her feeding. She became thin and gave less milk; it seemed to weigh on her mind too, as she was always watching nervously for that hateful dog, and in the mornings would hang around the stable as though afraid to venture off and subject herself at once to an onset.

This was going too far. All attempts to make Bingo more moderate

in his pleasure were failures, so he was compelled to give it up altogether. After this, though he dared not bring her home, he continued to
show his interest by lying at her stable door while she was being
milked.

As the summer came on the mosquitoes became a dreadful plague,
and the consequent vicious switching of Dunne's tail at milking-time
even more annoying than the mosquitoes.

Fred, the brother who did the milking, was of an inventive as well
as an impatient turn of mind, and he devised a simple plan to stop the
switching. He fastened a brick to the cow's tail, then set blithely about
his work assured of unusual comfort while the rest of us looked on in
doubt.

Suddenly through the mist of mosquitoes came a dull whack and
an outburst of 'language.' The cow went on placidly chewing till Fred
got on his feet and furiously attacked her with the milking-stool. It was
bad enough to be whacked on the ear with a brick by a stupid old cow,
but the uproarious enjoyment and ridicule of the bystanders made it
unendurable.

Bingo, hearing the uproar, and divining that he was needed,
rushed in and attacked Dunne on the other side. Before the affair
quieted down the milk was spilt, the pail and stool were broken, and
the cow and the dog severely beaten.

Poor Bingo could not understand it at all. He had long ago learned
to despise that cow, and now in utter disgust he decided to forsake
even her stable door, and from that time he attached himself exclus-
ively to the horses and their stable.

The cattle were mine, the horses were my brother's, and in trans-
ferring his allegiance from the cow-stable to the horse-stable Bingo
seemed to give me up too, and anything like daily companionship
ceased, and, yet, whenever any emergency arose Bingo turned to me
and I to him, and both seemed to feel that the bond between man and
dog is one that lasts as long as life.

The only other occasion on which Bingo acted as cowherd was in
the autumn of the same year at the annual Carberry Fair. Among the
dazzling inducements to enter one's stock there was, in addition to a

prospect of glory, a cash prize of 'two dollars,' for the 'best collie in training.'

Misled by a false friend, I entered Bingo and early on the day fixed, the cow was driven to the prairie just outside of the village. When the time came she was pointed out to Bingo and the word given—'Go fetch the cow.' It was the intention, of course, that he should bring her to me at the judge's stand.

But the animals knew better. They hadn't rehearsed all summer for nothing. When Dunne saw Bingo's careering form she knew that her only hope for safety was to get into her stable, and Bingo was equally sure that his sole mission in life was to quicken her pace in that direction. So off they raced over the prairie, like a wolf after a deer, and heading straight toward their home two miles away, they disappeared from view.

That was the last that judge or jury ever saw of dog or cow. The prize was awarded to the only other entry.

* * *

Bingo's loyalty to the horses was quite remarkable; by day he trotted beside them, and by night he slept at the stable door. Where the team went Bingo went, and nothing kept him away from them. This interesting assumption of ownership lent the greater significance to the following circumstance.

I was not superstitious, and up to this time had had no faith in omens, but was now deeply impressed by a strange occurrence in which Bingo took a leading part. There were but two of us now living on the De Winton Farm. One morning my brother set out for Boggy Creek for a load of hay. It was a long day's journey there and back, and he made an early start. Strange to tell, Bingo for once in his life did not follow the team. My brother called to him, but still he stood at a safe distance, and eyeing the team askance, refused to stir. Suddenly he raised his nose in the air and gave vent to a long, melancholy howl. He watched the wagon out of sight, and even followed for a hundred yards or so, raising his voice from time to time in the most doleful howlings. All that day he stayed about the barn, the only time that he was willingly separated from the horses, and at intervals howled a very death dirge. I was alone, and the dog's behaviour inspired me with an awful foreboding of calamity, that weighed upon me more and more as the hours passed away.

About six o'clock Bingo's howlings became unbearable, so that for lack of a better thought I threw something at him, and ordered him away. But oh, the feeling of horror that filled me! Why did I let my brother go away alone? Should I ever again see him alive? I might have known from the dog's actions that something dreadful was about to happen.

At length the hour for his return arrived, and there was John on his load. I took charge of the horses, vastly relieved, and with an air of assumed unconcern, asked, "All right?"

"Right," was the laconic answer.

Who now can say that there is nothing in omens?

And yet, when long afterward, I told this to one skilled in the occult, he looked grave, and said, "Bingo always turned to you in a crisis?"

"Yes."

"Then do not smile. It was you that were in danger that day; he stayed and saved your life, though you never knew from what."

* * *

Early in the spring I had begun Bingo's education. Very shortly afterward he began mine.

Midway on the two-mile stretch of prairie that lay between our shanty and the village of Carberry, was the corner-stake of the farm; it was a stout post in a low mound of earth, and was visible from afar.

I soon noticed that Bingo never passed without minutely examining this mysterious post. Next I learned that it was also visited by the prairie wolves as well as by all the dogs in the neighborhood, and at length, with the aid of a telescope, I made a number of observations that helped me to an understanding of the matter and enabled me to enter more fully into Bingo's private life.

The post was by common agreement a registry of the canine tribes. Their exquisite sense of smell enabled each individual to tell at once by the track and trace what other had recently been at the post. When the snow came much more was revealed. I then discovered that this post was but one of a system that covered the country; that in short, the entire region was laid out in signal stations at convenient intervals. These were marked by any conspicuous post, stone, buffalo skull, or other object that chanced to be in the desired locality, and extensive observation showed that it was a very complete system for getting and giving the news.

Each dog or wolf makes a point of calling at those stations that are near his line of travel to learn who has recently been there, just as a man calls at his club on returning to town and looks up the register.

I have seen Bingo approach the post, sniff, examine the ground about, then growl, and with bristling mane and glowing eyes, scratch fiercely and contemptuously with his hind feet, finally walking off very stiffly, glancing back from time to time. All of which, being interpreted, said:

"*Grrrh! woof!* there's that dirty cur of McCarthy's. *Woof!* I'll 'tend to him to-night. *Woof! woof!*" On another occasion, after the preliminaries, he became keenly interested and studied a coyote's track that came and went, saying to himself, as I afterward learned:

"A coyote track coming from the north, smelling of dead cow. Indeed? Pollworth's old Brindle must be dead at last. This is worth looking into."

At other times he would wag his tail, trot about the vicinity and come again and again to make his own visit more evident, perhaps for the benefit of his brother Bill just back from Brandon! So that it was not by chance that one night Bill turned up at Bingo's home and was taken to the hills where a delicious dead horse afforded a chance to suitably celebrate the reunion.

At other times he would be suddenly aroused by the news, take up the trail, and race to the next station for later information.

Sometimes his inspection produced only an air of grave attention, as though he said to himself, "Dear me, who the deuce is this?" or "It seems to me I met that fellow at the Portage last summer."

One morning on approaching the post Bingo's every hair stood on end, his tail dropped and quivered, and he gave proof that he was suddenly sick at the stomach, sure signs of terror. He showed no desire to follow up or know more of the matter, but returned to the house, and half an hour afterward his mane was still bristling and his expression one of hate or fear.

I studied the dreaded track and learned that in Bingo's language the half-terrified, deep-gurgled '*grr-wff*' means '*timber wolf*.'

These were among the things that Bingo taught me. And in the after time when I might chance to see him arouse from his frosty nest by the stable door, and after stretching himself and shaking the snow from his shaggy coat, disappear into the gloom at a steady trot, trot, trot, I used to think:

"Aha! old dog, I know where you are off to, and why you eschew the shelter of the shanty. Now I know why your nightly trips over the country are so well timed, and how you know just where to go for what you want, and when and how to seek it."

* * *

In the autumn of 1884, the shanty at De Winton farm was closed and Bingo changed his home to the establishment, that is, to the stable, not the house, of Gordon Wright, our most intimate neighbor.

Since the winter of his puppyhood he had declined to enter a house at any time excepting during a thunder-storm. Of thunder and guns he had a deep dread—no doubt the fear of the first originated in the second, and that arose from some unpleasant shot-gun experiences, the cause of which will be seen. His nightly couch was outside the stable, even during the coldest weather, and it was easy to see that he enjoyed to the full the complete nocturnal liberty entailed. Bingo's midnight wanderings extended across the plains for miles. There was plenty of proof of this. Some farmers at very remote points sent word to old Gordon that if he did not keep his dog home nights, they would use the shotgun, and Bingo's terror of firearms would indicate that the threats were not idle. A man living as far away as Petrel, said he saw a large black wolf kill a coyote on the snow one winter evening, but afterward he changed his opinion and 'reckoned it must 'a' been Wright's dog.' Whenever the body of a winter-killed ox or horse was exposed, Bingo was sure to repair to it nightly, and driving away the prairie wolves, feast to repletion.

Sometimes the object of a night foray was merely to maul some distant neighbor's dog, and notwithstanding vengeful threats, there seemed no reason to fear that the Bingo breed would die out. One man even avowed that he had seen a prairie wolf accompanied by three young ones which resembled the mother, excepting that they were very large and black and had a ring of white around the muzzle.

True or not as that may be, I know that late in March, while we were out in the sleigh with Bingo trotting behind, a prairie wolf was started from a hollow. Away it went with Bingo in full chase, but the wolf

Bingo and the she-wolf

did not greatly exert itself to escape, and within a short distance Bingo was close up, yet strange to tell, there was no grappling, no fight!

Bingo trotted amiably alongside and licked the wolf's nose.

We were astounded, and shouted to urge Bingo on. Our shouting and approach several times started the wolf off at speed and Bingo again pursued until he had overtaken it, but his gentleness was too obvious.

"It is a she-wolf, he won't harm her," I exclaimed as the truth dawned on me. And Gordon said: "Well, I be darned."

So we called our unwilling dog and drove on.

For weeks after this we were annoyed by the depredations of a prairie wolf who killed our chickens, stole pieces of pork from the end of the house, and several times terrified the children by looking into the window of the shanty while the men were away.

Against this animal Bingo seemed to be no safeguard. At length the wolf, a female, was killed, and then Bingo plainly showed his hand by his lasting enmity toward Oliver, the man who did the deed.

* * *

It is wonderful and beautiful how a man and his dog will stick to one another, through thick and thin. Butler tells of an undivided Indian tribe, in the Far North which was all but exterminated by an internecine feud over a dog that belonged to one man and was killed by his neighbor; and among ourselves we have lawsuits, fights, and deadly feuds, all pointing the same old moral, 'Love me, love my dog.'

One of our neighbors had a very fine hound that he thought the best and dearest dog in the world. I loved him, so I loved his dog, and when one day poor Tan crawled home terribly mangled and died by the door, I joined my threats of vengeance with those of his master and thenceforth lost no opportunity of tracing the miscreant, both by offering rewards and by collecting scraps of evidence. At length it was clear that one of three men to the southward had had a hand in the cruel affair. The scent was warming up, and soon we should have been in a position to exact rigorous justice at least, from the wretch who had murdered poor old Tan.

Then something took place which at once changed my mind and led me to believe that the mangling of the old hound was not by any means an unpardonable crime, but indeed on second thoughts was rather commendable than otherwise.

Gordon Wright's farm lay to the south of us, and while there one day, Gordon, Jr., knowing that I was tracking the murderer, took me aside and looking about furtively, he whispered, in tragic tones:

"It was Bing done it."

And the matter dropped right there. For I confess that from that moment I did all in my power to baffle the justice I had previously striven so hard to further.

I had given Bingo away long before, but the feeling of ownership did not die; and of this indissoluble fellowship of dog and man he was soon to take part in another important illustration.

Old Gordon and Oliver were close neighbors and friends; they joined in a contract to cut wood, and worked together harmoniously till late on in winter. Then Oliver's old horse died, and he, determining to profit as far as possible, dragged it out on the plain and laid poison baits for wolves around it. Alas for poor Bingo! He would lead a wolfish life, though again and again it brought him into wolfish misfortunes.

He was as fond of dead horse as any of his wild kindred. That very night, with Wright's own dog Curley, he visited the carcass. It seemed as though Bing had busied himself chiefly keeping off the wolves, but Curley feasted immoderately. The tracks in the snow told the story of the banquet; the interruption as the poison began to work, and of the

Bingo watched while Curley feasted

dreadful spasms of pain during the erratic course back home where Curley, falling in convulsions at Gordon's feet, died in the greatest agony.

'Love me, love my dog,' no explanations or apology were acceptable; it was useless to urge that it was accidental, the long-standing fued between Bingo and Oliver was now remembered as an important side-light. The wood-contract was thrown up, all friendly relations ceased, and to this day there is no county big enough to hold the rival factions which were called at once into existence and to arms by Curley's dying yell.

It was months before Bingo really recovered from the poison. We believed indeed that he never again would be the sturdy old-time Bingo. But when the spring came he began to gain strength, and bettering as the grass grew, he was within a few weeks once more in full health and vigor to be a pride to his friends and a nuisance to his neighbors.

* * *

Changes took me far away from Manitoba, and on my return in 1886 Bingo was still a member of Wright's household. I thought he would have forgotten me after two years absence, but not so. One day early in the winter, after having been lost for forty-eight hours, he crawled home to Wright's with a wolf-trap and a heavy log fast to one foot, and the foot frozen to stony hardness. No one had been able to approach to help him, he was so savage, when I, the stranger now, stooped down and laid hold of the trap with one hand and his leg with the other. Instantly he seized my wrist in his teeth.

Without stirring I said, "Bing, don't you know me?"

He had not broken the skin and at once released his hold and offered no further resistance, although he whined a good deal during the removal of the trap. He still acknowledged me his master in spite of his change of residence and my long absence, and notwithstanding my surrender of ownership I still felt that he was my dog.

Bing was carried into the house much against his will and his frozen foot thawed out. During the rest of the winter he went lame and two of his toes eventually dropped off. But before the return of warm weather his health and strength were fully restored, and to a casual glance he bore no mark of his dreadful experience in the steel trap.

* * *

During that same winter I caught many wolves and foxes who did not
have Bingo's good luck in escaping the traps, which I kept out right into
the spring, for bounties are good even when fur is not.

Kennedy's Plain was always a good trapping ground because it
was unfrequented by man and yet lay between the heavy woods and
the settlement. I had been fortunate with the fur here, and late in April
rode in on one of my regular rounds.

The wolf-traps are made of heavy steel and have two springs, each
of one hundred pounds power. They are set in fours around a buried
bait, and after being strongly fastened to concealed logs are carefully
covered in cotton and in fine sand so as to be quite invisible.

A prairie wolf was caught in one of these. I killed him with a club
and throwing him aside proceeded to reset the trap as I had done so
many hundred times before. All was quickly done. I threw the trap-
wrench over toward the pony, and seeing some fine sand near by, I
reached out for a handful of it to add a good finish to the setting.

Oh, unlucky thought! Oh, mad heedlessness born of long immunity! That fine sand was *on the next wolf-trap* and in an instant I was a
prisoner. Although not wounded, for the traps have no teeth, and my
thick trapping gloves deadened the snap, I was firmly caught across the
hand above the knuckles. Not greatly alarmed at this, I tried to reach
the trap-wrench with my right foot. Stretching out at full length, face
downward, I worked myself toward it, making my imprisoned arm as
long and straight as possible. I could not see and reach at the same
time, but counted on my toe telling me when I touched the little iron
key to my fetters. My first effort was a failure; strain as I might at the
chain my toe struck no metal. I swung slowly around my anchor, but
still failed. Then a painfully taken observation showed I was much too
far to the west. I set about working around, tapping blindly with my toe
to discover the key. Thus wildly groping with my right foot I forgot
about the other till there was a sharp 'clank' and the iron jaws of trap
No. 3 closed tight on my left foot.

The terrors of the situation did not, at first, impress me, but I soon
found that all my struggles were in vain. I could not get free from either
trap or move the traps together, and there I lay stretched out and firmly
staked to the ground.

What would become of me now? There was not much danger of
freezing for the cold weather was over, but Kennedy's Plain was never
visited excepting by the winter wood-cutters. No one knew where I had
gone, and unless I could manage to free myself there was no prospect
ahead but to be devoured by wolves, or else die of cold and starvation.

As I lay there the red sun went down over the spruce swamp west
of the plain, and a shorelark on a gopher mound a few yards off twit-
tered his evening song, just as one had done the night before at our
shanty door, and though the numb pains were creeping up my arm,
and a deadly chill possessed me, I noticed how long his little ear-tufts
were. Then my thoughts went to the comfortable supper-table at

Wright's shanty, and I thought, now they are frying the pork for supper, or just sitting down. My pony still stood as I left him with his bridle on the ground patiently waiting to take me home. He did not understand the long delay, and when I called, he ceased nibbling the grass and looked at me in dumb, helpless enquiry. If he would only go home the empty saddle might tell the tale and bring help. But his very faithfulness kept him waiting hour after hour while I was perishing of cold and hunger.

Then I remembered how old Girou the trapper had been lost, and in the following spring his comrades found his skeleton held by the leg in a bear-trap. I wondered which part of my clothing would show my identity. Then a new thought came to me. This is how a wolf feels when he is trapped. Oh! what misery have I been responsible for! Now I'm to pay for it.

Night came slowly on. A prairie wolf howled, the pony pricked up his ears and walking nearer to me, stood with his head down. Then another prairie wolf howled and another, and I could make out that they were gathering in the neighborhood. There I lay prone and helpless, wondering if it would not be strictly just that they should come and tear me to pieces. I heard them calling for a long time before I realized that dim, shadowy forms were sneaking near. The horse saw them first, and his terrified snort drove them back at first, but they came nearer next time and sat around me on the prairie. Soon one bolder than the others crawled up and tugged at the body of his dead relative. I shouted and he retreated growling. The pony ran to a distance in terror. Presently the wolf returned, and after two or three of these retreats and returns, the body was dragged off and devoured by the rest in a few minutes.

After this they gathered nearer and sat on their haunches to look at me, and the boldest one smelt the rifle and scratched dirt on it. He retreated when I kicked at him with my free foot and shouted, but growing bolder as I grew weaker he came and snarled right in my face. At this several others snarled and came up closer, and I realized that I was to be devoured by the foe that I most despised, when suddenly out of the gloom with a guttural roar sprang a great black wolf. The prairie wolves scattered like chaff except the bold one, which seized by the black new-comer was in a few moments a draggled corpse, and then, oh horrors! this mighty brute bounded at me and—Bingo—noble Bingo, rubbed his shaggy, panting sides against me and licked my cold face.

"Bingo—Bing—old—boy—Fetch me the trap-wrench!"

Away he went and returned dragging the rifle, for he knew only that I wanted something.

"No—Bing—the trap-wrench." This time it was my sash, but at last he brought the wrench and wagged his tail in joy that it was right. Reaching out with my free hand, after much difficulty I unscrewed the pillar-nut. The trap fell apart and my hand was released, and a minute later I was free. Bing brought the pony up, and after slowly walking to restore the circulation I was able to mount. Then slowly at first but soon at a gallop, with Bingo as herald careering and barking ahead, we set out for home, there to learn that the night before, though never taken on the trapping rounds, the brave dog had acted strangely, whimpering and watching the timber-trail; and at last when night came on, in spite of attempts to detain him he had set out in the gloom and guided by a knowledge that is beyond us had reached the spot in time to avenge me as well as set me free.

Stanch old Bing—he was a strange dog. Though his heart was with me, he passed me next day with scarcely a look, but responded with alacrity when little Gordon called him to a gopher-hunt. And it was so to the end; and to the end also he lived the wolfish life that he loved, and never failed to seek the winter-killed horses and found one again with a poisoned bait, and wolfishly bolted that; then feeling the pang, set out, not for Wright's but to find me, and reached the door of my shanty where I should have been. Next day on returning I found him dead in the snow with his head on the sill of the door—the door of his puppyhood's days; my dog to the last in his heart of hearts—it was my help he sought, and vainly sought, in the hour of his bitter extremity.

THE SPRINGFIELD FOX

The hens had been mysteriously disappearing for over a month; and when I came home to Springfield for the summer holidays it was my duty to find the cause. This was soon done. The fowls were carried away bodily one at a time, before going to roost or else after leaving, which put tramps and neighbors out of court; they were not taken from the high perches, which cleared all coons and owls; or left partly eaten, so that weasels, skunks, or minks were not the guilty ones, and the blame, therefore, was surely left at Reynard's door.

The great pine wood of Erindale was on the other bank of the river, and on looking carefully about the lower ford I saw a few fox-tracks and a barred feather from one of our Plymouth Rock chickens. On climbing the farther bank in search of more clews, I heard a great outcry of crows behind me, and turning, saw a number of these birds darting down at something in the ford. A better view showed that it was the old story, thief catch thief, for there in the middle of the ford was a fox with something in his jaws—he was returning from our barnyard with another hen. The crows, though shameless robbers themselves, are ever first to cry 'Stop thief,' and yet more than ready to take 'hush-money' in the form of a share in the plunder.

And this was their game now. The fox to get back home must cross the river, where he was exposed to the full brunt of the crow mob. He made a dash for it, and would doubtless have gotten across with his booty had I not joined in the attack, whereupon he dropped the hen, scarce dead, and disappeared in the woods.

This large and regular levy of provisions wholly carried off could mean but one thing, a family of little foxes at home; and to find them I now was bound.

That evening I went with Ranger, my hound, across the river into the Erindale woods. As soon as the hound began to circle, we heard the short, sharp bark of a fox from a thickly wooded ravine close by. Ranger dashed in at once, struck a hot scent and went off on a lively straight-away till his voice was lost in the distance away over the upland.

65

After nearly an hour he came back, panting and warm, for it was baking August weather, and lay down at my feet.

But almost immediately the same foxy '*Yap yurrr*' was heard close at hand and off dashed the dog on another chase.

Away he went in the darkness, baying like a foghorn, straight away to the north. And the loud '*Boo, boo,*' became a low '*oo, oo,*' and that a feeble '*o-o*' and then was lost. They must have gone some miles away, for even with ear to the ground I heard nothing of them though a mile was easy distance for Ranger's brazen voice.

As I waited in the black woods I heard a sweet sound of dripping water: '*Tink tank tenk tink, Ta tink tank tenk tonk.*'

I did not know of any spring so near, and in the hot night it was a glad find. But the sound led me to the bough of an oak-tree, where I found its source. Such a soft sweet song; full of delightful suggestion on such a night:

> *Tonk tank tenk tink*
> *Ta tink a tonk a tank a tink a*
> *Ta ta tink tank ta ta tonk tink*
> *Drink a tank a drink a drunk*

It was the 'water-dripping' song of the saw-whet owl.

But suddenly a deep raucous breathing and a rustle of leaves showed that Ranger was back. He was completely fagged out. His tongue hung almost to the ground and was dripping with foam, his flanks were heaving and spume-flecks dribbled from his breast and sides. He stopped panting a moment to give my hand a dutiful lick, then flung himself flop on the leaves to drown all other sounds with his noisy panting.

But again that tantalizing '*Yap yurrr*' was heard a few feet away, and the meaning of it all dawned on me.

We were close to the den where the little foxes were, and the old ones were taking turns in trying to lead us away.

It was late night now, so we went home feeling sure that the problem was nearly solved.

* * *

It was well known that there was an old fox with his family living in the neighborhood, but no one supposed them so near.

This fox had been called 'Scarface,' because of a scar reaching from his eye through and back of his ear; this was supposed to have been given him by a barbed-wire fence during a rabbit hunt, and as the hair came in white after it healed, it was always a strong mark.

The winter before I had met with him and had had a sample of his craftiness. I was out shooting, after a fall of snow, and had crossed the open fields to the edge of the brushy hollow back of the old mill. As my head rose to a view of the hollow I caught sight of a fox trotting at long range down the other side, in line to cross my course. Instantly I held motionless, and did not even lower or turn my head lest I should catch his eye by moving, until he went on out of sight in the thick cover at the bottom. As soon as he was hidden I bobbed down and ran to head him off where he should leave the cover on the other side, and was there in good time awaiting, but no fox came forth. A careful look showed the fresh track of a fox that had bounded from the cover, and following it with my eye I saw old Scarface himself far out of range behind me, sitting on his haunches and grinning as though much amused.

A study of the trail made all clear. He had seen me at the moment I saw him, but he, also like a true hunter, had concealed the fact, putting on an air of unconcern till out of sight, when he had run for his life around behind me and amused himself by watching my stillborn trick

In the springtime I had yet another instance of Scarface's cunning. I was walking with a friend along the road over the high pasture. We passed within thirty feet of a ridge on which were several gray and brown bowlders. When at the nearest point my friend said:

"Stone number three looks to me very much like a fox curled up."

But I could not see it, and we passed. We had not gone many yards farther when the wind blew on this bowlder as on fur.

My friend said, "I am sure that is a fox, lying asleep."

"We'll soon settle that," I replied, and turned back, but as soon as I had taken one step from the road, up jumped Scarface, for it was he, and ran. A fire had swept the middle of the pasture, leaving a broad belt of black; over this he skurried till he came to the unburnt yellow grass again, where he squatted down and was lost to view. He had been watching us all the time, and would not have moved had we kept to the road. The wonderful part of this is, not that he resembled the round stones and dry grass, but that he *knew he did*, and was ready to profit by it.

We soon found that it was Scarface and his wife Vixen that had made our woods their home and our barnyard their base of supplies.

Next morning a search of the pines showed a great bank of earth that had been scratched up within a few months. It must have come from a hole, and yet there was none to be seen. It is well known that a really cute fox, on digging a new den, brings all the earth out at the first hole made, but carries on a tunnel into some distant thicket. Then closing up for good the first made and too well-marked door, uses only the entrance hidden in the thicket.

So after a little search at the other side of a knoll, I found the real entry and good proof that there was a nest of little foxes inside.

Rising above the brush on the hillside was a great hollow basswood. It leaned a good deal and had a large hole at the bottom, and a smaller one at top.

We boys had often used this tree in playing Swiss Family Robinson, and by cutting steps in its soft punky walls had made it easy to go up and down in the hollow. Now it came in handy, for next day when the sun was warm I went there to watch, and from this perch on the roof, I soon saw the interesting family that lived in the cellar near by.

There were four little foxes; they looked curiously like little lambs, with their woolly coats, their long thick legs and innocent expressions, and yet a second glance at their broad, sharp-nosed, sharp-eyed visages showed that each of these innocents was the makings of a crafty old fox.

They played about, basking in the sun, or wrestling with each other till a slight sound made them skurry under ground. But their alarm was needless, for the cause of it was their mother; she stepped from the bushes bringing another hen—number seventeen as I remember. A low call from her and the little fellows came tumbling out. Then began a scene that I thought charming, but which my uncle would not have enjoyed at all.

They rushed on the hen, and tussled and fought with it, and each other, while the mother, keeping a sharp eye for enemies, looked on with fond delight. The expression on her face was remarkable. It was first a grinning of delight, but her usual look of wildness and cunning was there, nor were cruelty and nervousness lacking, but over all was the unmistakable look of the mother's pride and love.

The base of my tree was hidden in bushes and much lower than the knoll where the den was. So I could come and go at will without scaring the foxes.

For many days I went there and saw much of the training of the young ones. They early learned to turn to statuettes at any strange sound, and then on hearing it again or finding other cause for fear, to run for shelter.

Some animals have so much mother-love that it overflows and benefits outsiders. Not so old Vixen it would seem. Her pleasure in the cubs led to most refined cruelty. For she often brought home to them mice and birds alive, and with diabolic gentleness would avoid doing them serious hurt so that the cubs might have larger scope to torment them.

There was a woodchuck that lived over in the hill orchard. He was neither handsome nor interesting, but he knew how to take care of himself. He had digged a den between the roots of an old pine stump, so that the foxes could not follow him by digging. But hard work was not their way of life; wits they believed worth more than elbow-grease. This woodchuck usually sunned himself on the stump each morning. If he saw a fox near he went down in the door of his den, or if the enemy was very near he went inside and stayed long enough for the danger to pass.

One morning Vixen and her mate seemed to decide that it was time the children knew something about the broad subject of Woodchucks, and further that this orchard woodchuck would serve nicely for an object-lesson. So they went together to the orchard-fence unseen by old Chuckie on his stump. Scarface then showed himself in the orchard and quietly walked in a line so as to pass by the stump at a distance, but never once turned his head or allowed the ever watchful woodchuck to think himself seen. When the fox entered the field the woodchuck quietly dropped down to the mouth of his den; here he waited as the

They tussled and fought while their mother looked on with fond delight

fox passed, but concluding that after all wisdom is the better part, went into his hole.

This was what the foxes wanted. Vixen had kept out of sight, but now ran swiftly to the stump and hid behind it. Scarface had kept straight on, going very slowly. The woodchuck had not been frightened, so before long his head popped up between the roots and he looked around. There was that fox still going on, farther and farther away. The woodchuck grew bold as the fox went, and came out farther, and then seeing the coast clear, he scrambled onto the stump, and with one spring Vixen had him and shook him till he lay senseless. Scarface had watched out of the corner of his eye and now came running back. But Vixen took the chuck in her jaws and made for the den, so he saw he wasn't needed.

Back to the den came Vix, and carried the chuck so carefully that he was able to struggle a little when she got there. A low '*woof*' at the

Vix shows the cubs how to catch mice

den brought the little fellows out like schoolboys to play. She threw the wounded animal to them and they set on him like four little furies, uttering little growls and biting little bites with all the strength of their baby jaws, but the woodchuck fought for his life and beating them off slowly hobbled to the shelter of a thicket. The little ones pursued like a pack of hounds and dragged at his tail and flanks, but could not hold him back. So Vix overtook him with a couple of bounds and dragged him again into the open for the children to worry. Again and again this rough sport went on till one of the little ones was badly bitten, and his squeal of pain roused Vix to end the woodchuck's misery and serve him up at once.

Not far from the den was a hollow overgrown with coarse grass, the playground of a colony of field-mice. The earliest lesson in wood-craft that the little ones took, away from the den, was in this hollow. Here they had their first course of mice, the easiest of all game. In teaching, the main thing was example, aided by a deep-set instinct. The old fox, also, had one or two signs meaning "lie still and watch," "come, do as I do," and so on, that were much used.

So the merry lot went to this hollow one calm evening and Mother Fox made them lie still in the grass. Presently a faint squeak showed that the game was astir. Vix rose up and went on tip-toe into the grass—not crouching but as high as she could stand, sometimes on her hind legs so as to get a better view. The runs that the mice follow are hidden under the grass tangle, and the only way to know the where-abouts of a mouse is by seeing the slight shaking of the grass, which is the reason why mice are hunted only on calm days.

And the trick is to locate the mouse and seize him first and see him afterward. Vix soon made a spring, and in the middle of the bunch of dead grass that she grabbed was a field-mouse squeaking his last squeak.

He was soon gobbled, and the four awkward little foxes tried to do the same as their mother, and when at length the eldest for the first time in his life caught game, he quivered with excitement and ground his pearly little milk-teeth into the mouse with a rush of inborn savage-ness that must have surprised even himself.

Another home lesson was on the red-squirrel. One of these noisy, vulgar creatures, lived close by and used to waste part of each day scolding the foxes, from some safe perch. The cubs made many vain attempts to catch him as he ran across their glade from one tree to another, or spluttered and scolded at them a foot or so out of reach. But old Vixen was up in natural history—she knew squirrel nature and took the case in hand when the proper time came. She hid the children and lay down flat in the middle of the open glade. The saucy low-minded squirrel came and scolded as usual. But she moved no hair. He came nearer and at last right overhead to chatter:

"You brute you, you brute you."

But Vix lay as dead. This was very perplexing, so the squirrel came down the trunk and peeping about made a nervous dash across the grass, to another tree, again to scold from a safe perch.

"You brute you, you useless brute, scarrr-scarrrrr."

But flat and lifeless on the grass lay Vix. This was most tantalizing to the squirrel. He was naturally curious and disposed to be venturesome, so again he came to the ground and skurried across the glade nearer than before.

Still as death lay Vix, "surely she was dead." And the little foxes began to wonder if their mother wasn't asleep.

But the squirrel was working himself into a little craze of foolhardy curiosity. He had dropped a piece of bark on Vix's head, he had used up his list of bad words and he had done it all over again, without getting a sign of life. So after a couple more dashes across the glade he ventured within a few feet of the really watchful Vix, who sprang to her feet and pinned him in a twinkling.

"And the little ones picked the bones e-oh."

Thus the rudiments of their education were laid, and afterward as they grew stronger they were taken farther afield to begin the higher branches of trailing and scenting.

And the little ones picked the bones e-oh

For each kind of prey they were taught a way to hunt, for every animal has some great strength or it could not live, and some great weakness or the others could not live. The squirrel's weakness was foolish curiosity; the fox's that he can't climb a tree. And the training of the little foxes was all shaped to take advantage of the weakness of the other creatures and to make up for their own by defter play where they are strong.

From their parents they learned the chief axioms of the fox world. How, is not easy to say. But that they learned this in company with their parents was clear. Here are some that foxes taught me, without saying a word:—

Never sleep on your straight track.

Your nose is before your eyes, then trust it first.

A fool runs down the wind.

Running rills cure many ills.

Never take the open if you can keep the cover.

Never leave a straight trail if a crooked one will do.

If it's strange, it's hostile.

Dust and water burn the scent.

Never hunt mice in a rabbit-woods, or rabbits in a henyard.

Keep off the grass.

Inklings of the meanings of these were already entering the little one's minds—thus, 'Never follow what you can't smell,' was wise, they could see, because if you can't smell it, then the wind is so that it must smell you.

One by one they learned the birds and beasts of their home woods, and then as they were able to go abroad with their parents they learned new animals. They were beginning to think they knew the scent of everything that moved. But one night the mother took them to a field where was a strange black flat thing on the ground. She brought them on purpose to smell it, but at the first whiff their every hair stood on end, they trembled, they knew not why—it seemed to tingle through their blood and fill them with instinctive hate and fear. And when she saw its full effect she told them—

"That is man-scent."

* * *

Meanwhile the hens continued to disappear. I had not betrayed the den of cubs. Indeed, I thought a good deal more of the little rascals than I did of the hens; but uncle was dreadfully wrought up and made most disparaging remarks about my woodcraft. To please him I one day took the hound across to the woods and seating myself on a stump on the open hillside, I bade the dog go on. Within three minutes he sang out in the tongue all hunters know so well, "Fox! fox! fox! straight away down the valley."

After awhile I heard them coming back. There I saw the fox— Scarface—loping lightly across the river-bottom to the stream. In he went and trotted along in the shallow water near the margin for two hundred yards, then came out straight toward me. Though in full view, he saw me not but came up the hill watching over his shoulder for the hound. Within ten feet of me he turned and sat with his back to me while he craned his neck and showed an eager interest in the doings of the hound. Ranger came bawling along the trail till he came to the running water, the killer of scent, and here he was puzzled; but there was only one thing to do; that was by going up and down both banks find where the fox had left the river.

The fox before me shifted his position a little to get a better view and watched with a most human interest all the circling of the hound. He was so close that I saw the hair of his shoulder bristle a little when the dog came in sight. I could see the jumping of his heart on his ribs, and the gleam of his yellow eye. When the dog was wholly baulked by the water trick, it was comical to see:—he could not sit still, but rocked up and down in glee, and reared on his hind feet to get a better view of the slow-plodding hound. With mouth opened nearly to his ears, though not at all winded, he panted noisily for a moment, or rather he laughed gleefully, just as a dog laughs by grinning and panting.

Old Scarface wriggled in huge enjoyment as the hound puzzled over the trail so long that when he did find it, it was so stale he could barely follow it, and did not feel justified in tonguing on it at all.

As soon as the hound was working up the hill, the fox quietly went

to the woods. I had been sitting in plain view only ten feet away, but I had the wind and kept still and the fox never knew that his life had for twenty minutes been in the power of the foe he most feared. Ranger also would have passed me as near as the fox, but I spoke to him, and with a little nervous start he quit the trail and looking sheepish lay down by my feet.

This little comedy was played with variations for several days, but it was all in plain view from the house across the river. My uncle, impatient at the daily loss of hens, went out himself, sat on the open knoll, and when old Scarface trotted to his lookout to watch the dull hound on the river flat below, my uncle remorselessly shot him in the back, at the very moment when he was grinning over a new triumph.

* * *

But still the hens were disappearing. My uncle was wrathy. He determined to conduct the war himself, and sowed the woods with poison baits, trusting to luck that our own dogs would not get them. He indulged in contemptuous remarks on my by-gone woodcraft, and went out evenings with a gun and the two dogs, to see what he could destroy.

Vix knew right well what a poisoned bait was; she passed them by or else treated them with active contempt, but one she dropped down the hole of an old enemy, a skunk, who was never afterward seen. Formerly old Scarface was always ready to take charge of the dogs, and keep them out of mischief. But now that Vix had the whole burden of the brood, she could no longer spend time in breaking every track to the den, and was not always at hand to meet and mislead the foes that might be coming too near.

The end is easily foreseen. Ranger followed a hot trail to the den, and Spot, the fox-terrier, announced that the family was at home, and then did his best to go in after them.

The whole secret was out now, and the whole family doomed. The hired man came around with pick and shovel to dig them out, while we and the dogs stood by. Old Vix soon showed herself in the near woods, and led the dogs away off down the river, where she shook them off when she thought proper, by the simple device of springing on a sheep's back. The frightened animal ran for several hundred yards, then Vix got off, knowing that there was now a hopeless gap in the scent, and returned to the den. But the dogs, baffled by the break in the trail, soon did the same, to find Vix hanging about in despair, vainly trying to decoy us away from her treasures.

Meanwhile Paddy plied both pick and shovel with vigor and effect. The yellow, gravelly sand was heaping on both sides, and the shoulders of the sturdy digger were sinking below the level. After an hour's digging, enlivened by frantic rushes of the dogs after the old fox, who hovered near in the woods, Pat called:

"Here they are, sor!"

It was the den at the end of the burrow, and cowering as far back as they could, were the four little woolly cubs.

Before I could interfere, a murderous blow from the shovel, and a sudden rush for the fierce little terrier, ended the lives of three. The fourth and smallest was barely saved by holding him by his tail high out of reach of the excited dogs.

He gave one short squeal, and his poor mother came at the cry, and circled so near that she would have been shot but for the accidental protection of the dogs, who somehow always seemed to get between, and whom she once more led away on a fruitless chase. The little one saved alive was dropped into a bag, where he lay quite still. His unfortunate brothers were thrown back into their nursery bed, and buried under a few shovelfuls of earth.

We guilty ones then went back into the house, and the little fox was soon chained in the yard. No one knew just why he was kept alive, but in all a change of feeling had set in, and the idea of killing him was without a supporter.

He was a pretty little fellow, like a cross between a fox and a lamb. His woolly visage and form were strangely lamb-like and innocent, but one could find in his yellow eyes a gleam of cunning and savageness as unlamb-like as it possibly could be.

As long as anyone was near he crouched sullen and cowed in his shelter-box, and it was a full hour after being left alone before he ventured to look out.

My window now took the place of the hollow basswood. A number of hens of the breed he knew so well were about the cub in the yard. Late that afternoon as they strayed near the captive there was a sudden rattle of the chain, and the youngster dashed at the nearest one and

Slunk back into his box

would have caught him but for the chain which brought him up with a jerk. He got on his feet and slunk back to his box, and though he afterward made several rushes he so gauged his leap as to win or fail within the length of the chain and never again was brought up by its cruel jerk.

As night came down the little fellow became very uneasy, sneaking out of his box, but going back at each slight alarm, tugging at his chain, or at times biting it in fury while he held it down with his fore paws. Suddenly he paused as though listening, then raising his little black nose he poured out a short quavering cry.

Once or twice this was repeated, the time between being occupied in worrying the chain and running about. Then an answer came. The far-away *Yap-yurrr* of the old fox. A few minutes later a shadowy form appeared on the wood-pile. The little one slunk into his box, but at once returned and ran to meet his mother with all the gladness that a fox could show. Quick as a flash she seized him and turned to bear him away by the road she came. But the moment the end of the chain was reached the cub was rudely jerked from the old one's mouth, and she, scared by the opening of a window, fled over the wood-pile.

There she had lain, and mourned

An hour afterward the cub had ceased to run about or cry. I peeped out, and by the light of the moon saw the form of the mother at full length on the ground by the little one, gnawing at something—the clank of iron told what, it was that cruel chain. And Tip, the little one, meanwhile was helping himself to a warm drink.

On my going out she fled into the dark woods, but there by the shelter-box were two little mice, bloody and still warm, food for the cub brought by the devoted mother. And in the morning I found the chain was very bright for a foot or two next the little one's collar.

On walking across the woods to the ruined den, I again found signs of Vixen. The poor heart-broken mother had come and dug out the bedraggled bodies of her little ones.

There lay the three little baby foxes all licked smooth now, and by them were two of our hens fresh killed. The newly heaved earth was printed all over with tell-tale signs—signs that told me that here by the side of her dead she had watched like Rizpah. Here she had brought their usual meal, the spoil of her nightly hunt. Here she had stretched herself beside them and vainly offered them their natural drink and yearned to feed and warm them as of old; but only stiff little bodies under their soft wool she found, and little cold noses still and unresponsive.

A deep impress of elbows, breast, and hocks showed where she had laid in silent grief and watched them for long and mourned as a wild mother can mourn for its young. But from that time she came no more to the ruined den, for now she surely knew that her little ones were dead.

* * *

Tip the captive, the weakling of the brood, was now the heir to all her love. The dogs were loosed to guard the hens. The hired man had orders to shoot the old fox on sight—so had I, but was resolved never to see her. Chicken-heads, that a fox loves and a dog will not touch, had been poisoned and scattered through the woods; and the only way to the yard where Tip was tied, was by climbing the wood-pile after braving all other dangers. And yet each night old Vix was there to nurse her baby and bring it fresh-killed hens and game. Again and again I saw her, although she came now without awaiting the querulous cry of the captive.

The second night of the captivity I heard the rattle of the chain, and then made out that the old fox was there, hard at work digging a hole by the little one's kennel. When it was deep enough to half bury her, she gathered into it all the slack of the chain, and filled it again with earth. Then in triumph thinking she had gotten rid of the chain, she seized little Tip by the neck and turned to dash off up the woodpile, but alas only to have him jerked roughly from her grasp.

Poor little fellow, he whimpered sadly as he crawled into his box. After half an hour there was a great outcry among the dogs, and by their straight-away tonguing through the far woods I knew they were chasing Vix. Away up north they went in the direction of the railway and their noise faded from hearing. Next morning the hound had not come back. We soon knew why. Foxes long ago learned what a railroad is; they soon devised several ways of turning it to account. One way is when hunted to walk the rails for a long distance just before a train comes. The scent, always poor on iron, is destroyed by the train and there is always a chance of hounds being killed by the engine. But another way more sure, but harder to play, is to lead the hounds straight to a high trestle just ahead of the train, so that the engine overtakes them on it and they are surely dashed to destruction.

This trick was skilfully played, and down below we found the mangled remains of old Ranger and learned that Vix was already wreaking her revenge.

That same night she returned to the yard before Spot's weary limbs could bring him back and killed another hen and brought it to Tip, and stretched her panting length beside him that he might quench his thirst. For she seemed to think he had no food but what she brought.

It was that hen that betrayed to my uncle the nightly visits. My own sympathies were all turning to Vix, and I would have no hand in planning further murders. Next night my uncle himself watched, gun in hand, for an hour. Then when it became cold and the moon clouded over he remembered other important business elsewhere, and left Paddy in his place.

But Paddy was "onaisy" as the stillness and anxiety of watching worked on his nerves. And the loud bang! bang! an hour later left us sure only that powder had been burned.

In the morning we found Vix had not failed her young one. Again next night found my uncle on guard, for another hen had been taken. Soon after dark a single shot was heard, but Vix dropped the game she was bringing and escaped. Another attempt made that night called forth another gun-shot. Yet next day it was seen by the brightness of the chain that she had come again and vainly tried for hours to cut that hateful bond.

Such courage and stanch fidelity were bound to win respect, if not toleration. At any rate, there was no gunner in wait next night, when all was still. Could it be of any use? Driven off thrice with gun-shots, would she make another try to feed or free her captive young one?

Would she? Hers was a mother's love. There was but one to watch them this time, the fourth night, when the quavering whine of the little one was followed by that shadowy form above the wood-pile.

But carrying no fowl or food that could be seen. Had the keen huntress failed at last? Had she no head of game for this her only charge, or had she learned to trust his captors for his food?

No, far from all this. The wild-wood mother's heart and hate were true. Her only thought had been to set him free. All means she knew she tried, and every danger braved to tend him well and help him to be free. But all had failed.

Like a shadow she came and in a moment was gone, and Tip seized on something dropped, and crunched and chewed with relish what she brought. But even as he ate, a knife-like pang shot through and a scream of pain escaped him. Then there was a momentary struggle and the little fox was dead.

The mother's love was strong in Vix, but a higher thought was stronger. She knew right well the poison's power; she knew the poison bait, and would have taught him had he lived to know and shun it too. But now at last when she must choose for him a wretched prisoner's life or sudden death, she quenched the mother in her breast and freed him by the one remaining door.

It is when the snow is on the ground that we take the census of the woods, and when the winter came it told me that Vix no longer roamed the woods of Erindale. Where she went it never told, but only this, that she was gone.

Gone, perhaps, to some other far-off haunt to leave behind the sad remembrance of her murdered little ones and mate. Or gone, may be, deliberately, from the scene of a sorrowful life, as many a wild-wood mother has gone, by the means that she herself had used to free her young one, the last of all her brood.

Vix

THE PACING MUSTANG

Jo Calone threw down his saddle on the dusty ground, turned his horses loose, and went clanking into the ranch-house.

"Nigh about chuck time?" he asked.

"Seventeen minutes," said the cook glancing at the Waterbury, with the air of a train-starter, though this show of precision had never yet been justified by events.

"How's things on the Perico?" said Jo's pard.

"Hotter'n hinges," said Jo. "Cattle seem O.K.; lots of calves."

"I seen that bunch o' mustangs that waters at Antelope Springs; couple o' colts along; one little dark one, a fair dandy; a born pacer. I run them a mile or two, and he led the bunch, an' never broke his pace. Cut loose, an' pushed them jest for fun, an' darned if I could make him break."

"You didn't have no reefreshments along?" said Scarth, incredulously.

"That's all right, Scarth. You had to crawl on our last bet, an' you'll get another chance soon as you're man enough."

"Chuck," shouted the cook, and the subject was dropped. Next day the scene of the round-up was changed, and the mustangs were forgotten.

A year later the same corner of New Mexico was worked over by the roundup, and again the mustang bunch was seen. The dark colt was now a black yearling, with thin, clean legs and glossy flanks; and more than one of the boys saw with his own eyes this oddity—the mustang was a born pacer.

Jo was along, and the idea now struck him that that colt was worth having. To an Easterner this thought may not seem startling or original, but in the West, where an unbroken horse is worth $5, and where an ordinary saddle-horse is worth $15 or $20, the idea of a wild mustang being desirable property does not occur to the average cowboy, for mustangs are hard to catch, and when caught are merely wild animal prisoners, perfectly useless and untamable to the last. Not a few of the cattle-owners make a point of shooting all mustangs at sight, for they

80

are not only useless cumberers of the feeding-grounds, but commonly lead away domestic horses, which soon take to the wild life and are thenceforth lost.

Wild Jo Calone knew a 'bronk right down to subsoil.' "I never seen a white that wasn't soft, nor a chestnut that wasn't nervous, nor a bay that wasn't good if broke right, nor a black that wasn't hard as nails, an' full of the old Harry. All a black bronk wants is claws to be wus'n Daniel's hull outfit of lions."

Since then a mustang is worthless vermin, and a black mustang ten times worse than worthless, Jo's pard "didn't see no sense in Jo's wantin' to corral the yearling," as he now seemed intent on doing. But Jo got no chance to try that year.

He was only a cow-puncher on $25 a month, and tied to hours. Like most of the boys, he always looked forward to having a ranch and an outfit of his own. His brand, the hogpen, of sinister suggestion, was already registered at Santa Fé, but of horned stock it was borne by a single old cow, so as to give him a legal right to put his brand on any maverick (or unbranded animal) he might chance to find.

Yet each fall, when paid off, Jo could not resist the temptation to go to town with the boys and have a good time 'while the stuff held out.' So that his property consisted of little more than his saddle, his bed, and his old cow. He kept on hoping to make a strike that would leave him well fixed with a fair start, and when the thought came that the Black Mustang was his mascot, he only needed a chance to 'make his try.'

The roundup circled down to the Canadian River, and back in the fall by the Don Carlos Hills, and Jo saw no more of the Pacer, though he heard of him from many quarters, for the colt, now a vigorous, young horse, rising three, was beginning to be talked of.

Antelope Springs is in the middle of a great level plain. When the water is high it spreads into a small lake with a belt of sedge around it; when it is low there is a wide flat of black mud, glistening white with alkali in places, and the spring a water-hole in the middle. It has no flow or outlet and yet is fairly good water, the only drinking-place for many miles.

This flat, or prairie as it would be called farther north, was the favorite feeding-ground of the Black Stallion, but it was also the pasture of many herds of range horses and cattle. Chiefly interested was the 'L cross F' outfit. Foster, the manager and part owner, was a man of enterprise. He believed it would pay to handle a better class of cattle and horses on the range, and one of his ventures was ten half-blooded mares, tall, clean-limbed, deer-eyed creatures, that made the scrub cow-ponies look like pitiful starvelings of some degenerate and quite different species.

One of these was kept stabled for use, but the nine, after the weaning of their colts, managed to get away and wandered off on the range.

A horse has a fine instinct for the road to the best feed, and the nine mares drifted, of course, to the prairie of Antelope Springs, twenty miles to the southward. And when, later that summer Foster went to round them up, he found the nine indeed, but with them and guarding them with an air of more than mere comradeship was a coal-black stallion, prancing around and rounding up the bunch like an expert, his jet-black coat a vivid contrast to the golden hides of his harem.

The mares were gentle, and would have been easily driven homeward but for a new and unexpected thing. The Black Stallion became greatly aroused. He seemed to inspire them too with his wildness, and flying this way and that way drove the whole band at full gallop where he would. Away they went, and the little cow-ponies that carried the men were easily left behind.

This was maddening, and both men at last drew their guns and sought a chance to drop that 'blasted stallion.' But no chance came that was not 9 to 1 of dropping one of the mares. A long day of manoeuvring made no change. The Pacer, for it was he, kept his family together and disappeared among the southern sandhills. The cattlemen on their jaded ponies set out for home with the poor satisfaction of vowing vengeance for their failure on the superb cause of it.

One of the most aggravating parts of it was that one or two experiences like this would surely make the mares as wild as the Mustang, and there seemed to be no way of saving them from it.

Scientists differ on the power of beauty and prowess to attract female admiration among the lower animals, but whether it is admiration or the prowess itself, it is certain that a wild animal of uncommon gifts soon wins a large following from the harems of his rivals. And the great Black Horse, with his inky mane and tail and his green-lighted eyes, ranged through all that region and added to his following from many bands till not less than a score of mares were in his 'bunch.' Most were merely humble cow-ponies turned out to range, but the nine great mares were there, a striking group by themselves. According to all reports, this bunch was always kept rounded up and guarded with such energy and jealousy that a mare, once in it, was a lost animal so far as man was concerned, and the ranchmen realized soon that they had gotten on the range a mustang that was doing them more harm than all other sources of loss put together.

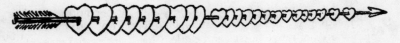

* * *

It was December, 1893. I was new in the country, and was setting out from the ranch-house on the Pinavetitos, to go with a wagon to the Canadian River. As I was leaving, Foster finished his remark by; "And if you get a chance to draw a bead on that accursed mustang, don't fail to drop him in his tracks."

This was the first I had heard of him, and as I rode along I gathered from Burns, my guide, the history that has been given. I was full of curiosity to see the famous three-year-old, and was not a little disappointed on the second day when we came to the prairie on Antelope Springs and saw no sign of the Pacer or his band.

But on the next day, as we crossed the Alamosa Arroyo, and were rising to the rolling prairie again, Jack Burns, who was riding on ahead, suddenly dropped flat on the neck of his horse, and swung back to me in the wagon, saying:

"Get out your rifle, here's that——stallion."

I seized my rifle, and hurried forward to a view over the prairie ridge. In the hollow below was a band of horses, and there at one end was the Great Black Mustang. He had heard some sound of our approach, and was not unsuspicious of danger. There he stood with head and tail erect, and nostrils wide, an image of horse perfection and beauty, as noble an animal as ever ranged the plains, and the mere notion of turning that magnificent creature into a mass of carrion was horrible. In spite of Jack's exhortation to 'shoot quick,' I delayed, and threw open the breach, whereupon he, always hot and hasty, swore at my slowness, growled, 'Gi' me that gun,' and as he seized it I turned the muzzle up, and *accidentally* the gun went off.

Instantly the herd below was all alarm, the great black leader snorted and neighed and dashed about. And the mares bunched, and away all went in a rumble of hoofs, and a cloud of dust.

The Stallion careered now on this side, now on that, and kept his eye on all and led and drove them far away. As long as I could see I watched, and never once did he break his pace.

Jack made Western remarks about me and my gun, as well as that mustang, but I rejoiced in the Pacer's strength and beauty, and not for all the mares in the bunch would I have harmed his glossy hide.

* * *

There are several ways of capturing wild horses. One is by creasing—that is, grazing the animal's nape with a rifle-ball so that he is stunned long enough for hobbling.

"Yes! I seen about a hundred necks broke trying it, but I never seen a mustang creased yet," was Wild Jo's critical remark.

Sometimes, if the shape of the country abets it, the herd can be driven into a corral; sometimes with extra fine mounts they can be run down, but by far the commonest way, paradoxical as it may seem, is to *walk* them down.

The fame of the Stallion that never was known to gallop was spreading. Extraordinary stories were told of his gait, his speed, and his wind, and when old Montgomery of the 'triangle-bar' outfit came out plump at Well's Hotel in Clayton, and in presence of witnesses said he'd give one thousand dollars cash for him safe in a box-car, providing the stories were true, a dozen young cow-punchers were eager to cut loose and win the purse, as soon as present engagements were up. But Wild Jo had had his eye on this very deal for quite a while; there was no time to lose, so ignoring present contracts he rustled all night to raise the necessary equipment for the game.

By straining his already overstrained credit, and taxing the already overtaxed generosity of his friends, he got together an expedition consisting of twenty good saddle-horses, a mess-wagon, and a fortnight's stuff for three men—himself, his 'pard,' Charley, and the cook.

Then they set out from Clayton, with the avowed intention of walking down the wonderfully swift wild horse. The third day they arrived at Antelope Springs, and as it was about noon they were not surprised to see the black Pacer marching down to drink with all his band behind him. Jo kept out of sight until the wild horses each and all had drunk their fill, for a thirsty animal always travels better than one laden with water.

Jo then rode quietly forward. The Pacer took alarm at half a mile, and led his band away out of sight on the soapweed mesa to the southeast. Jo followed at a gallop till he once more sighted them, then came back and instructed the cook, who was also teamster, to make for Alamosa Arroyo in the south. Then away to the southeast he went after the mustangs. After a mile or two he once more sighted them, and walked his horse quietly till so near that they again took alarm and circled away to the south. An hour's trot, not on the trail, but cutting across to where they ought to go, brought Jo again in close sight. Again he walked quietly toward the herd, and again there was the alarm and flight. And so they passed the afternoon, but circled ever more and more to the south, so that when the sun was low they were, as Jo had expected, not far from Alamosa Arroyo. The band was again close at hand, and Jo, after starting them off, rode to the wagon, while his pard, who had been taking it easy, took up the slow chase on a fresh horse.

After supper the wagon moved on to the upper ford of the Alamosa, as arranged, and there camped for the night.

Meanwhile, Charley followed the herd. They had not run so far as at first, for their pursuer made no sign of attack, and they were getting used to his company. They were more easily found, as the shadows fell, on account of a snow-white mare that was in the bunch. A young moon in the sky now gave some help, and relying on his horse to choose the path, Charley kept him quietly walking after the herd, represented by that ghost-white mare, till they were lost in the night. He then got off, unsaddled and picketed his horse, and in his blanket quickly went to sleep.

At the first streak of dawn he was up, and within a short half-mile, thanks to the snowy mare, he found the band. At his approach, the shrill neigh of the Pacer bugled his troop into a flying squad. But on the first mesa they stopped, and faced about to see what this persistent follower was, and what he wanted. For a moment or so they stood against the sky to gaze, and then deciding that he knew him as well as he wished to, that black meteor flung his mane on the wind, and led off at his tireless, even swing, while the mares came streaming after.

Away they went, circling now to the west, and after several repetitions of this same play, flying, following, and overtaking, and flying again, they passed, near noon, the old Apache look-out, Buffalo Bluff.

And here, on watch, was Jo. A long thin column of smoke told Charley to come to camp, and with a flashing pocket-mirror he made response.

Jo, freshly mounted, rode across, and again took up the chase, and back came Charley to camp to eat and rest, and then move on up stream.

All that day Jo followed, and managed, when it was needed, that the herd should keep the great circle of which the wagon cut a small chord. At sundown he came to Verde Crossing, and there was Charley with a fresh horse and food, and Jo went on in the same calm, dogged way. All the evening he followed, and far into the night, for the wild herd was now getting somewhat used to the presence of the harmless strangers, and were more easily followed; moreover, they were tiring out with perpetual travelling. They were no longer in the good grass country, they were not grain-fed like the horses on their track, and above all, the slight but continuous nervous tension was surely telling. It spoiled their appetites, but made them very thirsty. They were allowed, and as far as possible encouraged, to drink deeply at every chance. The effect of large quantities of water on a running animal is well known; it tends to stiffen the limbs and spoil the wind. Jo carefully guarded his own horse against such excess, and both he and his horse were fresh when they camped that night on the trail of the jaded mustangs.

At dawn he found them easily close to hand, and though they ran at first they did not go far before they dropped into a walk. The battle seemed nearly won now, for the chief difficulty in the 'walk-down' is to keep track of the herd the first two or three days when they are fresh.

All that morning Jo kept in sight, generally in close sight, of the band. About ten o'clock, Charley relieved him near José Peak and that day the mustangs walked only a quarter of a mile ahead with much less spirit than the day before and circled now more north again. At night Charley was supplied with a fresh horse and followed as before.

Next day the mustangs walked with heads held low, and in spite of the efforts of the Black Pacer at times they were less than a hundred yards ahead of their pursuer.

The fourth and fifth days passed the same way, and now the herd was nearly back to Antelope Springs. So far all had come out as expected. The chase had been in a great circle with the wagon following a lesser circle. The wild herd was back to its starting-point, worn out; and the hunters were back, fresh and on fresh horses. The herd was kept from drinking till late in the afternoon and then driven to the Springs to swell themselves with a perfect water gorge. Now was the chance for the skilful ropers on the grain-fed horses to close in, for the sudden heavy drink was ruination, almost paralysis, of wind and limb, and it would be easy to rope and hobble them one by one.

There was only one weak spot in the programme, the Black Stallion, the cause of the hunt, seemed made of iron, that ceaseless swinging pace seemed as swift and vigorous now as on the morning when the chase began. Up and down he went rounding up the herd and urging them on by voice and example to escape. But they were played out. The old white mare that had been such help in sighting them at night, had dropped out hours ago, dead beat. The half-bloods seemed to be losing all fear of the horsemen, the band was clearly in Jo's power. But the one who was the prize of all the hunt seemed just as far as ever out of reach.

Here was a puzzle. Jo's comrades knew him well and would not have been surprised to see him in a sudden rage attempt to shoot the Stallion down. But Jo had no such mind. During that long week of following he had watched the horse all day at speed and never once had he seen him gallop.

The horseman's adoration of a noble horse had grown and grown, till now he would as soon have thought of shooting his best mount as firing on that splendid beast.

Jo even asked himself whether he would take the handsome sum that was offered for the prize. Such an animal would be a fortune in himself to sire a race of pacers for the track.

But the prize was still at large—the time had come to finish up the hunt. Jo's finest mount was caught. She was a mare of Eastern blood, but raised on the plains. She never would have come into Jo's possession but for a curious weakness. The loco is a poisonous weed that grows in these regions. Most stock will not touch it; but sometimes an animal tries it and becomes addicted to it. It acts somewhat like morphine, but the animal, though sane for long intervals, has always a passion for the herb and finally dies mad. A beast with the craze is said to be locoed. And Jo's best mount had a wild gleam in her eye that to an expert told the tale.

But she was swift and strong and Jo chose her for the grand finish of the chase. It would have been an easy matter now to rope the mares, but was no longer necessary. They could be separated from their black leader and driven home to the corral. But that leader still had the look of untamed strength. Jo, rejoicing in a worthy foe, went bounding forth to try the odds. The lasso was flung on the ground and trailed to take out every kink, and gathered as he rode into neatest coils across his left palm. Then putting on the spur the first time in that chase he rode straight for the Stallion a quarter of a mile beyond. Away he went, and away went Jo, each at his best, while the fagged-out mares scattered right and left and let them pass. Straight across the open plain the fresh horse went at its hardest gallop, and the Stallion, leading off, still kept his start and kept his famous swing.

It was incredible, and Jo put on more spur and shouted to his horse, which fairly flew, but shortened up the space between by not a single inch. For the Black One whirled across the flat and up and passed a soapweed mesa and down across a sandy treacherous plain, then over a grassy stretch where prairie dogs barked, then hid below, and on came Jo, but there to see, could he believe his eyes, the Stallion's start grown longer still, and Jo began to curse his luck, and urge and spur his horse until the poor uncertain brute got into such a state of nervous fright, her eyes began to roll, she wildly shook her head from side to side, no longer picked her ground—a badger-hole received her foot and down she went, and Jo went flying to the earth. Though badly bruised, he gained his feet and tried to mount his crazy beast. But she, poor brute, was done for—her off fore-leg hung loose.

There was but one thing to do. Jo loosed the cinch, put Lightfoot out of pain, and carried back the saddle to the camp. While the Pacer steamed away till lost to view.

This was not quite defeat, for all the mares were manageable now, and Jo and Charley drove them carefully to the 'L cross F' corral and claimed a good reward. But Jo was more than ever bound to own the Stallion. He had seen what stuff was made of, he prized him more and more, and only sought to strike some better plan to catch him.

* * *

The cook on that trip was Bates—Mr. Thomas Bates, he called himself at the post-office where he regularly went for the letters and remittance which never came. Old Tom Turkeytrack, the boys called him, from his cattle-brand, which he said was on record at Denver, and which, according to his story, was also borne by countless beef and saddle stock on the plains of the unknown North.

When asked to join the trip as a partner, Bates made some sarcastic remarks about horses not fetching $12 a dozen, which had been literally true within the year, and he preferred to go on a very meagre salary. But no one who once saw the Pacer going had failed to catch the craze. Turkeytrack experienced the usual change of heart. He now wanted to own that mustang. How this was to be brought about he did not clearly see until one day there called at the ranch that had 'secured his services,' as he put it, one, Bill Smith, more usually known as Horseshoe Billy, from his cattle-brand. While the excellent fresh beef and bread and the vile coffee, dried peaches and molasses were being consumed, he of the horseshoe remarked, in tones which percolated through a huge stop-gap of bread:

"Wall, I seen that thar Pacer to-day, nigh enough to put a plait in his tail."

"What, you didn't shoot?"

"No, but I come mighty near it."

"Don't you be led into no sich foolishness," said a 'double-bar H' cow-puncher at the other end of the table. "I calc'late that maverick 'ill carry my brand before the moon changes."

"You'll have to be pretty spry or you'll find a 'triangle dot' on his weather side when you get there."

"Where did you run acrost him?"

"Wall, it was like this; I was riding the flat by Antelope Springs and I sees a lump on the dry mud inside the rush belt. I knowed I never seen that before, so rides up, thinking it might be some of our stock, an' seen it was a horse lying plump flat. The wind was blowing like—— from him to me, so I rides up close and seen it was the Pacer, dead as a mackerel. Still, he didn't look swelled or cut, and there wa'n't no smell, an' I didn't know what to think till I seen his ear twitch off a fly and then I knowed he was sleeping. I gits down me rope and coils it, and seen it was old and pretty shaky in spots, and me saddle a single cinch, an' me pony about 700 again a 1,200 lbs. stallion, an' I sez to meself, sez I: 'Tain't no use, I'll only break me cinch and git throwed an' lose me saddle.' So I hits the saddle-horn a crack with the hondu, and I wish't you'd a seen that mustang. He lept six foot in the air an' landed on all fours and snorted like he was shunting cars. His eyes fairly bugged out an' he lighted out lickety split for California, and he orter be there about now if he kep' on like he started—and I swear he never made a break the hull trip."

The story was not quite so consecutive as given here. It was much punctuated by present engrossments, and from first to last was more or less infiltrated through the necessaries of life, for Bill was a healthy young man without a trace of false shame. But the account was complete and everyone believed it, for Billy was known to be reliable. Of all those who heard, old Turkeytrack talked the least and probably thought the most, for it gave him a new idea.

During his after-dinner pipe he studied it out and deciding that he could not go it alone, he took Horseshoe Billy into his council and the result was a partnership in a new venture to capture the Pacer; that is, the $5,000 that was now said to be the offer for him safe in a box-car.

Antelope Springs was still the usual watering-place of the Pacer. The water being low left a broad belt of dry black mud between the sedge and the spring. At two places this belt was broken by a well-marked trail made by the animals coming to drink. Horses and wild animals usually kept to these trails, though the horned cattle had no hesitation in taking a short cut through the sedge.

In the most used of these trails the two men set to work with shovels and digged a pit 15 feet long, 6 feet wide and 7 feet deep. It was a hard twenty hours work for them as it had to be completed between the Mustang's drinks, and it began to be very damp work before it was finished. With poles, brush, and earth it was then cleverly covered over and concealed. And the men went to a distance and hid in pits made for the purpose.

About noon the Pacer came, alone now since the capture of his band. The trail on the opposite side of the mud belt was little used, and old Tom, by throwing some fresh rushes across it, expected to make sure that the Stallion would enter by the other, if indeed he should by any caprice try to come by the unusual path.

What sleepless angel is it watches over and cares for the wild animals? In spite of all reasons to take the usual path, the Pacer came along the other. The suspicious-looking rushes did not stop him; he walked calmly to the water and drank. There was only one way now to prevent utter failure; when he lowered his head for the second draft which horses always take, Bates and Smith quit their holes and ran swiftly toward the trail behind him, and when he raised his proud head Smith sent a revolver-shot into the ground behind him.

Away went the Pacer at his famous gait straight to the trap. Another second and he would be into it. Already he is on the trail, and already they feel they have him, but the Angel of the wild things is with him, that incomprehensible warning comes, and with one mighty bound he clears the fifteen feet of treacherous ground and spurns the earth as he fades away unharmed, never again to visit Antelope Springs by either of the beaten paths.

* * *

Wild Jo never lacked energy. He meant to catch that Mustang, and when he learned that others were bestirring themselves for the same purpose he at once set about trying the best untried plan he knew—the plan by which the coyote catches the fleeter jackrabbit, and the mounted Indian the far swifter antelope—the old plan of the relay chase.

The Canadian River on the south, its affluent, the Piñavetitos Arroyo, on the northeast, and the Don Carlos Hills with the Ute Creek Cañon on the west, formed a sixty-mile triangle that was the range of the Pacer. It was believed that he never went outside this, and at all times Antelope Springs was his headquarters. Jo knew this country well, all the water-holes and cañon crossings as well as the ways of the Pacer.

If he could have gotten fifty good horses he could have posted them to advantage so as to cover all points, but twenty mounts and five good riders were all that proved available.

The horses, grain-fed for two weeks before, were sent on ahead; each man was instructed now to play his part and sent to his post the day before the race. On the day of the start Jo with his wagon drove to the plain of Antelope Springs and, camping far off in a little draw, waited.

At last he came, that coal-black Horse, out from the sand-hills at the south, alone as always now, and walked calmly down to the Springs and circled quite around it to sniff for any hidden foe. Then he approached where there was no trail at all and drank.

Jo watched and wished he would drink a hogshead. But the moment that he turned and sought the grass Jo spurred his steed. The Pacer heard the hoofs, then saw the running horse, and did not want a nearer view but led away. Across the flat he went down to the south, and kept the famous swinging gait that made his start grow longer. Now through the sandy dunes he went, and steadying to an even pace he gained considerably and Jo's too-laden horse plunged through the sand and sinking fetlock deep, lost at every bound. Then came a level stretch where the runner seemed to gain, and then a long decline where Jo's horse dared not run his best, so lost again at every step.

But on they went, and Jo spared neither spur nor quirt. A mile—a mile—and another mile, and the far-off rock at Arriba loomed up ahead.

And there Jo knew fresh mounts were held, and on they dashed. But the night-black mane out level on the breeze ahead was gaining more and more.

Arriba Cañon reached at last, the watcher stood aside, for it was not wished to turn the race, and the Stallion passed—dashed down, across and up the slope, with that unbroken pace, the only one he knew.

And Jo came bounding on his foaming steed, and leaped on the waiting mount, then urged him down the slope and up upon the track, and on the upland once more drove in the spurs, and raced and raced, and raced, but not a single inch he gained.

Ga-lump, ga-lump, ga-lump with measured beat he went—an hour— an hour, and another hour—Arroyo Alamosa just ahead with fresh relays, and Jo yelled at his horse and pushed him on and on. Straight for the place the Black One made, but on the last two miles some strange foreboding turned him to the left, and Jo foresaw escape in this, and pushed his jaded mount at any cost to head him off, and hard as they had raced this was the hardest race of all, with gasps for breath and leather squeaks at every straining bound. Then cutting right across, Jo seemed to gain, and drawing his gun he fired shot after shot to toss the dust, and so turned the Stallion's head and forced him back to take the crossing to the right.

Down they went. The Stallion crossed and Jo sprang to the ground. His horse was done, for thirty miles had passed in the last stretch, and Jo himself was worn out. His eyes were burnt with flying alkali dust. He was half blind so he motioned to his 'pard' to "go ahead and keep him straight for Alamosa ford."

Out shot the rider on a strong, fresh steed, and away they went— up and down on the rolling plain—the Black Horse flecked with snowy foam. His heaving ribs and noisy breath showed what he felt—but on and on he went.

And Tom on Ginger seemed to gain, then lose and lose, when in an hour the long decline of Alamosa came. And there a freshly mounted lad took up the chase and turned it west, and on they went past towns of prairie dogs, through soapweed tracts and cactus brakes by scores, and pricked and wrenched rode on. With dust and sweat the Black was now a dappled brown, but still he stepped the same. Young Carrington, who followed, had hurt his steed by pushing at the very start, and spurred and urged him now to cut across a gulch at which the Pacer shied. Just one misstep and down they went.

The boy escaped, but the pony lies there yet, and the wild Black Horse kept on.

This was close to old Gallego's ranch, where Jo himself had cut across refreshed to push the chase. Within thirty minutes he was again scorching the Pacer's trail.

Far in the west the Carlos Hills were seen, and there Jo knew fresh men and mounts were waiting, and that way the indomitable rider tried

Away went the mustang at his famous pace

to turn the race, but by a sudden whim, of the inner warning born per-haps—the Pacer turned. Sharp to the north he went, and Jo, the skilful wrangler, rode and rode and yelled and tossed the dust with shots, but down a gulch the wild black meteor streamed and Jo could only follow. Then came the hardest race of all; Jo, cruel to the Mustang, was crueller to his mount and to himself. The sun was hot, the scorching plain was dim in shimmering heat, his eyes and lips were burnt with sand and salt, and yet the chase sped on. The only chance to win would be if he could drive the Mustang back to Big Arroyo Crossing. Now almost for the first time he saw signs of weakening in the Black. His mane and tail were not just quite so high, and his short half mile of start was down by more than half, but still he stayed ahead and paced and paced and paced.

An hour and another hour, and still they went the same. But they turned again, and night was near when big Arroyo ford was reached—fully twenty miles. But Jo was game, he seized the waiting horse. The one he left went gasping to the stream and gorged himself with water till he died.

Then Jo held back in hopes the foaming Black would drink. But he was wise; he gulped a single gulp, splashed through the stream and then passed on with Jo at speed behind him. And when they last were seen the Black was on ahead just out of reach and Jo's horse bounding on.

It was morning when Jo came to camp on foot. His tale was briefly told:—eight horses dead—five men worn out—the matchless Pacer safe and free.

"'Tain't possible; it can't be done. Sorry I didn't bore his hellish carcass through when I had the chance," said Jo, and gave it up.

* * *

Old Turkeytrack was cook on this trip. He had watched the chase with as much interest as anyone, and when it failed he grinned into the pot and said: "That mustang's mine unless I'm a darned fool." Then falling back on Scripture for a precedent, as was his habit, he still addressed the pot:

"Reckon the Philistines tried to run Samson down and they got done up, an' would a stayed done ony for a nat'ral weakness on his part. An' Adam would a loafed in Eden yit ony for a leetle failing which we all onderstand. An' it aint $5000 I'll take for him nuther."

Much persecution had made the Pacer wilder than ever. But it did not drive him away from Antelope Springs. That was the only drink-ing-place with absolutely no shelter for a mile on every side to hide an enemy. Here he came almost every day about noon, and after thor-oughly spying the land approached to drink.

His had been a lonely life all winter since the capture of his harem, and of this old Turkeytrack was fully aware. The old cook's chum had a nice little brown mare which he judged would serve his ends, and taking a pair of the strongest hobbles, a spade, a spare lasso, and a stout post he mounted the mare and rode away to the famous Springs.

A few antelope skimmed over the plain before him in the early freshness of the day. Cattle were lying about in groups, and the loud, sweet song of the prairie lark was heard on every side. For the bright snowless winter of the mesas was gone and the springtime was at hand. The grass was greening and all nature seemed turning to thoughts of love.

It was in the air, and when the little brown mare was picketed out to graze she raised her nose from time to time to pour forth a long shrill whinny that surely was her song, if song she had, of love.

Old Turkeytrack studied the wind and the lay of the land. There was the pit he had labored at, now opened and filled with water that was rank with drowned prairie dogs and mice. Here was the new trail the animals were forced to make by the pit. He selected a sedgy clumb near some smooth, grassy ground, and first firmly sunk the post, then dug a hole large enough to hide in, and spread his blanket in it. He shortened up the little mare's tether, till she could scarcely move; then on the ground between he spread his open lasso, tying the long end to the post, then covered the rope with dust and grass, and went into his hiding-place.

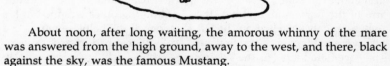

About noon, after long waiting, the amorous whinny of the mare was answered from the high ground, away to the west, and there, black against the sky, was the famous Mustang.

Down he came at that long swinging gait, but grown crafty with much pursuit, he often stopped to gaze and whinny, and got answer that surely touched his heart. Nearer he came again to call, then took alarm, and paced all around in a great circle to try the wind for his foes, and seemed in doubt. The Angel whispered "Don't go." But the brown mare called again. He circled nearer still, and neighed once more, and got reply that seemed to quell all fears, and set his heart aglow.

Nearer still he pranced, till he touched Solly's nose with his own, and finding her as responsive as he well could wish, thrust aside all thoughts of danger, and abandoned himself to the delight of conquest, until, as he pranced around, his hind legs for a moment stood within the evil circle of the rope. One deft sharp twitch, the noose flew tight, and he was caught.

A snort of terror and a bound in the air gave Tom the chance to add the double hitch. The loop flashed up the line, and snake-like bound those mighty hoofs.

Terror lent speed and double strength for a moment, but the end of the rope was reached, and down he went a captive, a hopeless prisoner at last. Old Tom's ugly, little crooked form sprang from the pit to complete the mastering of the great glorious creature whose mighty strength had proved as nothing when matched with the wits of a little old man. With snorts and desperate bounds of awful force the great beast dashed and struggled to be free; but all in vain. The rope was strong.

The second lasso was deftly swung, and the forefeet caught, and then with a skilful move the feet were drawn together, and down went the raging Pacer to lie a moment later 'hog-tied' and helpless on the ground. There he struggled till worn out, sobbing great convulsive sobs while tears ran down his cheeks.

Tom stood by and watched, but a strange revulsion of feeling came over the old cow-puncher. He trembled nervously from head to foot, as he had not done since he roped his first steer, and for a while could do nothing but gaze on his tremendous prisoner. But the feeling soon passed away. He saddled Delilah, and taking the second lasso, roped the great horse about the neck, and left the mare to hold the Stallion's head, while he put on the hobbles. This was soon done, and sure of him now old Bates was about to loose the ropes, but on a sudden thought he stopped. He had quite forgotten, and had come unprepared for something of importance. In Western law the Mustang was the property of the first man to mark him with his brand; how was this to be done with the nearest branding-iron twenty miles away?

Old Tom went to his mare, took up her hoofs one at a time and examined each shoe. Yes! one was a little loose; he pushed and pried it with the spade, and got it off. Buffalo chips and kindred fuel were plentiful about the plain, so a fire was quickly made, and he soon had one arm of the horse-shoe red hot, then holding the other wrapped in his sock he rudely sketched on the left shoulder of the helpless mustang a turkeytrack, his brand, the first time really that it had ever been used. The Pacer shuddered as the hot iron seared his flesh, but it was quickly done, and the famous Mustang Stallion was a maverick no more.

Now all there was to do was to take him home. The ropes were loosed, the Mustang felt himself freed, thought he was free, and sprang to his feet only to fall as soon as he tried to take a stride. His forefeet were strongly tied together, his only possible gait a shuffling walk, or else a desperate labored bounding with feet so unnaturally held that within a few yards he was inevitably thrown each time he tried to break away. Tom on the light pony headed him off again and again, and by dint of driving, threatening, and manoeuvring, contrived to force his foaming, crazy captive northward toward the Piñavetitos Cañon. But the wild horse would not drive, would not give in. With snorts of terror or of rage and maddest bounds, he tried and tried to get away. It was one long cruel fight; his glossy sides were thick with dark foam, and the foam was stained with blood. Countless hard falls and exhaustion that a long day's chase was powerless to produce was telling on him; his straining bounds first this way and then that, were not now quite so strong, and the spray he snorted as he gasped was half a spray of blood. But his captor, relentless, masterful and cool, still forced him on. Down the slope toward the cañon they had come, every yard a fight, and now they were at the head of the draw that took the trail down to the only crossing of the cañon, the northmost limit of the Pacer's ancient range.

From this the first corral and ranch-house were in sight. The man rejoiced, but the Mustang gathered his remaining strength for one more desperate dash. Up, up the grassy slope from the trail he went, defied the swinging, slashing rope and the gunshot fired in air, in vain attempt to turn his frenzied course. Up, up and on, above the sheerest cliff he dashed then sprang away into the vacant air, down—down— two hundred downward feet to fall, and land upon the rocks below, a lifeless wreck—but free.

WULLY

The Story of a Yaller Dog

Wully was a little yaller dog. A yaller dog, be it understood, is not necessarily the same as a yellow dog. He is not simply a canine whose capillary covering is highly charged with yellow pigment. He is the mongrelest mixture of all mongrels, the least common multiple of all dogs, the breedless union of all breeds, and though of no breed at all, he is yet of older, better breed than any of his aristocratic relations, for he is nature's attempt to restore the ancestral jackal, the parent stock of all dogs.

Indeed, the scientific name of the jackal (*Canis aureus*) means simply 'yellow dog,' and not a few of that animal's characteristics are seen in his domesticated representative. For the plebeian cur is shrewd, active, and hardy, and far better equipped for the real struggle of life than any of his 'thoroughbred' kinsmen.

If we were to abandon a yaller dog, a greyhound, and a bulldog on a desert island, which of them after six months would be alive and well? Unquestionably it would be the despised yellow cur. He has not the speed of the greyhound, but neither does he bear the seeds of lung and skin diseases. He has not the strength or reckless courage of the bulldog, but he has something a thousand times better, he has *common sense.* Health and wit are no mean equipment for the life struggle, and when the dog-world is not 'managed' by man, they have never yet failed to bring out the yellow mongrel as the sole and triumphant survivor.

Once in a while the reversion to the jackal type is more complete, and the yaller dog has pricked and pointed ears. Beware of him then. He is cunning and plucky and can bite like a wolf. There is a strange, wild streak in his nature too, that under cruelty or long adversity may develop into deadliest treachery in spite of the better traits that are the foundation of man's love for the dog.

96

The three maroons

* * *

Away up in the Cheviots little Wully was born. He and one other of the litter were kept; his brother because he resembled the best dog in the vicinity, and himself because he was a little yellow beauty.

His early life was that of a sheep-dog, in company with an experienced collie who trained him, and an old shepherd who was scarcely inferior to them in intelligence. By the time he was two years old Wully was full grown and had taken a thorough course in sheep. He knew them from ram-horn to lamb-hoof, and old Robin, his master, at length had such confidence in his sagacity that he would frequently stay at the tavern all night while Wully guarded the woolly idiots in the hills. His education had been wisely bestowed and in most ways he was a very bright little dog with a future before him. Yet he never learned to despise that addle-pated Robin. The old shepherd, with all his faults, his continual striving after his ideal state—intoxication—and his mind-shrivelling life in general was rarely brutal to Wully, and Wully repaid him with an exaggerated worship that the greatest and wisest in the land would have aspired to in vain.

Wully could not have imagined any greater being than Robin, and yet for the sum of five shillings a week all Robin's vital energy and mental force were pledged to the service of a not very great cattle and sheep dealer, the real proprietor of Wully's charge, and when this man, really less great than the neighboring laird, ordered Robin to drive his flock by stages to the Yorkshire moors and markets, of all the 376 mentalities concerned, Wully's was the most interested and interesting.

The journey through Northumberland was uneventful. At the River Tyne the sheep were driven on to the ferry and landed safely in smoky South Shields. The great factory chimneys were just starting up

for the day and belching out fogbanks and thunder-rollers of opaque leaden smoke that darkened the air and hung low like a storm-cloud over the streets. The sheep thought that they recognized the fuming dun of an unusually heavy Cheviot storm. They became alarmed, and in spite of their keepers stampeded through the town in 374 different directions.

Robin was vexed to the inmost recesses of his tiny soul. He stared stupidly after the sheep for half a minute, then gave the order, "Wully, fetch them in." After this mental effort he sat down, lit his pipe, and taking out his knitting began to work on a half-finished sock.

To Wully the voice of Robin was the voice of God. Away he ran in 374 different directions, and headed off and rounded up the 374 different wanderers, and brought them back to the ferry-house before Robin, who was stolidly watching the process, had toed off his sock.

Finally Wully—not Robin—gave the sign that all were in. The old shepherd proceeded to count them—370, 371, 372, 373.

"Wully," he said reproachfully, "thar no' a' here. Thur's anither." And Wully, stung with shame, bounded off to scour the whole city for the missing one. He was not long gone when a small boy pointed out to Robin that the sheep were all there, the whole 374. Now Robin was in a quandary. His order was to hasten on to Yorkshire, and yet he knew that Wully's pride would prevent his coming back without another sheep, even if he had to steal it. Such things had happened before, and resulted in embarrassing complications. What should he do? There was five shillings a week at stake. Wully was a good dog, it was a pity to lose him, but then, his orders from the master; and again, if Wully stole an extra sheep to make up the number, then what—in a foreign land too? He decided to abandon Wully, and push on alone with the sheep. And how he fared no one knows or cares.

Meanwhile, Wully careered through miles of streets hunting in vain for his lost sheep. All day he searched, and at night, famished and worn out, he sneaked shamefacedly back to the ferry, only to find that master and sheep had gone. His sorrow was pitiful to see. He ran about whimpering, then took the ferryboat to the other side, and searched everywhere for Robin. He returned to South Shields and searched there, and spent the rest of the night seeking for his wretched idol. The next day he continued his search, he crossed and recrossed the river many times. He watched and smelt everyone that came over, and with significant shrewdness he sought unceasingly in the neigboring taverns for his master. The next day he set to work systematically to smell everyone that might cross the ferry.

The ferry makes fifty trips a day, with an average of one hundred persons a trip, yet never once did Wully fail to be on the gang-plank and smell every pair of legs that crossed—5,000 pairs, 10,000 legs that day did Wully examine after his own fashion. And the next day, and the next, and all the week he kept his post, and seemed indifferent to feeding himself. Soon starvation and worry began to tell on him. He grew thin and ill-tempered. No one could touch him, and any attempt to interfere with his daily occupation of leg-smelling roused him to desperation.

Day after day, week after week Wully watched and waited for his master, who never came. The ferry men learned to respect Wully's fidelity. At first he scorned their proffered food and shelter, and lived no one knew how, but starved to it at last, he accepted the gifts and learned to tolerate the givers. Although embittered against the world, his heart was true to his worthless master.

Fourteen months afterward I made his acquaintance. He was still on rigid duty at his post. He had regained his good looks. His bright, keen face set off by his white ruff and pricked ears made a dog to catch the eye anywhere. But he gave me no second glance, once he found my legs were not those he sought, and in spite of my friendly overtures during the ten months following that he continued his watch, I got no farther into his confidence than any other stranger.

For two whole years did this devoted creature attend that ferry. There was only one thing to prevent him going home to the hills, not the distance nor the chance of getting lost, but the conviction that Robin, the godlike Robin, wished him to stay by the ferry; and he stayed.

But he crossed the water as often as he felt it would serve his purpose. The fare for a dog was one penny, and it was calculated that Wully owed the company hundreds of pounds before he gave up his quest. He never failed to sense every pair of nethers that crossed the gangplank—6,000,000 legs by computation had been pronounced upon by this expert. But all to no purpose. His unswerving fidelity never faltered, though his temper was obviously souring under the long strain.

We had never heard what became of Robin, but one day a sturdy drover strode down the ferry-slip and Wully mechanically assaying the new personality, suddenly started, his mane bristled, he trembled, a low growl escaped him, and he fixed his every sense on the drover.

One of the ferry hands not understanding called to the stranger,

"Hoot mon, ye maunna hort oor dawg."

"Whaes hortin 'im, ye fule; he is mair like to hort me." But further explanation was not necessary. Wully's manner had wholly changed. He fawned on the drover, and his tail was wagging violently for the first time in years.

A few words made it all clear. Dorley, the drover, had known Robin very well, and the mittens and comforter he wore were of Robin's own make and had once been part of his wardrobe. Wully recognized the traces of his master, and despairing of any nearer approach to his lost idol, he abandoned his post at the ferry and plainly

Once more a sheep-dog in charge of a flock

announced his intention of sticking to the owner of the mittens, and Dorley was well-pleased to take Wully along to his home among the hills of Derbyshire, where he became once more a sheep-dog in charge of a flock.

* * *

Monsaldale is one of the best-known valleys in Derbyshire. The Pig and Whistle is its single but celebrated inn, and Jo Greatorex, the landlord, is a shrewd and sturdy Yorkshireman. Nature meant him for a frontiersman, but circumstances made him an innkeeper and his inborn tastes made him a—well, never mind; there was a great deal of poaching done in that country.

Wully's new home was on the upland east of the valley above Jo's inn, and that fact was not without weight in bringing me to Monsaldale. His master, Dorley, farmed in a small way on the lowland, and on the moors had a large number of sheep. These Wully guarded with his old-time sagacity, watching them while they fed and bringing them to the fold at night. He was reserved and preoccupied for a dog, and rather too ready to show his teeth to strangers, but he was so unremitting in his attention to his flock that Dorley did not lose a lamb that year, although the neighboring farmers paid the usual tribute to eagles and to foxes.

The dales are poor fox-hunting country at best. The rocky ridges, high stone walls, and precipices are too numerous to please the riders, and the final retreats in the rocks are so plentiful that it was a marvel the foxes did not overrun Monsaldale. But they didn't. There had been but little reason for complaint until the year 1881, when a sly old fox quartered himself on the fat parish, like a mouse inside a cheese, and laughed equally at the hounds of the huntsmen and the lurchers of the farmers.

He was several times run by the Peak hounds, and escaped by making for the Devil's Hole. Once in this gorge, where the cracks in the rocks extend unknown distances, he was safe. The country folk began to see something more than chance in the fact that he always escaped at the Devil's Hole, and when one of the hounds who nearly caught this Devil's Fox soon after went mad, it removed all doubt as to the spiritual paternity of said fox.

He continued his career of rapine, making audacious raids and hair-breadth escapes, and finally began, as do many old foxes, to kill from a mania for slaughter. Thus it was that Digby lost ten lambs in one night. Carroll lost seven the next night. Later, the vicarage duck-pond was wholly devastated, and scarcely a night passed but someone in the region had to report a carnage of poultry, lambs or sheep, and, finally even calves.

Of course all the slaughter was attributed to this one fox of the Devil's Hole. It was known only that he was a very large fox, at least one that made a very large track. He never was clearly seen, even by the huntsmen. And it was noticed that Thunder and Bell, the stanchest hounds in the pack, had refused to tongue or even to follow the trail when he was hunted.

His reputation for madness sufficed to make the master of the Peak hounds avoid the neighborhood. The farmers in Monsaldale, led by Jo, agreed among themselves that if it would only come on a snow, they would assemble and beat the whole country, and in defiance of all rules of the hunt, get rid of the 'daft' fox in any way they could. But the snow did not come, and the red-haired gentleman lived his life. Notwithstanding his madness, he did not lack method. He never came two successive nights to the same farm. He never ate where he killed, and he never left a track that betrayed his retreat. He usually finished up his night's trail on the turf, or on a public highway.

Once I saw him. I was walking to Monsaldale from Bakewell late one night during a heavy storm, and as I turned the corner of Stead's sheep-fold there was a vivid flash of lightning. By its light, there was fixed on my retina a picture that made me start. Sitting on his haunches by the roadside, twenty yards away, was a very large fox gazing at me with malignant eyes, and licking his muzzle in a suggestive manner. All this I saw, but no more, and might have forgotten it, or thought myself mistaken, but the next morning, in that very fold, were found the bodies of twenty-three lambs and sheep, and the unmistakable signs that brought home the crime to the well-known marauder.

There was only one man who escaped, and that was Dorley. This was the more remarkable because he lived in the centre of the region raided, and within one mile of the Devil's Hole. Faithful Wully proved himself worth all the dogs in the neighborhood. Night after night he brought in the sheep, and never one was missing. The Mad Fox might prowl about the Dorley homestead if he wished, but Wully, shrewd, brave, active Wully was more than a match for him, and not only saved his master's flock, but himself escaped with a whole skin. Everyone entertained a profound respect for him, and he might have been a popular pet but for his temper which, never genial, became more and more crabbed. He seemed to like Dorley, and Huldah, Dorley's eldest daughter, a shrewd, handsome, young woman, who, in the capacity of general manager of the house, was Wully's special guardian. The other members of Dorley's family Wully learned to tolerate, but the rest of the world, men and dogs, he seemed to hate.

His uncanny disposition was well shown in the last meeting I had with him. I was walking on a pathway across the moor behind Dorley's house. Wully was lying on the doorstep. As I drew near he arose, and without appearing to see me trotted toward my pathway and placed himself across it about ten yards ahead of me. There he stood silently and intently regarding the distant moor, his slightly bristling mane the only sign that he had not been suddenly turned to stone. He did not stir as I came up, and not wishing to quarrel, I stepped around past his nose and walked on. Wully at once left his position and in the same eerie silence trotted on some twenty feet and again stood across the pathway. Once more I came up and, stepping into the grass, brushed past his nose. Instantly, but without a sound, he seized my left heel, I kicked out with the other foot, but he escaped. Not having a stick, I flung a large stone at him. He leaped forward and the stone struck him in the ham, bowling him over into a ditch. He gasped out a savage growl as he fell, but scrambled out of the ditch and limped away in silence.

Yet sullen and ferocious as Wully was to the world, he was always gentle with Dorley's sheep. Many were the tales of rescues told of him. Many a poor lamb that had fallen into a pond or hole would have perished but for his timely and sagacious aid, many a far-weltered ewe did he turn right side up; while his keen eye discerned and his fierce courage baffled every eagle that had appeared on the moor in his time.

* * *

The Monsaldale farmers were still paying their nightly tribute to the Mad Fox, when the snow came, late in December. Poor Widow Gelt lost her entire flock of twenty sheep, and the fiery cross went forth early in the morning. With guns unconcealed the burly farmers set out to follow to the finish the tell-tale tracks in the snow, those of a very large fox, undoubtedly the multo-murderous villain. For awhile the trail was clear enough, then it came to the river and the habitual cunning of the animal was shown. He reached the water at a long angle pointing down stream and jumped into the shallow, unfrozen current. But at the other side there was no track leading out, and it was only after long searching that, a quarter of a mile higher up the stream, they found where he had come out. The track then ran to the top of Henley's high stone wall, where there was no snow left to tell tales. But the patient hunters persevered. When it crossed the smooth snow from the wall to the high road there was a difference of opinion. Some claimed that the track went up, others down the road. But Jo settled it, and after another long search they found where apparently the same trail, though some said a larger one had left the road to enter a sheep-fold, and leaving this without harming the occupants, the track-master had stepped in the foot-marks of a countryman, thereby getting to the moor road, along which he had trotted straight to Dorley's farm.

That day the sheep were kept in on account of the snow and Wully, without his usual occupation, was lying on some planks in the sun. As the hunters drew near the house, he growled savagely and sneaked around to where the sheep were. Jo Greatorex walked up to where Wully had crossed the fresh snow, gave a glance, looked dumb-founded, then pointing to the retreating sheep-dog, he said, with emphasis:

"Lads, we're off the track of the Fox. But there's the killer of the Widder's yowes."

Some agreed with Jo, others recalled the doubt in the trail and were for going back to make a fresh follow. At this juncture, Dorley himself came out of the house.

"Tom," said Jo, "that dog o' thine 'as killed twenty of Widder Gelt's sheep, last night. An' ah fur one don't believe as it is first killin'."

"Why, mon, thou art crazy," said Tom, "Ah never 'ad a better sheep-dog—'e fair loves the sheep."

"Aye! We's seen summat o' that in las' night's work," replied Jo.

In vain the company related the history of the morning. Tom swore that it was nothing but a jealous conspiracy to rob him of Wully.

"Wully sleeps i' the kitchen every night. Never is oot till he's let to

Wully studied her calm face

bide wi' the yowes. Why, mon, he's wi' oor sheep the year round, and never a hoof have ah lost."

Tom became much excited over this abominable attempt against Wully's reputation and life. Jo and his partisans got equally angry, and it was a wise suggestion of Huldah's that quieted them.

"Feyther," said she, "ah'll sleep i' the kitchen the night. If Wully 'as ae way of gettin' oot ah'll see it, an' if he's no oot an' sheep's killed on the country-side, we'll ha' proof it's na Wully."

That night Huldah stretched herself on the settee and Wully slept as usual underneath the table. As night wore on the dog became restless. He turned on his bed and once or twice got up, stretched, looked at Huldah and lay down again. About two o'clock he seemed no longer able to resist some strange impulse. He arose quietly, looked toward the low window, then at the motionless girl. Huldah lay still and breathed as though sleeping. Wully slowly came near and sniffed and breathed his doggy breath in her face. She made no move. He nudged her gently with his nose. Then, with his sharp ears forward and his head on one side he studied her calm face. Still no sign. He walked quietly to the window, mounted the table without noise, placed his nose under the sash-bar and raised the light frame until he could put one paw underneath. Then changing, he put his nose under the sash and raised it high enough to slip out, easing down the frame finally on his rump and tail with an adroitness that told of long practice. Then he disappeared into the darkness.

From her couch Huldah watched in amazement. After waiting for some time to make sure that he was gone, she arose, intending to call her father at once, but on second thought she decided to await more conclusive proof. She peered into the darkness, but no sign of Wully was to be seen. She put more wood on the fire, and lay down again. For over an hour she lay wide awake listening to the kitchen clock, and starting at each trifling sound, and wondering what the dog was doing. Could it be possible that he had really killed the widow's sheep? Then the recollection of his gentleness to their own sheep came, and completed her perplexity.

Another hour slowly tick-tocked. She heard a slight sound at the window that made her heart jump. The scratching sound was soon followed by the lifting of the sash, and in a short time Wully was back in the kitchen with the window closed behind him.

By the flickering fire-light Huldah could see a strange, wild gleam in his eye, and his jaws and snowy breast were dashed with fresh blood. The dog ceased his slight panting as he scrutinized the girl. Then, as she did not move, he lay down, and began to lick his paws and muzzle, growling lowly once or twice as though at the remembrance of some recent occurrence.

Huldah had seen enough. There could no longer be any doubt that Jo was right and more—a new thought flashed into her quick brain, she realized that the weird fox of Monsal was before her. Raising herself she looked straight at Wully, and exclaimed:

"Wully! Wully! so it's a true—oh, Wully, ye terrible brute."

Her voice was fiercely reproachful, it rang in the quiet kitchen, and Wully recoiled as though shot. He gave a desperate glance toward the closed window. His eye gleamed, and his mane bristled. But he cowered under her gaze, and grovelled on the floor as though begging for mercy. Slowly he crawled nearer and nearer, as if to lick her feet, until quite close, then, with the fury of a tiger, but without a sound, he sprang for her throat.

The girl was taken unawares, but she threw up he arm in time, and Wully's long, gleaming tusks sank into her flesh, and grated on the bone.

"Help! help! feyther! feyther!" she shrieked.

Wully was a light weight, and for a moment she flung him off. But there could be no mistaking his purpose. The game was up, it was his life or hers now.

"Feyther! feyther!" she screamed, as the yellow fury, striving to kill her, bit and tore the unprotected hands that had so often fed him.

In vain she fought to hold him off, he would soon have had her by the throat, when in rushed Dorley.

Straight at him, now in the same horrid silence sprang Wully, and savagely tore him again and again before a deadly blow from the fagot-hook disabled him, dashing him, gasping and writhing, on the stone floor, desperate, and done for, but game and defiant to the last. Another quick blow scattered his brains on the hearthstone, where so long he had been a faithful and honored retainer—and Wully, bright, fierce, trusty, treacherous Wully, quivered a moment, then straightened out, and lay forever still.

REDRUFF

The Story of the Don Valley Partridge

Down the wooded slope of Taylor's Hill the Mother Partridge led her brood; down toward the crystal brook that by some strange whim was called Mud Creek. Her little ones were one day old but already quick on foot, and she was taking them for the first time to drink.

She walked slowly, crouching low as she went, for the woods were full of enemies. She was uttering a soft little cluck in her throat, a call to the little balls of mottled down that on their tiny pink legs came toddling after, and peeping softly and plaintively if left even a few inches behind, and seeming so fragile they made the very chicadees look big and coarse. There were twelve of them, but Mother Grouse watched them all, and she watched every bush and tree and thicket, and the whole woods and the sky itself. Always for enemies she seemed seeking—friends were too scarce to be looked for—and an enemy she found. Away across the level beaver meadow was a great brute of a fox. He was coming their way, and in a few moments would surely wind them or strike their trail. There was no time to lose.

'*Krrr! Krrr!*' (Hide! Hide!) cried the mother in a low firm voice, and the little bits of things, scarcely bigger than acorns and but a day old, scattered far (a few inches) apart to hide. One dived under a leaf, another between two roots, a third crawled into a curl of birchbark, a fourth into a hole, and so on, till all were hidden but one who could find no cover, so squatted on a broad yellow chip and lay very flat, and closed his eyes very tight, sure that now he was safe from being seen. They ceased their frightened peeping and all was still.

Mother Partridge flew straight toward the dreaded beast, alighted fearlessly a few yards to one side of him, and then flung herself on the ground, flopping as though winged and lame—oh, so dreadfully lame—and whining like a distressed puppy. Was she begging for mercy—

107

mercy from a bloodthirsty, cruel fox? Oh, dear no! She was no fool.
One often hears of the cunning of the fox. Wait and see what a fool he
is compared with a mother-partridge. Elated at the prize so suddenly
within his reach, the fox turned with a dash and caught—at least, no,
he didn't quite catch the bird; she flopped by chance just a foot out of
reach. He followed with another jump and would have seized her this
time surely, but somehow a sapling came just between, and the partridge dragged herself awkwardly away and under a log, but the great
brute snapped his jaws and bounded over the log, while she, seeming a
trifle less lame, made another clumsy forward spring and tumbled
down a bank, and Reynard, keenly following, almost caught her tail,
but, oddly enough, fast as he went and leaped, she still seemed just a
trifle faster. It was most extraordinary. A winged partridge and he, Reynard, the Swift-foot, had not caught her in five minutes' racing. It was
really shameful. But the partridge seemed to gain strength as the fox
put forth his, and after a quarter of a mile race, racing that was somehow all away from Taylor's Hill, the bird got unaccountably quite well,
and, rising with a derisive whirr, flew off through the woods leaving
the fox utterly dumfounded to realize that he had been made a fool of,
and, worst of all, he now remembered that this was not the first time he
had been served this very trick, though he never knew the reason for it.

Meanwhile Mother Partridge skimmed in a great circle and came
by a roundabout way back to the little fuzz-balls she had left hidden in
the woods.

With a wild bird's keen memory for places, she went to the very
grass-blade she last trod on, and stood for a moment fondly to admire
the perfect stillness of her children. Even at her step not one had
stirred, and the little fellow on the chip, not so very badly concealed
after all, had not budged, nor did he now; he only closed his eyes a tiny
little bit harder, till the mother said:

 '*K-reet!*' (Come, children) and instantly like a fairy story, every hole
gave up its little baby-partridge, and the wee fellow on the chip, the
biggest of them all really, opened his big-little eyes and ran to the shelter of her broad tail, with a sweet little '*peep peep*' which an enemy could
not have heard three feet away, but which his mother could not have
missed thrice as far, and all the other thimblefuls of down joined in,
and no doubt thought themselves dreadfully noisy, and were proportionately happy.

The sun was hot now. There was an open space to cross on the
road to the water, and, after a careful lookout for enemies, the mother
gathered the little things under the shadow of her spread fantail and
kept off all danger of sunstroke until they reached the brier thicket by
the stream.

Here a cottontail rabbit leaped out and gave them a great scare. But
the flag of truce he carried behind was enough. He was an old friend;
and among other things the little ones learned that day that Bunny
always sails under a flag of truce, and lives up to it too.

And then came the drink, the purest of living water, though silly
men called it Mud Creek.

At first the little fellows didn't know how to drink, but they copied their mother, and soon learned to drink like her and give thanks after every sip. There they stood in a row along the edge, twelve little brown and golden balls on twenty-four little pink-toed, in-turned feet, with twelve sweet little golden heads gravely bowing, drinking and giving thanks like their mother.

Then she led them by short stages, keeping the cover, to the far side of the beaver-meadow, where was a great grassy dome. The mother had made a note of this dome some time before. It takes a number of such domes to raise a brood of partridges. For this was an ant's nest. The old one stepped on top, looked about a moment, then gave half a dozen vigorous rakes with her claws. The friable ant-hill was broken open, and the earthen galleries scattered in ruins down the slope. The ants swarmed out and quarrelled with each other for lack of a better plan. Some ran around the hill with vast energy and little purpose, while a few of the more sensible began to carry away fat white eggs. But the old partridge, coming to the little ones, picked up one of these juicy-looking bags and clucked and dropped it, and picked it up again and again and clucked, then swallowed it. The young ones stood around, then one little yellow fellow, the one that sat on the chip, picked up an ant-egg, dropped it a few times, then yielding to a sudden impulse, swallowed it, and so had learned to eat. Within twenty minutes even the runt had learned, and a merry time they had scrambling after the delicious eggs as their mother broke open more ant-galleries, and sent them and their contents rolling down the bank, till every little partridge had so crammed his little crop that he was positively misshapen and could eat no more.

Then all went cautiously up the stream, and on a sandy bank, well screened by brambles, they lay for all that afternoon, and learned how pleasant it was to feel the cool powdery dust running between their hot little toes. With their strong bent for copying, they lay on their sides like their mother and scratched with their tiny feet and flopped with their wings, though they had no wings to flop with, only a little tag among the down on each side, to show where the wings would come. That night she took them to a dry thicket near by, and there among the crisp, dead leaves that would prevent an enemy's silent approach on foot, and under the interlacing briers that kept off all foes of the air, she cradled them in their feather-shingled nursery and rejoiced in the fulness of a mother's joy over the wee cuddling things that peeped in their sleep and snuggled so trustfully against her warm body.

* * *

The third day the chicks were much stronger on their feet. They no longer had to go around an acorn; they could even scramble over pine-cones, and on the little tags that marked the place for their wings, were now to be seen blue rows of fat blood-quills.

Their start in life was a good mother, good legs, a few reliable instincts, and a germ of reason. It was instinct, that is, inherited habit, which taught them to hide at the word from their mother; it was instinct that taught them to follow her, but it was reason which made them keep under the shadow of her tail when the sun was smiting down, and from that day reason entered more and more into their expanding lives.

Next day the blood-quills had sprouted the tips of feathers. On the next, the feathers were well out, and a week later the whole family of down-clad babies were strong on the wing.

And yet not all—poor little Runtie had been sickly from the first. He bore his half-shell on his back for hours after he came out; he ran less and cheeped more than his brothers, and when one evening at the onset of a skunk the mother gave the word '*Kwit, kwit*' (Fly, fly), Runtie was left behind, and when she gathered her brood on the piney hill he was missing, and they saw him no more.

Meanwhile, their training had gone on. They knew that the finest grasshoppers abounded in the long grass by the brook; they knew that the currant-bushes dropped fatness in the form of smooth, green worms; they knew that the dome of an ant-hill rising against the distant woods stood for a garner of plenty; they knew strawberries, though not really insects, were almost as delicious; they knew that the huge danaid butterflies were good, safe game, if they could only catch them, and that a slab of bark dropping from the side of a rotten log was sure to abound in good things of many different kinds; and they had learned, also, that yellow-jackets, mud-wasps, woolly worms, and hundred-leggers were better let alone.

It was now July, the Moon of Berries. The chicks had grown and flourished amazingly during this last month, and were now so large that in her efforts to cover them the mother was kept standing all night.

They took their daily dust-bath, but of late had changed to another higher on the hill. It was one in use by many different birds, and at first the mother disliked the idea of such a second-hand bath. But the dust was of such a fine, agreeable quality, and the children led the way with such enthusiasm, that she forgot her mistrust.

After a fortnight the little ones began to droop and she herself did not feel very well. They were always hungry, and though they ate enormously, they one and all grew thinner and thinner. The mother was the last to be affected. But when it came, it came as hard on her—a ravenous hunger, a feverish headache, and a wasting weakness. She never knew the cause. She could not know that the dust of the much-used dust-bath, that her true instinct taught her to mistrust at first, and now again to shun, was sown with parasitic worms, and that all of the family were infested.

No natural impulse is without a purpose. The mother-bird's

knowledge of healing was only to follow natural impulse. The eager, feverish craving for something, she knew not what, led her to eat, or try, everything that looked eatable and to seek the coolest weeds. And there she found a deadly sumach laden with its poison fruit. A month ago she would have passed it by, but now she tried the unattractive berries. The acrid burning juice seemed to answer some strange demand of her body; she ate and ate, and all her family joined in the strange feast of physic. No human doctor could have hit it better; it proved a biting, drastic purge, the dreadful secret foe was downed, the danger passed. But not for all—Nature, the old nurse, had come too late for two of them. The weakest, by inexorable law, dropped out. Enfeebled by the disease, the remedy was too severe for them. They drank and drank by the stream, and next morning did not move when the others followed the mother. Strange vengeance was theirs now, for a skunk, the same that could have told where Runtie went, found and devoured their bodies and died of the poison they had eaten.

Seven little partridges now obeyed the mother's call. Their individual characters were early shown and now developed fast. The weaklings were gone, but there were still a fool and a lazy one. The mother could not help caring for some more than for others, and her favorite was the biggest, he who once sat on the yellow chip for concealment. He was not only the biggest, strongest, and handsomest of the brood, but best of all, the most obedient. His mother's warning '*rrr*' (danger) did not always keep the others from a risky path or a doubtful food, but obedience seemed natural to him, and he never failed to respond to her soft '*K-reet*' (Come), and of this obedience he reaped the reward, for his days were longest in the land.

August, the Molting Moon, went by; the young ones were now three parts grown. They knew just enough to think themselves wonderfully wise. When they were small it was necessary to sleep on the ground so their mother could shelter them, but now they were too big to need that, and the mother began to introduce grown-up ways of life. It was time to roost in the trees. The young weasels, foxes, skunks, and minks were beginning to run. The ground grew more dangerous each night, so at sundown Mother Partridge called '*K-reet*,' and flew into a thick, low tree.

The little ones followed, except one, an obstinate little fool who persisted in sleeping on the ground as heretofore. It was all right that time, but the next night his brothers were awakened by his cries. There was a slight scuffle, then stillness, broken only by a horrid sound of crunching bones and a smacking of lips. They peered down into the terrible darkness below, where the glint of two close-set eyes and a peculiar musty smell told them that a mink was the killer of their fool brother.

Six little partridges now sat in a row at night, with their mother in the middle, though it was not unusual for some little one with cold feet to perch on her back.

Their education went on, and about this time they were taught 'whirring.' A partridge can rise on the wing silently if it wishes, but

In the moonlight

whirring is so important at times that all are taught how and when to
rise on thundering wings. Many ends are gained by the whirr. It warns
all other partridges near that danger is at hand, it unnerves the gunner,
or it fixes the foe's attention on the whirrer, while the others sneak off
in silence, or by squatting, escape notice.

A partridge adage might well be 'foes and food for every moon.'
September came, with seeds and grain in place of berries and ant-eggs,
and gunners in place of skunks and minks.

  The partridges knew well what a fox was, but had scarcely seen a
dog. A fox they knew they could easily baffle by taking to a tree, but
when in the Gunner Moon old Cuddy came prowling through the
ravine with his bob-tailed yellow cur, the mother spied the dog and

cried out, '*Kwit! kwit!*' (Fly, fly). Two of the brood thought it a pity their mother should lose her wits so easily over a fox, and were pleased to show their superior nerve by springing into a tree in spite of her earnestly repeated '*Kwit! kwit!*' and her example of speeding away on silent wings.

Meanwhile, the strange bob-tailed fox came under the tree and yapped and yapped at them. They were much amused at him and at their mother and brothers, so much so that they never noticed a rustling in the bushes till there was a loud *Bang! bang!* and down fell two bloody, flopping partridges, to be seized and mangled by the yellow cur until the gunner ran from the bushes and rescued the remains.

* * *

Cuddy lived in a wretched shanty near the Don, north of Toronto. His was what Greek philosophy would have demonstrated to be an ideal existence. He had no wealth, no taxes, no social pretensions, and no property to speak of. His life was made up of a very little work and a great deal of play, with as much out-door life as he chose. He considered himself a true sportsman because he was 'fond o' huntin',' and 'took a sight o' comfort out of seein' the critters hit the mud' when his gun was fired. The neighbors called him a squatter, and looked on him merely as an anchored tramp. He shot and trapped the year round, and varied his game somewhat with the season perforce, but had been heard to remark he could tell the month by the 'taste o' the partridges,' if he didn't happen to know by the almanac. This, no doubt, showed keen observation, but was also unfortunate proof of something not so creditable. The lawful season for murdering partridges began September 15th, but there was nothing surprising in Cuddy's being out a fortnight ahead of time. Yet he managed to escape punishment year after year, and even contrived to pose in a newspaper interview as an interesting character.

He rarely shot on the wing, preferring to pot his birds, which was not easy to do when the leaves were on, and accounted for the brood in the third ravine going so long unharmed; but the near prospect of other gunners finding them now, had stirred him to go after 'a mess o' birds.' He had heard no roar of wings when the mother-bird led off her four survivors, so pocketed the two he had killed and returned to the shanty.

The little grouse thus learned that a dog is not a fox, and must be differently played; and an old lesson was yet more deeply graven— 'Obedience is long life.'

The rest of September was passed in keeping quietly out of the way of gunners as well as some old enemies. They still roosted on the long thin branches of the hardwood trees among the thickest leaves, which protected them from foes in the air; the height saved them from foes on the ground, and left them nothing to fear but coons, whose slow, heavy tread on the limber boughs never failed to give them timely warning. But the leaves were falling now—every month its foes and its food. This was nut time, and it was owl time, too. Barred owls coming down from the north doubled or trebled the owl population. The nights were getting frosty and the coons less dangerous, so the mother changed the place of roosting to the thickest foliage of a hemlock-tree.

Only one of the brood disregarded the warning '*Kreet, kreet.*' He stuck to his swinging elm-bough, now nearly naked, and a great yellow-eyed owl bore him off before morning.

Mother and three young ones now were left, but they were as big as she was; indeed one, the eldest, he of the chip, was bigger. Their ruffs had begun to show. Just the tips, to tell what they would be like when grown, and not a little proud they were of them.

The ruff is to the partridge what the train is to the peacock—his chief beauty and his pride. A hen's ruff is black with a slight green gloss. A cock's is much larger and blacker and is glossed with more vivid bottle-green. Once in a while a partridge is born of unusual size and vigor, whose ruff is not only larger, but by a peculiar kind of intensification is of a deep coppery red, iridescent with violet, green, and gold. Such a bird is sure to be a wonder to all who know him, and the little one who had squatted on the chip, and had always done what he was told, developed before the Acorn Moon had changed, into all the glory of a gold and copper ruff—for this was Redruff, the famous partridge of the Don Valley.

* * *

One day late in the Acorn Moon, that is, about mid-October, as the grouse family were basking with full crops near a great pine log on the sunlit edge of the beaver-meadow, they heard the far-away bang of a gun, and Redruff, acting on some impulse from within, leaped on the log, strutted up and down a couple of times, then, yielding to the elation of the bright, clear, bracing air, he whirred his wings in loud defiance. Then, giving fuller vent to this expression of vigor, just as a colt frisks to show how well he feels, he whirred yet more loudly, until, unwittingly, he found himself drumming, and tickled with the discovery of his new power, thumped the air again and again till he filled the near woods with the loud tattoo of the fully grown cock-partridge. His brother and sister heard and looked on with admiration and surprise; so did his mother, but from that time she began to be a little afraid of him.

In early November comes the moon of a weird foe. By a strange law of nature, not wholly without parallel among mankind, all partridges go crazy in the November moon of their first year. They become possessed of a mad hankering to get away somewhere, it does not matter much where. And the wisest of them do all sorts of foolish things at this period. They go drifting, perhaps, at speed over the country by night, and are cut in two by wires, or dash into lighthouses, or locomotive headlights. Daylight finds them in all sorts of absurd places, in buildings, in open marshes, perched on telephone wires in a great city, or even on board of coasting vessels. The craze seems to be a relic of a bygone habit of migration, and it has at least one good effect, it breaks up the families and prevents the constant intermarrying, which would surely be fatal to their race. It always takes the young badly their first year, and they may have it again the second fall, for it is very catching; but in the third season it is practically unknown.

Redruff's mother knew it was coming as soon as she saw the frost grapes blackening, and the maples shedding their crimson and gold. There was nothing to do but care for their health and keep them in the quiestest part of the woods.

Redruff's calendar

The first sign of it came when a flock of wild geese went *honking* southward overhead. The young ones had never before seen such long-necked hawks, and were afraid of them. But seeing that their mother had no fear, they took courage, and watched them with intense interest. Was it the wild, clanging cry that moved them, or was it solely the inner prompting then come to the surface? A strange longing to follow took possession of each of the young ones. They watched those arrowy trumpeters fading away to the south, and sought out higher perches to watch them farther yet, and from that time things were no more the same. The November moon was waxing, and when it was full, the November madness came.

The least vigorous of the flock were most affected. The little family was scattered. Redruff himself flew on several long erratic night journeys. The impulse took him southward, but there lay the boundless stretch of Lake Ontario, so he turned again, and the waning of the Mad Moon found him once more in the Mud Creek Glen, but absolutely alone.

* * *

Food grew scarce as winter wore on. Redruff clung to the old ravine and the piney sides of Taylor's Hill, but every month brought its food and its foes. The Mad Moon brought madness, solitude, and grapes; the Snow Moon came with rosehips; and the Stormy Moon brought browse of birch and silver storms that sheathed the woods in ice, and made it hard to keep one's perch while pulling off the frozen buds. Redruff's beak grew terribly worn with the work, so that even when closed there was still an opening through behind the hook. But nature had prepared him for the slippery footing; his toes, so slim and trim in September, had sprouted rows of sharp, horny points, and these grew with the growing cold, till the first snow had found him fully equipped with snow-shoes and ice-creepers. The cold weather had driven away most of the hawks and owls, and made it impossible for his four-footed enemies to approach unseen, so that things were nearly balanced.

His flight in search of food had daily led him farther on, till he had discovered and explored the Rosedale Creek, with its banks of silver-birch, and Castle Frank, with its grapes and rowan berries, as well as

MAR. WAKENING MOON

APRIL PUSSY-WILLOW MOON

APR-MAY DRUMMING MOON

MAY LOVE MOON

JUNE CHICK MOON

JULY BERRY MOON

AUGUST MOLTING MOON

SEPT. GUNNER MOON

OCT. ACORN MOON

NOV. MAD MOON

DEC. SNOW MOON

JAN. STORMY MOON

FEB. HUNGRY MOON

Chester woods, where amelanchier and Virginia-creeper swung their fruit-bunches, and checkerberries glowed beneath the snow.

He soon found out that for some strange reason men with guns did not go within the high fence of Castle Frank. So among these scenes he lived his life, learning new places, new foods, and grew wiser and more beautiful every day.

He was quite alone so far as kindred were concerned, but that scarcely seemed a hardship. Wherever he went he could see the jolly chickadees scrambling merrily about, and he remembered the time when they had seemed such big, important creatures. They were the most absurdly cheerful things in the woods. Before the autumn was fairly over they had begun to sing their famous refrain, '*Spring Soon,*'

and kept it up with good heart more or less all through the winter's direst storms, till at length the waning of the Hungry Moon, our February, seemed really to lend some point to the ditty, and they redoubled their optimistic announcement to the world in an 'I-told-you-so' mood. Soon good support was found, for the sun gained strength and melted the snow from the southern slope of Castle Frank Hill, and exposed great banks of fragrant wintergreen, whose berries were a bounteous feast for Redruff, and, ending the hard work of pulling frozen browse, gave his bill the needed chance to grow into its proper shape again. Very soon the first bluebird came flying over and warbled as he flew '*The spring is coming.*' The sun kept gaining, and early one day in the dark of the Wakening Moon of March there was a loud '*Caw, caw,*' and old Silverspot, the king-crow, came swinging along from the south at the head of his troops and officially announced

'THE SPRING HAS COME.'

All nature seemed to respond to this, the opening of the bird's New Year, and yet it was something within that chiefly seemed to move them. The chickadees went simply wild; they sang their '*Spring now, spring now now—Spring now now,*' so persistently that one wondered how they found time to get a living.

And Redruff felt it thrill him through and through. He sprang with joyous vigor on a stump and sent rolling down the little valley, again and again, a thundering '*Thump, thump, thump, thunderrrrrrrrr,*' that wakened dull echoes as it rolled, and voiced his gladness in the coming of the spring.

Away down the valley was Cuddy's shanty. He heard the drum-call on the still morning air and 'reckoned there was a cock patridge to git,' and came sneaking up the ravine with his gun. But Redruff skimmed away in silence, nor rested till once more in Mud Creek Glen. And there he mounted the very log where first he had drummed and rolled his loud tattoo again and again, till a small boy who had taken a short cut to the mill through the woods, ran home, badly scared, to tell his mother he was sure the Indians were on the war-path, for he heard their war-drums beating in the glen.

Why does a happy boy holla? Why does a lonesome youth sigh? They don't know any more than Redruff knew why every day now he mounted some dead log and thumped and thundered to the woods; then strutted and admired his gorgeous blazing ruffs as they flashed their jewels in the sunlight, and then thundered out again. Whence now came the strange wish for someone else to admire the plumes? And why had such a notion never come till the Pussywillow Moon?

'*Thump, thump, thunder-r-r-r-r-r-rrrr*'
'*Thump, thump, thunder-r-r-r-r-r-rrrr*'
he rumbled again and again.

Day after day he sought the favorite log, and a new beauty, a rose-red comb, grew out above each clear, keen eye, and the clumsy snow-shoes were wholly shed from his feet. His ruff grew finer, his eye brighter, and his whole appearance splendid to behold, as he strutted and flashed in the sun. But—oh! he was *so lonesome now.*

Yet what could he do but blindly vent his hankering in this daily drum-parade, till on a day early in loveliest May, when the trilliums had fringed his log with silver stars, and he had drummed and longed, then drummed again, his keen ear caught a sound, a gentle footfall in the brush. He turned to a statue and watched; he knew he had been watched. Could it be possible? Yes! there it was—a form—another—a shy little lady grouse, now bashfully seeking to hide. In a moment he was by her side. His whole nature swamped by a new feeling—burnt up with thirst—a cooling spring in sight. And how he spread and flashed his proud array! How came he to know that that would please? He puffed his plumes and contrived to stand just right to catch the sun, and strutted and uttered a low, soft chuckle that must have been just as good as the 'sweet nothings' of another race, for clearly now her heart was won. Won, really, days ago, if only he had known. For full three days she had come at the loud tattoo and coyly admired him from afar, and felt a little piqued that he had not yet found out her, so close at hand. So it was not quite all mischance, perhaps, that little stamp that caught his ear. But now she meekly bowed her head with sweet, sub-missive grace—the desert passed, the parch-burnt wanderer found the spring at last.

Oh, those were bright, glad days in the lovely glen of the unlovely name. The sun was never so bright, and the piney air was balmier sweet than dreams. And that great noble bird came daily on his log, sometimes with her and sometimes quite alone, and drummed for very joy of being alive. But why sometimes alone? Why not forever with his Brownie bride? Why should she stay to feast and play with him for hours, then take some stealthy chance to slip away and see him no more for hours or till next day, when his martial music from the log announced him restless for her quick return? There was a woodland mystery here he could not clear. Why should her stay with him grow daily less till it was down to minutes, and one day at last she never came at all. Nor the next, nor the next, and Redruff, wild, careered on lightning wing and drummed on the old log, then away up-stream on another log, and skimmed the hill to another ravine to drum and drum. But on the fourth day, when he came and loudly called her, as of old, at their earliest tryst, he heard a sound in the bushes, as at first, and there was his missing Brownie bride with ten little peeping partridges following after.

Redruff skimmed to her side, terribly frightening the bright-eyed downlings, and was just a little dashed to find the brood with claims far stronger than his own. But he soon accepted the change, and thenceforth joined himself to the brood, caring for them as his father never had for him.

* * *

Good fathers are rare in the grouse world. The mother-grouse builds her nest and hatches out her young without help. She even hides the place of the nest from the father and meets him only at the drum-log and the feeding-ground, or perhaps the dusting-place, which is the club-house of the grouse kind.

When Brownie's little ones came out they had filled her every thought, even to the forgetting of their splendid father. But on the third day, when they were strong enough, she had taken them with her at the father's call.

Some fathers take no interest in their little ones, but Redruff joined at once to help Brownie in the task of rearing the brood. They had learned to eat and drink just as their father had learned long ago, and could toddle along, with their mother leading the way, while the father ranged near by or followed far behind.

The very next day, as they went from the hill-side down toward the creek in a somewhat drawn-out string, like beads with a big one at each end, a red squirrel, peeping around a pine-trunk, watched the procession of downlings with the Runtie straggling far in the rear. Redruff, yards behind, preening his feathers on a high log, had escaped the eye of the squirrel, whose strange perverted thirst for birdling blood was roused at what seemed so fair a chance. With murderous intent to cut off the hindmost straggler, he made a dash. Brownie could not have seen him until too late, but Redruff did. He flew for that red-haired cut-throat; his weapons were his fists, that is, the knob-joints of the wings, and what a blow he could strike! At the first onset he struck the squirrel square on the end of the nose, his weakest spot, and sent him reeling; he staggered and wriggled into a brush-pile, where he had expected to carry the little grouse, and there lay gasping with red drops trickling down his wicked snout. The partridges left him lying there, and what became of him they never knew, but he troubled them no more.

The family went on toward the water, but a cow had left deep tracks in the sandy loam, and into one of these fell one of the chicks

Redruff saving Runtie

and peeped in dire distress when he found he could not get out.

This was a fix. Neither one seemed to know what to do, but as they trampled vainly round the edge, the sandy bank caved in, and, running down, formed a long slope, up which the young one ran and rejoined his brothers under the broad veranda of their mother's tail.

Brownie was a bright little mother, of small stature, but keen of wit and sense, and was, night and day, alert to care for her darling chicks. How proudly she stepped and clucked through the arching woods with her dainty brood behind her; how she strained her little brown tail almost to a half-circle to give them a broader shade, and never flinched at sight of any foe, but held ready to fight or fly, whichever seemed the best for her little ones.

Before the chicks could fly they had a meeting with old Cuddy; though it was June, he was out with his gun. Up the third ravine he went, and Tike, his dog, ranging ahead, came so dangerously near the Brownie brood that Redruff ran to meet him, and by the old but never failing trick led him on a foolish chase away back down the valley of the Don.

But Cuddy, as it chanced, came right along, straight for the brood, and Brownie, giving the signal to the children, 'Krrr, krrr' (Hide, hide), ran to lead the man away just as her mate had led the dog. Full of a mother's devoted love, and skilled in the learning of the woods, she ran in silence till quite near, then sprang with a roar of wings right in his face, and tumbling on the leaves she shammed a lameness that for a moment deceived the poacher. But when she dragged one wing and whined about his feet, then slowly crawled away, he knew just what it meant—that it was all a trick to lead him from her brood, and he struck at her a savage blow; but little Brownie was quick, she avoided the blow and limped behind a sapling, there to beat herself upon the leaves again in sore distress, and seem so lame that Cuddy made another try to strike her down with a stick. But she moved in time to balk him, and bravely, steadfast still to lead him from her helpless little ones, she flung herself before him and beat her gentle breast upon the ground, and moaned as though begging for mercy. And Cuddy, failing again to strike her, raised his gun, and firing charge enough to kill a bear, he blew poor brave, devoted Brownie into quivering, bloody rags.

This gunner brute knew the young must be hiding near, so looked about to find them. But no one moved or peeped. He saw not one, but as he trampled about with heedless, hateful feet, he crossed and crossed again their hiding-ground, and more than one of the silent little sufferers he trampled to death, and neither knew nor cared.

Redruff had taken the yellow brute away off down-stream, and now returned to where he left his mate. The murderer had gone, taking her remains, to be thrown to the dog. Redruff sought about and found the bloody spot with feathers, Brownie's feathers, scattered around, and now he knew the meaning of that shot.

Who can tell what his horror and his mourning were? The outward signs were few, some minutes dumbly gazing at the place with down-cast, draggled look, and then a change at the thought of their helpless brood. Back to the hiding-place he went, and called the well-known 'Kreet, kreet.' Did every grave give up its little inmate at the magic word? No, barely more than half; six little balls of down unveiled their lustrous eyes, and, rising, ran to meet him, but four feathered little bodies had found their graves indeed. Redruff called again and again, till he was sure that all who could respond had come, and led them from that dreadful place, far, far away up-stream, where barb-wire fences and bramble thickets were found to offer a less grateful, but more reliable, shelter.

Here the brood grew and were trained by their father just as his mother had trained him; though wider knowledge and experience gave him many advantages. He knew so well the country round and all the feeding-grounds, and how to meet the ills that harass partridge-life, that the summer passed and not a chick was lost. They grew and flourished, and when the Gunner Moon arrived they were a fine family of six grown-up grouse with Redruff, splendid in his gleaming copper feathers, at their head. He had ceased to drum during the summer after the loss of Brownie, but drumming is to the partridge what singing is to the lark; while it is his love-song, it is also an expression of exuberance born of health, and when the molt was over and September food and weather had renewed his splendid plumes and braced him up again, his spirits revived, and finding himself one day near the old log he mounted impulsively, and drummed again and again.

From that time he often drummed, while his children sat around, or one who showed his father's blood would mount some nearby stump or stone, and beat the air in the loud tattoo.

The black grapes and the Mad Moon now came on. But Redruff's brood were of a vigorous stock; their robust health meant robust wits, and though they got the craze, it passed within a week, and only three had flown away for good.

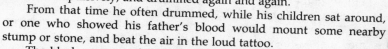

Redruff, with his remaining three, was living in the glen when the snow came. It was light, flaky snow, and as the weather was not very cold, the family squatted for the night under the low, flat boughs of a cedar-tree. But next day the storm continued, it grew colder, and the drifts piled up all day. At night, the snow-fall ceased, but the frost grew harder still, so Redruff, leading the family to a birch-tree above a deep drift, dived into the snow, and the others did the same. Then into the holes the wind blew the loose snow—their pure white bed-clothes, and thus tucked in they slept in comfort, for the snow is a warm wrap, and the air passes through it easily enough for breathing. Next morning each partridge found a solid wall of ice before him from his frozen breath, but easily turned to one side and rose on the wing at Redruff's morning '*Kreet, kreet, kwit.*' (Come children, come children, fly.)

This was the first night for them in a snowdrift, though it was an old story to Redruff, and next night they merrily dived again into bed, and the north wind tucked them in as before. But a change of weather was brewing. The night wind veered to the east. A fall of heavy flakes gave place to sleet, and that to silver rain. The whole wide world was sheathed in ice, and when the grouse awoke to quit their beds, they found themselves sealed in with a great cruel sheet of edgeless ice.

The deeper snow was still quite soft, and Redruff bored his way to the top, but there the hard, white sheet defied his strength. Hammer and struggle as he might he could make no impression, and only bruised his wings and head. His life had been made up of keen joys and dull hardships, with frequent sudden desperate straits, but this seemed the hardest brunt of all, as the slow hours wore on and found him weakening with his struggles, but no nearer to freedom. He could hear the struggling of his family, too, or sometimes heard them calling to him for help with their long-drawn plaintive '*p-e-e-e-e-t-e, p-e-e-e-e- t-e.*'

They were hidden from many of their enemies, but not from the pangs of hunger, and when the night came down the weary prisoners, worn out with hunger and useless toil, grew quiet in despair. At first they had been afraid the fox would come and find them imprisoned there at his mercy, but as the second night went slowly by they no longer cared, and even wished he would come and break the crusted snow, and so give them at least a fighting chance for life.

But when the fox really did come padding over the frozen drift, the deep-laid love of life revived, and they crouched in utter stillness till he passed. The second day was one of driving storm. The north wind sent his snow-horses, hissing and careering over the white earth, tossing and curling their white manes and kicking up more snow as they dashed on. The long, hard grinding of the granular snow seemed to be thinning the snow-crust, for though far from dark below, it kept on growing lighter. Redruff had pecked and pecked at the under side all day, till his head ached and his bill was wearing blunt, but when the sun went down he seemed as far as ever from escape. The night passed like the others, except no fox went trotting overhead. In the morning he renewed his pecking, though now with scarcely any force, and the voices or struggles of the others were no more heard. As the daylight grew stronger he could see that his long efforts had made a brighter spot above him in the snow, and he continued feebly pecking. Outside, the storm-horses kept on trampling all day, the crust was really growing thin under their heels, and late that afternoon his bill went through into the open air. New life came with this gain, and he pecked away, till just before the sun went down he had made a hole that his head, his neck, and his ever-beautiful ruffs could pass. His great broad shoulders were too large, but he could now strike downward, which gave him fourfold force; the snow-crust crumbled quickly, and in a little while he sprang from his icy prison once more free. But the young ones! Redruff flew to the nearest bank, hastily gathered a few red hips to stay his gnawing hunger, then returned to the prison-drift and clucked and stamped. He got only one reply, a feeble '*peete, peete,*' and scratching with his sharp claws on the thinned granular sheet he soon broke through, and Graytail feebly crawled out of the hole. But that was all; the others, scattered he could not tell where in the drift, made no reply, gave no sign of life, and he was forced to leave them. When the snow melted in the spring their bodies came to view, skin, bones, and feathers—nothing more.

* * *

It was long before Redruff and Graytail fully recovered, but food and rest in plenty are sure cure-alls, and a bright clear day in midwinter had the usual effect of setting the vigorous Redruff to drumming on the log. Was it the drumming, or the tell-tale tracks of their snowshoes on the omnipresent snow, that betrayed them to Cuddy? He came prowling again and again up the ravine, with dog and gun, intent to hunt the partridges down. They knew him of old, and he was coming now to know them well. That great copper-ruffed cock was becoming famous up and down the valley. During the Gunner Moon many a one had tried to end his splendid life, just as a worthless wretch of old sought fame by burning the Ephesian wonder of the world. But Redruff was deep in woodcraft. He knew just where to hide, and when to rise on silent wing, and when to squat till overstepped, then rise on thunder wing within a yard to shield himself at once behind some mighty tree-trunk and speed away.

But Cuddy never ceased to follow with his gun that red-ruffed cock; many a long snapshot he tried, but somehow always found a tree, a bank, or some safe shield between, and Redruff lived and throve and drummed.

When the Snow Moon came he moved with Graytail to the Castle Frank woods, where food was plenty as well as grand old trees. There was in particular, on the east slope among the creeping hemlocks, a splendid pine. It was six feet through, and its first branches began at the tops of the other trees. Its top in summer-time was a famous resort for the bluejay and his bride. Here, far beyond the reach of shot, in warm spring days the jay would sing and dance before his mate, spread his bright blue plumes and warble the sweetest fairyland music, so sweet and soft that few hear it but the one for whom it is meant, and books knew nothing at all about it.

This great pine had an especial interest for Redruff, now living near with his remaining young one, but its base, not its far-away crown, concerned him. All around were low, creeping hemlocks, and among them the partridge-vine and the wintergreen grew, and the sweet black acorns could be scratched from under the snow. There was no better feeding-ground, for when that insatiable gunner came on them there it was easy to run low among the hemlock to the great pine, then rise with a derisive *whirr* behind its bulk, and keeping the huge trunk in line with the deadly gun, skim off in safety. A dozen times at least the pine had saved them during the lawful murder season, and here it was that Cuddy, knowing their feeding habits, laid a new trap. Under the bank he sneaked and watched in ambush while an accomplice went around the Sugar Loaf to drive the birds. He came trampling through the low thicket where Redruff and Graytail were feeding, and long before the gunner was dangerously near Redruff gave a low warning '*rrr-rrr*' (danger) and walked quickly toward the great pine in case they had to rise.

Graytail was some distance up the hill, and suddenly caught sight
of a new foe close at hand, the yellow cur, coming right on. Redruff,
much farther off, could not see him for the bushes, and Graytail became
greatly alarmed.

'*Kwit, kwit*' (Fly, fly), she cried, running down the hill for a start.
'*Kreet, k-r-r-r*' (This way, hide), cried the cooler Redruff, for he saw that
now the man with the gun was getting in range. He gained the great
trunk, and behind it, as he paused a moment to call earnestly to Graytail, 'This way, this way,' he heard a slight nose under the bank before
him that betrayed the ambush, then there was a terrified cry from
Graytail as the dog sprang at her, she rose in air and skimmed behind
the shielding trunk, away from the gunner in the open, right into the
power of the miserable wretch under the bank.

Whirr, and up she went, a beautiful, sentient, noble being.

Bang, and down she fell—battered and bleeding, to gasp her life
out and to lie a rumpled mass of carrion in the snow.

It was a perilous place for Redruff. There was no chance for a safe
rise, so he squatted low. The dog came within ten feet of him, and the
stranger, coming across to Cuddy, passed at five feet, but he never
moved till a chance came to slip behind the great trunk away from both.
Then he safely rose and flew to the lonely glen by Taylor's Hill.

One by one the deadly cruel gun had stricken his near ones down,
till now, once more, he was alone. The Snow Moon slowly passed with
many a narrow escape, and Redruff, now known to be the only survivor of his kind, was relentlessly pursued, and grew wilder every day.

It seemed, at length, a waste of time to follow him with a gun, so
when the snow was deepest, and food scarcest, Cuddy hatched a new
plot. Right across the feeding-ground, almost the only good one now in
the Stormy Moon, he set a row of snares. A cottontail rabbit, an old
friend, cut several of these with his sharp teeth, but some remained,
and Redruff, watching a far-off speck that might turn out a hawk, trod
right in one of them, and in an instant was jerked into the air to dangle
by one foot.

Have the wild things no moral or legal rights? What right has man
to inflict such long and fearful agony on a fellow-creature, simply
because that creature does not speak his language? All that day, with
growing, racking pains, poor Redruff hung and beat his great, strong
wings in helpless struggles to be free. All day, all night, with growing
torture, until he only longed for death. But no one came. The morning
broke, the day wore on, and still he hung there, slowly dying; his very

The owl

strength a curse. The second night crawled slowly down, and when, in the dawdling hours of darkness, a great Horned Owl, drawn by the feeble flutter of a dying wing, cut short the pain, the deed was wholly kind.

The wind blew down the valley from the north. The snow-horses went racing over the wrinkled ice, over the Don Flats, and over the marsh toward the lake, white, for they were driven snow, but on them, scattered dark, were riding plumy fragments of partridge ruffs—the famous rainbow ruffs. And they rode on the wind that night, away, away to the south, over the dark lake, as they rode in the gloom of his Mad Moon flight, riding and riding on till they were engulfed, the last trace of the last of the Don Valley race.

For no partridge is heard in Castle Frank now—and in Mud Creek Ravine the old pine drum-log, unused, has rotted in silence away.

LIVES
OF THE
HUNTED

CONTENTS

KRAG THE KOOTENAY RAM

A great broad web of satin, shining white, and, strewn across, long clumps and trailing wreaths of lilac, almost white, wistaria bloom,—pendent, shining, and so delicately wrought in palest silk that still the web was white; and in and out and trailed across, now lost, now plain, two slender, twining, intertwining chains of golden thread.

* * *

I see a broken upland in the far Northwest. Its gray and purple rocks are interpatched with colors rich and warm, the new-born colors of the upland spring, the greatest springtime in the world; for where there is no winter there can be no spring. The gloom is measure of the light. So, in this land of long, long winter night, where Nature stints her joys for six hard months, then owns her debt and pays it all at once, the spring is glorious compensation for the past. Six months' arrears of joy are paid in one vast lavish outpour. And latest May is made the date of payment. Then spring, great, gorgeous, sixfold spring, holds carnival on every ridge.

Even the sullen Gunder Peak, that pierces the north end of the ridge, unsombres just a whit. The upland beams with all the flowers it might have grown in six lost months; yet we see only one. Here by our feet, and farther on, and right and left and onward far away, in great, broad acre beds, the purple lupine blooming. Irregular, broken, straggling patches near, but broader, denser, farther on; till on the distant slopes they lie, long, devious belts, like purple clouds at rest.

But late May though it be, the wind is cold; the pools tell yet of frost at night. The White Wind blows. Broad clouds come up, and down comes driving snow, over the peaks, over the upland, and over the upland flowers. Hoary, gray, and white the landscape grows in turn; and one by one the flowers are painted out. But the lupines, on their taller, stiffer stems, can fight the snow for long: they bow their whitened heads beneath its load; then, thanks no little to the wind itself, shake free and stand up defiantly straight, as fits their royal purple. And when the snowfall ends as suddenly as it began, the clouds roll by, and the blue sky sees an upland shining white, but streaked and patched with blots and belts of lovely purple bloom.

And wound across, and in and out, are two long trails of track.

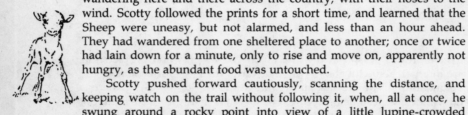

* * *

Late snow is good trailing, and Scotty MacDougall took down his rifle and climbed the open hills behind his shanty on Tobacco Creek, toward the well-known Mountain Sheep range. The broad white upland, with its lupine bands and patches, had no claim on Scotty's notice, nor was his interest aroused until he came on the double trail in the new snow. At a glance he read it—two full-grown female Mountain Sheep wandering here and there across the country, with their noses to the wind. Scotty followed the prints for a short time, and learned that the Sheep were uneasy, but not alarmed, and less than an hour ahead. They had wandered from one sheltered place to another; once or twice had lain down for a minute, only to rise and move on, apparently not hungry, as the abundant food was untouched.

Scotty pushed forward cautiously, scanning the distance, and keeping watch on the trail without following it, when, all at once, he swung around a rocky point into view of a little lupine-crowded hollow, and from the middle of it leaped the two Sheep.

Up went his rifle, and in a moment one or both would have fallen, had not Scotty's eye, before he pulled, rested on two tiny new-born Lambs, that got up on their long, wabbly legs, in doubt, for a moment, whether to go to the newcomer or to follow their mothers.

The old Sheep bleated a shrill alarm to their young, and circled back. The Lambs' moment of indecision was over; they felt that their duty lay with the creatures that looked and smelled like themselves, and coolly turned their uncertain steps to follow their mothers.

Of course Scotty could have shot any or all of the Sheep, as he was within twenty yards of the farthest; but there is in man an unreasoning impulse, a wild hankering to "catch alive"; and without thinking of what he could do with them afterward, Scotty, seeing them so easily in his power, leaned his gun in a safe place and ran after the Lambs. But the distressed mothers had by now communicated a good deal of their alarm to their young; the little things were no longer in doubt that they should avoid the stranger; and when he rushed forward, his onset added the necessary final touch, and for the first time in their brief lives they knew danger, and instinctively sought to escape it. They were not yet an hour old, but Nature had equipped them with a set of valuable instincts. And though the Lambs were slow of foot compared with the man, they showed at once a singular aptitude at dodging, and Scotty failed to secure them—as he had expected.

Meanwhile the mothers circled about, bleating piteously and urging the little ones to escape. Scotty, plunging around in his attempt, alarmed them more and more, and they put forth all the strength of their feeble limbs in the effort to go to their mothers. The man slipping and scrambling after them was unable to catch either, although more than once he touched one with his hand. But very soon this serious game of tag was adroitly steered by the timid mothers away from the lupine bed, and once on the smooth, firmer ground, the Lambs got an advantage that quite offset the weariness they began to feel; and Scotty, plunging and chasing first this way and then that, did not realize that the whole thing was being managed by the old ones, till they reached the lowest spur of the Gunder Peak, a ragged, broken, rocky cliff, up which the mothers bounded. Then the little ones felt a new power, just as a young Duck must when first he drops in the water. Their little black rubber hoofs gripped the slippery rocks as no man's foot can do it, and they soared on their new-found mountain wings, up and away, till led by their mothers out of sight.

It was well for them that Scotty had laid aside his rifle, for a Sheep at a hundred yards was as good as dead when he pulled on it. He now rushed back for his weapon, but before he could harm them, a bank of fog from the Peak came rolling between. The same White Wind that brought the treacherous trailing snow that had betrayed them to their deadliest foe, now brought the fog that screened them from his view.

So Scotty could only stare up the cliff and, half in admiration, mutter: "The little divils, the little divils—too smart for me, and them less'n an hour old."

For now he fully knew the meaning of the uneasy wandering that he had read in the old ones' trails.

He spent the rest of the day in bootless hunting, and at night went home hungry, to dine off a lump of fat bacon.

* * *

The rugged peaks are not the chosen home, but rather the safe and final refuge, of the Sheep. Once there, the mothers felt no fear, and thenceforth, in the weeks that followed, they took care that in feeding they should never wander far on the open away from their haven on the crags.

The Lambs were of a sturdy stock, and grew so fast that within a week they were strong enough to keep up with their mothers when the sudden appearance of a Mountain Lion forced them all to run for their lives.

The snow of the Lambs' birthday had gone again within a few

hours, and all the hills were now carpeted with grass and flowers. The abundant food for the mothers meant plenty of the best for the young ones, and they waggled their tails in satisfaction as they helped themselves.

One of the Lambs, whose distinguishing mark was a very white nose, was stockily built, while his playmate, slightly taller and more graceful, was peculiar in having little nubbins of horns within a few days of his birth.

They were fairly matched, and frisked and raced alongside their mothers or fought together the livelong day. One would dash away, and the other behind him try to butt him; or if they came to an inviting hillock they began at once the world-old, world-wide game of King of the Castle. One would mount and hold his friend at bay. Stamping and

The world-wide game of King of the Castle

shaking his little round head, he would give the other to understand that *he* was King of the Castle; and then back would go their pretty pink ears, the round woolly heads would press together, and the innocent brown eyes roll as they tried to look terribly fierce and push and strive, till one, forced to his knees, would wheel and kick up his heels as though to say: "I didn't want your old castle, anyway," but would straightway give himself the lie by seeking out a hillock for himself, and, posing on its top with his fiercest look, would stamp and shake his head, after the way that, in their language, stands for the rhyming challenge in ours, and the combat scene would be repeated.

In these encounters Whitenose generally had the best of it because of his greater weight; but in the races Nubbins was easily first. His activity was tireless; from morning till evening he seemed able to caper and jump.

At night they usually slept close against their mothers, in some sheltered nook where they could see the sunrise, or rather where they could feel it, for that was more important; and Nubbins, always active, was sure to be up first of the Lambs. Whitenose was inclined to be lazy, and would stay curled up, the last of the family to begin the day of activity. His snowy nose was matched by a white patch behind, as in all Bighorn Sheep, only larger and whiter than usual, and this patch afforded so tempting a mark that Nubbins never could resist a good chance to charge at it. He was delighted if, in the morning, he could waken his little friend by what he considered a tremendous butt on his beautiful patch of white.

Mountain Sheep usually go in bands; the more in the band, the more eyes for danger. But the hunters had been very active in the Kootenay country; Scotty in particular had been relentless. His shanty roof was littered over with horns of choice Rams, and inside it was half-filled with a great pile of Sheepskins awaiting a market. So the droves of Bighorn were reduced to a few scattering bands, the largest of which was less than thirty, and many, like that of which I speak, had but three or four in it.

Once or twice during the first fortnight of June old Scotty had crossed the Sheep range, with his rifle ready, for game was always in season for him; but each time, one or the other of the alert mothers saw him afar, and either led quickly away, or, by giving a short, peculiar *sniff*, had warned the others not to move; then all stood still as stones, and so escaped, when a single move might easily have brought sure death. When the enemy was out of sight they quickly changed to some distant part of the range.

But one day, as they rounded a corner of the pine woods, they smelled an unknown smell. They stopped to know what it was, when a large dark animal sprang from a rock and struck Whitenose's mother down.

Nubbins and his mother fled in terror, and the Wolverine, for that was the enemy, put a quick end to her life; but before he began to feast he sprang on Whitenose, who was standing stupefied, and with merciful mercilessness laid him by his mother.

* * *

Nubbins's mother was a medium-sized, well-knit creature. She had horns longer and sharper than usual for a Ewe, and they were of the kind called Spikehorns or Spikers; she also had plenty of good Sheep sense. The region above Tobacco Creek had been growing more dangerous each month, thanks chiefly to Scotty, and the Mother Sheep's intention to move out was decided for her by the morning's tragedy.

She careered along the slope of the Gunder Peak at full speed, but before going over each rising ground she stopped and looked over it, ahead and back, remaining still as a lichen-patched rock for a minute or more in each place while she scanned the range around.

Once she did this she saw a dark, moving figure on a range behind her. It was old Scotty. She was in plain view, but she held as still as could be, and so escaped notice; and when the man was lost behind the rocks she bounded away faster than before, with little Nubbins scampering after. At each ridge she looked out carefully; but seeing no more of either her enemy or her friends, she pushed on quietly all that day, travelling more slowly as the danger-field was left behind.

Toward evening, as she mounted the Yak-in-i-kak watershed, she caught a glimpse of moving forms on a ridge ahead. After a long watch she made out that they were in the uniform of Sheep—gray, with white-striped stockings and white patches on face and stern. They were going up wind. Keeping out of view, she made so as to cross their back trail, which she soon found, and thus learned that her guess was right: there were the tracks of two large Bighorn; but the trail also said that they were Rams. According to Mountain Sheep etiquette, the Rams form one community and the Ewes and Lambs another. They must not mix or seek each other's society, excepting during the early winter, the festal months, the time of love and mating.

Nubbins's mother, or the Spikerdoe, as we may call her, left the trail and went over the watershed, glad to know that this was a Sheep region. She rested for the night in a hollow, and next morning she journeyed on, feeding as she went. Presently the mother caught a scent that made her pause. She followed it a little. Others joined on or crisscrossed, and she knew now that she had found the trail of a band of Ewes and Lambs. She followed steadily, and Nubbins skipped alongside, missing his playmate, but making up as far as possible by doing double work.

Within a very few minutes she sighted the band, over a dozen in all—her own people. The top of her head was just over a rock, so that she saw them first; but when Nubbins poked up his round head to see, the slight movement caught the eye of a watchful mother in the flock. She gave the signal that turned all the band to statues, with heads their way. It was now the Spiker's turn. She walked forth in plain view. The band galloped over the hill, but circled behind it to the left, while Nubbins and his mother went to the right.

In this way their positions in the wind were reversed. Formerly she could smell them; now they could smell her; and having already seen her uniform from afar, they were sure her credentials were right. She came cautiously up to them. A leading Ewe walked out to meet her. They sniffed and gazed. The leader stamped her feet, and the Spikerdoe got ready to fight. They advanced; their heads met with a whack! then, as they pushed, the Spikerdoe twisted so that one of her sharp points rested on the other Ewe's ear. The pressure became very unpleasant. The enemy felt she was getting the worst of it, so she sniffed, turned, and, shaking her head, rejoined her friends. The Spikerdoe walked after her, while little Nubbins, utterly puzzled, stuck close to her side. The flock wheeled and ran, but circled back, and as the Spiker stood her ground, they crowded around her, and she was admitted one of their number. This was the ceremony, so far as she was concerned. But Nubbins had to establish his own footing. There were some seven or eight Lambs in the flock. Most of them were older and bigger than he, and, in common with some other animals, they were ready to persecute the stranger simply because he was strange.

The first taste of this that Nubbins had was an unexpected "bang!" behind. It had always seemed very funny to him when he used to give Whitenose a surprise of this kind, but now there seemed nothing funny about it; it was simply annoying. And when he turned to face the enemy, another one charged from another direction; and whichever way he turned, there was a Lamb ready to butt at him, till poor Nubbins was driven to take refuge under his mother. Of course she could protect him, but he could not stay there always, and the rest of the day with the herd was an unhappy one for poor Nubbins, but a very amusing one for the others. He was so awed by their numbers, the suddenness of it all, that he did not know what to do. His activity helped but little. Next morning it was clear that the others intended to have some more fun at his expense. One of these, the largest, was a stocky little Ram. He had no horns yet, but when they did come they were just like himself, thick-set and crooked and rough, so that, reading ahead, we may style him "Krinklehorn." He came over, and just as Nubbins rose, hind legs first, as is Sheep fashion, the other hit him square and hard. Nubbins went sprawling, but jumped up again, and in something like a little temper went for the bully. Their small heads came together with about as much noise as two balls of yarn, but they both meant to win. Nubbins was aroused now, and he dashed for that other fellow. Their heads slipped past, and now it was head to shoulder, both pounding away. At first Nubbins was being forced back; but soon his unusual sprouts of horns did good service, and after getting one or two punches in his ribs from them, the bully turned and ran. The others, standing round, realized that the newcomer was fit. They received him as one of their number, and the hazing of Nubbins was ended.

* * *

It is quite common to hear conventionality and social rules derided as
though they were silly man-made tyrannies. They are really important
laws that, like gravitation, were here before human society began, and
shaped it when it came. In all wild animals we see them grown with the
mental growth of the species.

When a new Hen or Cow appears in the barn-yard, she must find
her level. She must take rank exactly according to the sum of her
powers. Those already there have long ago ranged themselves in a scale
of precedence; no one can climb in this scale without fighting all those
over whom she would go. Somewhere in this scale there must be a
place for the newcomer, and until this is settled, her life is one of
battles.

No doubt strength, courage, and activity fix her standing in most
cases, but sometimes wisdom and keenness of sense are of greater
importance. Which one is the leader of a band of wild animals? Not
necessarily the strongest or fiercest. That one might *drive* the rest, but
not lead them. The leader is not formally elected, as with man, but is
rather slowly selected, thus, *that individual* who can impress the rest
with the idea that he or she is *the best one to follow* becomes the leader,
and the government is wholly by consent of the governed. The election
is quite unanimous. For if in the herd are some who do not care to
follow, they are free to go the other way. In many kinds of animals that
go in herds, the leader whose courage and prowess have so often stood
all tests, and who has inspired all the rest with confidence in his
sagacity, is usually not the strongest male, but an *elderly female*. This is
especially the case with Elk, Buffalo, Blacktail, and the summer bands
of Mountain Sheep.

The Gunder Peak band of Sheep was made up of six or seven Ewes
with their Lambs, three or four Yearlings, and a promising young rising
Ram, two years of age, and just beginning to be very proud of his
horns, now in what is called the "ibex" stage. He was the largest
member of the band, but not by any means the most important. The
leader was a sagacious old Ewe; not the one that had tried a round with
the Spikerdoe, but a smaller one with short, stubby horns, who was
none other than the mother of Krinklehorn, the little bully.

The Sheep think of this leader, not as one *to be obeyed*, but as the
one *safe to follow*, the one who is always wise; and though they do not
give one another names, they have this idea; therefore I shall speak of
her as the Wise One.

The Spikerdoe was a very active Sheep, in her early prime, cool,
sagacious, keen of eye, nose, and ear, and forever on the watch. At least
once in three steps she raised her head to look around, and if she saw
anything strange or anything moving, she did not cease gazing until
she had made it out and went on grazing again, or else gave the long
snoof that made them all stand like stocks. Of course she was only
doing what they all did, but happened to do it better than they. The
Wise One, however, was rarely far behind her, and sometimes ahead in

seeing things, and had the advantage of knowing the country; but they were so nearly matched in gifts that very soon the Wise One felt that in the Spikerdoe she had a dangerous rival for the leadership.

The band was not without its cranks. There was a young Ewe that had a lazy fashion of feeding on her front "knees." The others did not copy her methods; they vaguely felt that they were not good. The effect of this original way of feeding was to bring a great callous pad on each knee (in reality the wrist). Then those growing pads and the improper use of her front legs began to rob Miss Kneepads of her suppleness. She could not spring quickly aside and back as the others could. Ordinarily this does not matter much, but there are times when it is very needful. All animals that must save themselves by flight have developed this trick of zigzag bounding. It is the couching Hare's best foil when sprung at by the Fox or the Hound; it is the sleeping Rabbit's only counter to the onset of the Wild Cat; it is the resting Deer's one balk to the leap of a Wolf; and it is the plan by which the Snipe, springing zigzag from the marsh, can set at naught the skill of the gunner as well as the speed of the Hawk, until she herself is under full headway.

Another odd Sheep in the band was a nervous little Ewe. She obeyed the leader, except in one thing. When the short *snoof* turned all the rest to stone, she would move about, fidgeting nervously, instead of heeding the Wise One's timely order to "freeze."

* * *

Some weeks went by in frequent alarms and flights. But the band was ably sentried, and all went well. As summer drew near a peculiar feverish restlessness came over the Sheep. They would stand motionless for a few minutes, neither grazing nor chewing the cud. They showed signs of indigestion, and kept on, seeking for something—they did not know what. As soon as the Wise One herself felt this listlessness and loss of appetite, she rose to the occasion. She led the whole band to a lower level, down among the timber, and lower still. Where was she going? The road was new to most of them. The Spikerdoe was full of distrust; she stopped again and again; she did not like these sinister lower levels. But the leader went calmly on. If any of the band had been disposed to stop and go back with her, the Spikerdoe would certainly have made a split. But all went listlessly after the Wise One, whose calm decision really inspired confidence. When far below the safety-line, the leader began to prick up her ears and gaze forward. Those near her also brightened up. They were neither hungry nor thirsty, but their stomachs craved something which they felt was near at last. A wide slope ahead appeared, and down it a white streak. Up to the head of this streak the Wise One led her band. They needed no telling; the bank and all about was white with something that the Sheep eagerly licked up. Oh, it was the most delicious thing they had ever tasted! It seemed they could not get enough; and as they licked and licked, the dryness left their throats, the hotness went from eye and ear, the headache quit their brains, their fevered itching skins grew cool and their stomachs sweetened, their listlessness was gone, and all their nature toned. It was like a most delicious drink of life-giving cordial, but it was only *common salt*.

This was what they had needed—and this was the great healing Salt-lick to which the leader's wisdom had been their guide.

* * *

For a young animal there is no better gift than obedience. It is obedience to the mother that gives him the benefit of all his mother's experience without the risk of getting it. Courage is good; speed and strength are good; but his best courage, speed, and strength are far below those of his mother, and they are at his service to the uttermost, if only he will obey. Brains are all-powerful, but among very young Bighorn Sheep at least, an obedient fool is far better off then the wisest headstrong Lamb that ever drew the breath of life.

When they had lingered an hour or two and licked the salt till nature was satisfied, the Wise One turned to go back to the range. The grass in the valley was uncommonly good, rich, rank, and abundant, and the Lambs just beginning to feed were revelling in the choicest of pasture; but this was down among the timber, with all its furtive dangers. The Wise One, as well as the Spikerdoe, wanted to get back to their own safe feeding-ground. She led the way, and the rest, though unwilling, would have followed, but litle Krinklehorn was too much engrossed with the rich food. He would not follow. His mother missed him, and when he bleated she came back to him. He did not positively refuse to come, but he lingered so that he held his mother back and encouraged the others to do the same. And when night fell the band was still below timber-line, and went to sleep in the woods.

A Mountain Lion does not make much noise as he sneaks up after his prey; he goes like a shadow: and not a sound was made by the great hungry Lion of the Yak-in-i-kak until by chance one little pebble touched by his velvet foot rolled down the bank. It was a slight noise, but the Spikerdoe heard it, and blowing the long *snoooof*, she called little Nubbins, and, in spite of the darkness, dashed up the cliff toward her safe home land. The others also leaped to their feet, but the Lion was among them. The Wise One leaped up, with a sign to Krinklehorn to follow. She also bounded toward safety—was saved; but her Lamb, always wilful, thought he saw a better way of escape, and finding himself alone, he bleated, "*Mother*"; and she, forgetting her own danger, dashed down again, and in a moment the Lion laid her low. Another Sheep forged by, and another, in the hurry and uproar of flight. At each of these in turn the Lion sprang, but each offset his pounce by a succession of bewildering zigzag jumps, and so escaped, till, last of all, poor Kneepads made past for the rocks, and when the Lion leaped she failed to play the only balk. The power that would have saved her she had long ago resigned; so now she fell.

Far up the bench the Sheep went bounding after the one that led. One by one they came up as she slacked her speed, and then they saw that the leader now was Spiker. They never saw the Wise One again, and so they knew that she must have fallen.

When they had reunited and turned to look back, they heard from far below a faint *baah* of a Lamb. All cocked their ears and waited. It is not wise to answer too quickly; it may be the trick of some enemy. But it came again—the familiar *baah* of one of their own flock; and Spikerdoe answered it.

A rattling of stones, a scrambling up banks, another *baah* for guidance, and there appeared among them little Krinklehorn—an orphan now.

Of course he did not know this yet, any more than the others did. But as the day wore on and no mother came in response to his plaintive calls, and as his little stomach began also to cry out for something more than grass or water, he realized his desolation, and *baahed* more and more plaintively. When night came he was cold as well as hungry; he must snuggle up to some one or freeze. No one took much notice of him, but Spikerdoe, seemingly the new leader, called once or twice in answer to his call, and almost by accident he drifted near her when she lay down and warmed himself against her beside his ancient enemy, young Nubbins.

In the morning he seemed to Mother Spikerdoe to be her own, in a limited sense. Rubbing against Nubbins made him smell like her own. And when Nubbins set about helping himself to a breakfast of warm milk, poor hungry Krinklehorn took the liberty of joining in on the other side. Thus Nubbins found himself nose to nose and dividing his birthright with his old-time enemy. But neither he nor his mother made any objection, and thus it was that Krinklehorn was adopted by his mother's rival.

* * *

There was no one of the others that could equal Spikerdoe in sagacity. She knew all the range now, and it was soon understood that she was to lead. It was also understood that Krinklehorn, as well as Nubbins, was her Lamb. The two were like brothers in many things. But Krinklehorn had no sense of gratitude to his foster-mother, and he always nursed his old grudge against Nubbins, and now that they

Dividing his birthright

drank daily of the same drink, he viewed Nubbins as his rival, and soon showed his feeling by a fresh attempt to master him. But Nubbins was better able to take care of himself now than ever. Krinklehorn got nothing but a few good prods for his pains, and their relative status was settled.

During the rest of the season they grew up side by side: Krinklehorn thick-set and sulky, with horns fast growing, but thick and crinkly; and Nubbins—well! it is not fair to call him Nubbins any longer, as his horns were growing fast and long; so that we may henceforth speak of him as Krag, a name that he got years afterward in the country around Gunder Peak, and the name by which he went down in history.

During the summer Krag and Krinklehorn grew in wit as well as in size. They learned all the ordinary rules of life among Bighorn. They knew how to give the warning *sniff* when they saw something, and the danger *snoo-of* when they were sure it was dangerous. They were acquainted with all the pathways and could have gone alone to any of the near salt-licks when they felt the need of it.

They could do the zigzag bounding that baffles the rush of an enemy, as well as the stiff-legged jumping which carries them safely up glassy, slippery slopes. Krag even excelled his mother in these accomplishments. They were well equipped to get their own living, they could eat grass, and so it was time they were weaned, for Spikerdoe had to lay on her fat to keep warm in the coming winter. The youngsters themselves would have been in no hurry to give up their comforting breakfast, but the supply began to run short, and the growing horns of the Lambs began to interfere with the mother's comfort so much that she proceeded firmly and finally with their weaning, and long before the earliest snow flurry grizzled the upland, she had them quite independent of her for their daily food.

* * *

Among the numbers of the band that met their fate that summer was the two-year-old Ram. He had no companion of his age and sex, and his sense of superiority developed a cock-sureness which resulted in his skin being added to the pile in Scotty's shanty. When the earliest snows of winter came, all the Lambs were weaned and doing for themselves, and the Ewes were fat and flourishing, but, being free from maternal cares, had thoughts for other matters. With the early frosts and the bracing air came the mating season, and, determined to find their mates, the sheep travelled about the likeliest parts of the hills.

Several times during the summer they had seen one or two great Rams in the distance, but an exchange of signals had made clear to each what the other was, and they had avoided each other's company. But now, when a pair of large Sheep were sighted, and the usual signals exchanged, there seemed no sign of a wish to avoid each other. As the two tall strangers came on, their great size, majestic forms, and vast curling horns left no doubt as to their sex, and, proud of their honors and powers, they pranced forward. But the forwardness of Spikerdoe and her band now gave place to a decided bashfulness. They turned as though to avoid the newcomers. This led to pursuit and to much manœuvring before the two Rams were permitted to join the herd. Then came the inevitable quarrel. The Rams had so far been good friends—were evidently chums; but chumship and love rivalry cannot dwell together. It was the old story—the jealous pang, the seeking for cause, the challenge, and the duel. But these are not always duels to the death. The Rams charged at each other; their horns whacked together till the chips flew from them; but after a few rounds one of them, the lighter, of course, was thrown backward, and, leaping up, he tried to escape. The other followed for a quarter of a mile, and, as he declined a further fight, the victor came proudly back, and claimed and was allowed the position and joys of Sultan of the band.

Krag and Krinklehorn were ignored. They were in awe of the great Ram who now took charge, and they felt that their safest plan was to keep as far as possible away from the present social activities of the flock, as they were not very sure of their own standing.

During the first part of that winter they were under guidance of the Ram. He was a big, handsome fellow, devoted to his female following, but not without a streak of masculine selfishness that made him take care to have the best of the food and to keep a sharp lookout for danger. Food was plentiful, for the Ram knew enough to lead them not into the sheltered ravines where the snow was deep, but up on the bleakest ridges of the upland, where the frigid wind lays bare the last year's grass, and, furthermore, where no enemy can approach unseen; so all went well.

* * *

The springtime came, with its thrilling sounds and feelings. Obedient to their ancient law, the Ram and the Band of Ewes had parted company in midwinter. The feeling had been growing for days. They were less disposed to follow him, and sometimes he lingered far away for hours. One day he did not rejoin them, and thenceforth to the end of the winter they followed the Spikerdoe as of old.

The little ones came about the first of June. Many of the mothers had two each, but Spikerdoe, now the Wise One, had but one, as before, and this little one displaced Krag for good and engrossed all the mother's attention. He even hindered her in her duties as a leader; and one day, as she was feeding him and watching the happy wagging of his tail, another Sheep gave an alarm. All froze except Fidgets. She crossed before the Wise One. There was a far-away "*crack!*" Fidgets dropped dead, and the Spikerdoe fell with a stifled *baah*! But she sprang to her feet, fogetting her own pain, and looking wildly about her for her Lamb, she leaped on the ridge to follow the others. Bang! went the rifle again, and the old Sheep got a first glimpse of the enemy. It was the man who had once so nearly caught the Lambs. He was a long way off, but the ball whistled before the Sheep's nose. She sprang back and changed her course, thereby leaving the rest, then leaped over the ridge, bleating to her little one to follow—bleating, too, from pain, for she was hard hit. But she leaped headlong down a rocky place, and the high ground came between. Down the gully she bounded, and out along the farther ridge, keeping out of sight so well that, though Scotty ran as fast as he could to the edge, he never saw her again. He chuckled as he noted the spots of blood; but these soon ceased, and after a long attempt to keep the trail, he gave it up, cursed his luck, and went back to the victim he had secured.

Away went Spikerdoe and her Lamb, the mother guiding, but the little one ahead. Her instinct told her that upward was the way to safety. Up the Gunder Peak she must go, but keep from being seen. So she went on, in spite of a burning wound, always keeping a ridge between, till round the nearest rocks she paused to look. She saw no sign either of her friends or her foe. She felt she had a deadly wound. She must escape lest her strength give out. She set off again at a run, forging upward, and the little one following or running ahead as he pleased. On they went till the timber-line was reached, and upward still her instinct urged her on.

Another lofty bench was scaled, and then she sighted a long white streak, a snow-drift lingering in a deep ravine. She eagerly made for that. There was a burning pain through her loins, and on each side was a dark stain on her coat. She craved a cooling touch, and on reaching the white patch sank on her side, her wound against the snow.

His mother . . . was so cold and still

There could be only one end to such a wound: two hours, three hours at furthest, and then—well, never mind.

And the little one? He stood dumbly gazing at her. He did not understand. He only knew that he was cold and hungry now, and that his mother, to whom he had looked for everything,—food, warmth, guidance, and sympathy,—was so cold and still!

He did not understand it. He did not know what next. But we do— the lingering misery, and the inevitable finish, soon or late, according to his strength; and the Raven on the rock knew, and waited. Better for the Lamb, far better, quicker, and more merciful, had the rifle served him as it did his mother.

* * *

Krag was a fine young Ram now, taller than any of the Ewes, and with long cimetars of horns. Krinklehorn also was well grown, as heavy as Krag, but not so tall, and with horns that looked diseased, they were so short, thick, and bumpy.

The autumn came again, with the grand reunion of the families, the readvent of the Ram, and also with a readjustment that Krag had not looked for. He was just beginning to realize that he was a Ram, and to take an interest in certain Ewes in the flock, when the great Ram came, with his curling horns and thick bull neck; and the first thing he did was to bundle Krag out of the flock. Krag, Krinklehorn, and three or four more of their age were packed off by themselves, for such is etiquette among Sheep. As soon as the young males reach, or nearly reach, maturity they must go off to study life for themselves, just as a boy leaves home for college. And during the four years that followed Krag led a roving bachelor life with a half-dozen companions. He became the leader, for he inherited his mother's wit, and they travelled into far countries, learning new pastures, new ways, and new wisdom, and fitting themselves to become fathers of large and successful families; for such is the highest ambition of every good Mountain Ram.

It was not choice that left Krag unmated, but a combination of events against which he vainly chafed, and he was still left with his bachelor crew. It was really better so. It seemed hard at the time, but it proved his making, for he was thus enabled to develop to the full his wonderful powers before being hampered and weakened by the responsibilities and mingled joys of a family. Each year the bachelor Rams grew handsomer. Even sulky Krinklehorn became a tall and strong, if not a fine-looking, Ram. He had never gotten over his old dislike of Krag. Once or twice he put forth his strength to worst him, and even tried to put him over a cliff; but he got so severely punished for it that thenceforth he kept away from his foster-brother. But Krag was a joy to behold. As he bounded up the jagged cliffs, barely touching each successive point with his clawed and padded hoofs, floating up like a bird, deriding all foes that thought of following afoot, and the sunbeams changing and flashing from his back as the supple muscles working changed the surface form, he was more like a spirit thing, that had no weight and knew no fear of falling, than a great three-hundred-pound Ram with five year-rings on his horns.

And such horns! The bachelors that owned his guidance had various horns, reflecting each the owner's life and gifts: some rough half-moons, some thick, some thin. But Krag's curled in one great sweep, three quarters of a circle, and the five year-marks told, first, beginning at the point, of the year when he was a Lamb, and grew the straight long spikes that had helped him so well in his early fight; next year the growth thicker and much longer; the next two years told of yet more robust growth with lesser length; but the last was record of a year of good food, of perfect health, and unexampled growth, for the span grown then was longer, wider, and cleaner horns than any of the others.

Tucked away under the protecting shadow of each rugged base, like things too precious to expose, were his beautiful eyes. Dark brown when he was a Lamb, yellowish brown when a yearling, they were now, in his early prime, great orbs of shining gold, or splendid amber jewels, with a long, dark, misty depth in each, through which the whole bright world was born and mirrored on his brain.

There is no greater joy to the truly living thing than the joy of being alive, of feeling alive in every part and power. It was a joy to Krag now to stretch his perfect limbs in a shock of playful battle with his friends. It was a joy to press his toes on some thin ledge, then sail an impossible distance across some fearful chasm to another ledge, whose size and distance he gauged with absolute precision. It was a joy to him to set the Mountain Lions at naught by a supple ricochet from rock to rock, or to turn and drive the bounding Blacktail band down pell-mell backward to their own, the lower, levels. There was a subtle pleasure in every move, and a glorying in his glorious strength, which, after all, is beauty. And when to such a being the early winter brought also the fire of love and set him all aglow, he was indeed a noble thing to see. In very wantonness of strength and power, he bounded, ball-like, up or down long, rugged slopes, leaping six feet high where one would have fully answered every end except the pleasure of doing it. But so he went, seeking, searching—for what? He could not have told; but he would know when he found it. Away he careered at the head of his band, till they crossed the trail of another band, and, instinct-guided, he followed after. In a mile or two the other band was sighted, a group of Ewes. They fled, of course, but being cornered on a rugged bench, they stood, and after due punctilio they allowed the Rams to approach.

The Bighorn is no monogamist. The finest Ram claims all of the Ewes in the flock, and any question of his claim must be settled on the spot in mortal fight. Hitherto there had been a spirit of good-fellowship among the Rams, but now that was changed; and when great Krag

bounded forward, snorting out a challenge to all the rest to disprove his right of might, there was none to face him, and, strange to tell, with many claimants, there was no fight. There was nothing now for the rest to do but to wheel at his command and leave him to the devotion and admiration of his conquest.

If, as they say, beauty and prowess are winning cards in all walks of animal life, then Krag must have been the idol of his band. For matched with Rams he had seemed a wonder, and among the Ewes his strength, his size, and the curling horns must have made of him a demigod, and the winged heart and the brimming cup were his.

But on the second day of joy two Rams appeared, and after manœuvring came near. One was a fine big animal, as heavy in the body as Krag, but with smaller horns, and the other was—yes, it surely was—Krinklehorn. The new Ram snuffed a challenge as he came near, then struck the ground with his foot, meaning, "I am a better Ram than you, and mean to oust you from your present happy position."

Krag's eyes blazed. He curled his massive neck. He threw his chin up and down like a champing horse, shook his great horns as though they were yet mere points, laid back his ears, and charged; and forward sprang the foe. *Choch!* they came together; but the stranger had an advantage of ground, which left the first onset a draw.

The Rams backed off, each measuring the other and the distance, and, seeking for firm footing, kept on the edge of the great bench; then, with a whoof! they came on again. Whack! and the splinters flew, for they both were prime. But this time Krag clearly had the best of it. He followed up his advantage at once with a second whack! at short range, and twisting around, his left horn hooked under the right of his foe, when, to his utter dismay, he received a terrific blow on his flank from an unknown enemy. He was whirled around, and would have been dashed over the cliff but that his horn was locked in that of his first foe, and so he was saved; for no Ram has weight enough in his hind quarter to oppose the headlong charge of another. Krag scrambled to his feet again, just in time to see the new enemy irresistibly carried by the violence of his own charge over the ledge and down.

It was a long time before a far-away crash told to those on the ledge that Krinklehorn had found the very end he plotted for his foster-brother. Ram fights are supposed to be fair duels. Krinklehorn, failing in fair fight, had tried foul, and had worked his own destruction; for not even a Bighorn can drop two hundred feet on rock and live.

Krag now turned on his other foe with double fury. One more shock and the stranger was thrown, defeated. He leaped to his feet and bounded off. For a time Krag urged him to further flight by the same means that Krinklehorn once used to persecute him, then returned in triumph to live unmolested with his family.

* * *

Scotty had gone from his Tobacco Creek location in 1887. The game was pretty well hunted out. Sheep had become very scarce, news of new gold strikes in Colorado had attracted him southward, and the old shanty was deserted. Five years went by with Krag as the leading Ram. It was five years under a good genius, with an evil genius removed—five years of prosperity, then, for the Bighorn.

Krag carried further the old ideas that were known to his mother. He taught his band to abjure the lowlands entirely. The forest coverts were full of evil, and the only land of safety was the open, wind-swept peaks, where neither Lions nor riflemen could approach unseen. He found more than one upland salt-lick where their natural need could be supplied without the dangerous lowland journeys that they once had thought necessary. He taught his band never to walk along the top of a ridge, but always along one side, so as to look down both ways without being conspicuous. And he added one famous invention of his own. This was the "hide." If a hunter chances close to a band of Sheep before they see him, the old plan was to make a dash for safety—a good enough plan in the days of bows and arrows or even of muzzle-loading rifles, but the repeating rifle is a different arm. Krag himself learned, and then taught his tribe, to crouch and lie perfectly still when thus surprised. In nine cases out of ten this will baffle a human hunter, as Krag found times without number.

It is always good for a race when a great one arises in it. Krag marked a higher level for the Bighorns. His children multiplied on the Yak-in-i-kak around the Gunder Peak, and eastward as far as Kintla Lake at least. They were healthier and much wiser than had been the Bighorn of other days, and being so, their numbers steadily increased.

Five years had made some changes in Krag's appearance, but his body was square and round and muscular as ever; his perfect legs seemed unchanged in form or in force; his head was as before, with the heart-shaped white patch on his nose; and his jewel eyes blazed as of old. But his horns, how they had changed! Before they were uncommon; now they were unique. The massive sweeps—the graven records of his life—were now a circle and a quarter, and they told of years of joy and years of strife, and one year, tallied in a narrow band of dark and wrinkled horn, told of the year when all the mountains were scourged by the epidemic of grip—when numbers of Lambs and their mothers died; when many strong Rams succumbed; when Krag himself had been smitten, but recovered, thanks to his stalwart growth and native force, and after a time of misery had shown no traces of those wretched months, except in the yearly growth of horn. For that year, 1889, it was barely an inch in width, plain for those who read such things—a record of a time of want.

* * *

At length old Scotty came back. Like all mountaineers, he was a wanderer, and he once more returned alone to his shanty on Tobacco Creek. The sod roof had fallen in, and he hesitated to repair it. Anyhow he would prospect awhile first. He took his rifle and sought the familiar upland. Before he returned he had sighted two large bands of Mountain

Sheep. That decided him. He spent a couple of days repairing the shanty, and the curse of the Yak-in-i-kak returned.

Scotty was now a middle-aged man. His hand was strong and steady, but his eyes had lost some of their power. As a youth he had scorned all aids to sight; but now he carried a field-glass. In the weeks that followed he scanned a thousand benches through the glass, and many a time his eye rested on the form of the Gunder Ram. The first time he saw him, he exclaimed, "Heavens, what horns!" then added prophetically, "Them's mine!" and he set out to make them his. But the Bighorn of his early days were fools to these, and month after month passed without his ever getting a nearer view of the great Ram. The Ram had more than once seen him at short range, but Scotty never knew it.

Several times, through the glass, he marked old Krag from afar on a bench; then, after a labor of hours, stalked round to the place only to find him gone. Sometimes he really was gone, but on more than one occasion the Ram was close at hand and hidden, watching his foe.

Then came a visitor to Scotty's shanty—a cattle-man named Lee, a sportsman by instinct, and a lover of Dogs and Horses. His Horses were of little use in mountain hunting, but his Wolf-hounds, three beautiful Russian Borzois, were his constant companions, and he suggested to Scotty that it would be a good plan to try the Dogs on the Bighorn.

Scotty grinned. "Guess you're from the plains, pard. Wait till you see the kind of place whar ole Krag hangs around."

* * *

Where the Yak-in-i-kak River leaves its parent mountains, south of Gunder Peak, it comes from a tremendous gorge called Skinkler's Gulch. This is a mere crack in the vast granite hill, but is at least five hundred feet in depth. Southward from the back of Gunder Peak is a broken upland that runs to a point at this cañon, and ends in a long promontory over the raging walled-in stream.

This upland is good Sheep range, and by a strange chance Scotty, coming up there with Lee and the three Wolf-hounds, got a glimpse of the Gunder Ram. The men kept out of sight and hurried along by the hollows toward the spot. But it was the old story. No sign of their quarry. They found his great hoof-mark just where they had seen him, so it was no illusion; but the hard rocks about refused further information, and no doubt Scotty would have had another mysterious disappearance to add to his list, but that the Dogs, nosing about in all of the near hollows and thickets of dwarf birch, broke out suddenly into a loud clamor, and as they did so, up jumped a huge, gray, white-sterned animal—the Ram, the wonderful Gunder Ram. Over the low bushes, over the broken rocks, bounding, soaring, floating, supple, certain, splendid, he bore the great curling wonders on his head as lightly as a lady might wear her ear-rings; and then, from various other coverts, sprang up his band and joined him. Up flew the rifles; but in a moment the three great Dogs, closing in, gave unwilling screen to the one victim on which every thought was fixed, and not a shot was heard. Away they went, the Ram forging quickly to the lead, and the others stringing along after. Over the upland, flying, sailing, leaping, and swerving, they went. Over the level plains the Dogs would soon have caught the hindmost or perhaps their noblest prey, but on the rugged rocks it was clear that the Sheep were gaining. The men ran, one to the right, the other to the left, the better to keep sight; and Krag, cut off from the peak, dashed southward over the bench-land. Now it was a straight race. On it went—on, southward. The Dogs gained, and were near catching the hindmost Sheep; then it seemed that the Ram dropped back and now ran the rearmost. A rugged stretch was reached, and there the Sheep gained steadily, though little. One, two, three miles, and the chase was sweeping along the rocky ridge that ends in the sudden gash of Skinkler's Gulch. A minute more and the crowd of Sheep were rounded up and cornered on the final rock. They huddled together in terror, five hundred feet of dizzy cañon all around, three fierce Dogs and two fiercer men behind. Then, a few seconds later, old Krag dashed up. Cornered at last, he wheeled to fight; for the wild thing never yields.

He was now so far from the bounding Dogs that two rifle-balls whistled near. Of the Dogs he had no fears—them he could fight; but the rifles were sure death. There was one chance left. The granite walls of the Yak-in-i-kak could prove no harder than the human foe. The Dogs were within forty rods now, fine courageous animals, keen for fight, fearless of death; and behind, the hunters, remorseless and already triumphant. Sure death from them, or doubtful life in the gulch. There was no time to hesitate; he, the leader, must act. He wheeled to the edge, and *leaped*—down—down, not to the bottom, not blindly. Thirty feet downward, across the dizzy chasm, was a little jut of rock, no bigger than his nose—the only one in sight, all the rest smooth, sheer, or over-hanging. But Krag landed fairly, poised just a heart-beat.

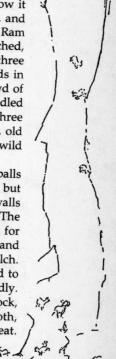

In a flash his blazing eyes took in another point, his only hope, on the other side, hidden under the overhanging rocks he had leaped from. His supple loins and corded limbs bent, pulsed, and floated him across, there got fresh guidance to his flight, then back, sometimes to a mere roughness of the rock, on which his hoofs, of horn and rubber built, gripped for an instant, and took fresh ricochet to another point. Then sidewise fifteen feet, and down, down with modulated impact from point to point, till, with a final drop of twenty feet, he reached a ledge of safety far below.

And the others, inspired by his example, followed fast—a long cascade of Sheep. Had he failed at one point all must have failed. But now they came down headlong. It was splendid, it was inspiring! Hop, skip, down they came, one after the other, now ten, now twenty feet, first to last leaping, sailing, bounding from point to ledge, from ledge to point, with masterly command of thew and hoof, with marvellous poise, and absolute success.

But just as the last had reached the second slender, speck-like foothold for its life, three white-and-yellow creatures whirled past her in the air, with gurgled gasps of horror, to perish far below. The Hounds, impetuous and brave, never hesitated to follow a foe, and never knew how far more gifted was that foe than themselves until it was too late. Down below, almost at the water's edge, Krag paused at length. Far above he heard the yells and whistles of the hunters; below in the boiling Yak-in-i-kak he saw a battered white-and-yellow form being hurried to the sea.

Lee and Scotty stood blankly at the edge. Sheep and Dogs had vanished; no possibility of escape for any. Scotty uttered words that had no bearing on the case, only they were harsh, blasphemous words, and seemed to be necessary. Lee had a choking feeling in his throat, and he felt as no man can comprehend who has not lost a noble Dog by a sudden, tragic, and untimely end.

"Bran! Rollo! Ida!" he called in lingering hope; but the only response was from the Western Wind, that "snoofed" and whistled as it swept down Skinkler's Gulch.

* * *

Lee was a young, warm-hearted, impulsive cattle-man. For a day or two he hung about the shanty. The loss of his three friends was a sad blow: he had no heart for more mountaineering. But a few days later a spell of bracing weather helped his spirits, and he agreed when Scotty suggested a hunt. They reached the upper level, when Scotty, who had from time to time been scanning the hills with his glass, suddenly exclaimed:

"H—l! If thar ain't the old Gunder Ram. Thought he was smashed in Skinkler's Gulch!" and he sat down in amazement. Lee took the glass, and he recognized the wonderful Ram by his superb horns. The color rushed to the young man's face. Now was his chance for glory and revenge at once! "Poor old Bran! good Rollo and Ida!"

Few animals have cunning enough to meet the combined drive and ambush. Scotty knew the lay of the land as well as the habits of the Ram.

"He ain't a-goin' to run down the wind, and he ain't a-goin' to quit the rocks. That means he'll pass up by the Gunder Peak, if he moves at all, an' he must take one side or the other. He won't go the west side if I show meself once that ar way. So you take the east; I'll give you two hours to get placed. I've a notion he'll cross the spur by that ledge."

Lee set out for his post. Scotty waited two hours, then moved on to a high ridge, and, clear against the sky, he waved his arms and walked up and down a few times. The Ram was not in sight, but Scotty knew he would see.

Then the old mountaineer circled back by hidden ways to the south, and began to walk and cut over the ridges toward the place where the Ram had been. He did not expect to see old Krag, but he did expect the Ram to see him. Lee was at his post, and, after a brief spell, he sighted the great Ram himself, bounding lightly down a ridge a mile away, and close behind him were three Ewes. They disappeared down a pine-clad hollow, and when they reappeared on the next ridge they were running as though in great alarm, their ears laid back; and from the hollow behind came, not, as Lee expected, the crack of Scotty's rifle or the sound of his yell, but the hunting chorus of Timber Wolves. Among the rocks the Sheep could easily escape, but among the timber or on the level such as now lay ahead, the advantage was with the Wolves; and a minute later these swept up in sight—five shaggy, furry brutes. The level open was crossed at whirling speed. The Sheep, racing for their lives, soon lengthened out into a procession in order of speed: far ahead the great Ram; behind him, with ten-yard gaps between them, the three Ewes; and forty yards behind the last, the five grim Wolves, closing, gaining at every leap. The bench-land narrowed eastward to pass a rocky shoulder. Long years and countless perils had taught the Sheep that in the rocks was safety, and that way led the Ram. But in the tangled upland birch the last of the Ewes was losing ground; she gasped a short *baah* as, thrown by a curling root, she lost a few more precious yards. The Wolves were almost within leaping distance when Krag reached the shoulder-ledge. But a shoulder above means a ravine below. In a moment, at that call of distress, Krag wheeled on the narrow ledge and faced the foe. He stood to one side, and the three Ewes leaped past him and on to safety. Then on came the Wolves, with a howl of triumph. Many a Sheep had they pulled down, and now they knew they soon would feast. Without a pause they closed, but in such a narrow pass, it was one at a time. The leader sprang; but those death-dealing fangs closed only on a solid mass of horn, and back of that was a force that crushed his head against himself, and dashed him at his friend behind with such a fearful vim that both were hurled over the cliff to perish on the rocks. On came the rest. The Ram had no time to back up for a charge, but a sweep of that

Krag wheeled and faced the foe

great head was enough. The points, forefronting now, as they did when he was a Lamb, speared and hurled the next Wolf, and the next; and then Krag found a chance to back up and gather his force. None but a mad Wolf could have failed to take warning; but on he came, and Krag, in savage glory of the fight, let loose that living thunderbolt,— himself,—and met the last of the furry monsters with a shock that crushed him flat against the rock, then picked him up on his horns as he might a rag, and hurled him farthest yet, and standing on the edge he watched him whirl and gasp till swallowed in the chasm.

The great Ram raised his splendid head, blew a long blast from his nostrils, like a war-horse, and gazed a moment to see if more were coming; then turned and lightly bounded after the Ewes he had so ably guarded.

From his hiding-place young Lee took in the whole scene with eager, sparkling eyes. Only fifty yards away from him it had passed.

He was an easy mark—fifty yards, standing; he was a splendid mark, all far beyond old Scotty's wildest talk. But Lee had seen a deed that day that stirred his blood. He felt no wish to end that life, but sat with brightened eyes, and said with fervor: "You grand old warrior! I do not care if you did kill my Dogs. You did it fair. I'll never harm you. For me, you may go in safety."

But the Ram never knew; and Scotty never understood.

* * *

There was once a wretch who, despairing of other claims to notice, thought to achieve a name by destroying the most beautiful building on earth. This is the mind of the head-hunting sportsman. The nobler the thing that he destroys, the greater the deed, the greater his pleasure, and the greater he considers his claim to fame.

During the years that followed more than one hunter saw the great Ram and feasted his covetous eyes on his unparalleled horns. His fame even reached the cities. Dealers in the wonderful offered fabulous prices for the head that bore them—set blood-money on the life that grew them; and many came to try their luck, and failed. Then Scotty, always needy, was fired by a yet larger money offer, and setting out with his partner, they found the Ram, with his harem about him. But in three days of hard following they never got a second glimpse; and the partner "reckoned thar was easier money to git," and returned home.

But back of Scotty's sinister gray eyes was the fibre of dogged persistency that has made his race the masters of the world. He returned with Mitchell to the shanty, but only to prepare for a long and obstinate hunt. His rifle, his blanket, his pipe, with matches, tobacco, a pot, a bundle of jerked venison, and three or four pounds of chocolate were all he carried. He returned alone next day to the place where he had left the track of the Ram, and followed it fast in the snow, winding about, in and out, and obscured by those of his band, but always distinguishable by its size. Once or twice Scotty came on the spots where the band had been lying down, and from time to time he scanned the distance with his glass. But he saw nothing of them. At night he camped on their trail; next day he took it up again. After following for hours, he came on the place where evidently the Ram had stopped to watch him afar, and so knew of his pursuer. Thenceforth the trail of the band for a long time was a single line as they headed for distant pastures.

Scotty followed doggedly behind; all day he followed, and at night, in a little hollow, crouched like a wild beast in his lair, with this difference only: he had a fire, and he smoked a pipe in very human fashion. In the morning he went on as before. Once or twice in the far distance he saw the band of Sheep travelling steadily southward. Next day passed, and the Sheep were driven to the south end of the Yak-in-i-kak range, just north of Whitefish Lake.

South of this was the Half-moon Prairie, east the broken land that stretched toward the north fork of the Flathead, and north of them their pertinacious and deadly foe. The Sheep were in doubt now, and as old Krag sought to sneak back by the lower benches of the east slope, he heard a "crack!" and a stinging something touched one horn and tore the hair from his shoulder.

The touch of a rifle-ball on the horn of a Ram has a more or less stunning effect; and Krag, dazed for a moment, gave the signal which in our speech is, "Every one for himself now"; and so the band was scattered. Some went this way and some that, running more or less openly.

But Scotty's one thought was old Krag: he heeded no other; and when the Ram made straight away eastward down the hill, Scotty again took up his trail, and cursed and gasped as he followed.

The Flathead River was only a few miles away. The Ram crossed on the ice, and keeping the roughest ground, turning when the wind turned, he travelled all day northeastward, with Scotty steadily behind. On the fifth day they passed near Terry's Lake. Scotty knew the ground. The Ram was going east, and would soon run into a lot of lumber-camps; then turn he must, for the region was a box cañon; there was only one way out. Scotty quit the trail, and crossing northward to this one defile, down which the Ram must go, he waited. The West—the Chinook—Wind had been rising for an hour or more, the one damp wind of the Rockies, the Snow Wind of the Hills; and as it rose the flakes began to fly. In half an hour more it was a blinding snow-storm. Things twenty yards away were lost to view. But it did not last; the heaviest of it was over in a few minutes, and in two hours the skies were clear again. Scotty waited another hour, but seeing nothing, he left his post and searched about for sign; and found it, too—a dimpling row of tracks, much hidden by the recent snow, but clear in one place under a ledge. The Ram had passed unseen, had given him the slip, saved by the storm-wind and the snow.

Oh, Chinook! Mother West Wind! that brings the showers of spring and the snows of winter; that makes the grass grow on these great rolling uplands; that sustains the grass and all flesh that the grass sustains; that carved these uplands themselves, as well as made all things that live upon them—are you only a puff of air, or are you, as Greek and Indian both alike have taught, a something better, a living, thinking thing, that first creates, then loves and guards its own? Why did you come that day and hold your muffler about the eyes of the wolfish human brute, if it were not that you meant he should not see or harm your splendid dear one as he passed?

And was there not purpose in the meeting of these very two, that you brought about long years ago, the day the Ram was born?

* * *

Now Scotty thought there must be an object in the Ram's bold dash for the east side of the Flathead, and that object must be to reach the hills around Kintla Lake, on which he was well known and had many times been seen. He might keep west all day to-day, while the Chinook blew, but if the wind changed in the night he would surely turn eastward. So Scotty made no further attempt to keep the trail, or to make the west point of the Kintla Range, but cut straight northward over the divide toward the lake. The wind did change in the night. And next day, as Scotty scanned the vast expanse between him and the lake, he saw a moving speck below. He quickly got out of sight, then ran to intercept the traveller. But when he got to the spot he aimed at, and cautiously peered, there, five hundred yards away, on the next ridge, he stood— the famous Ram. Each was in plain view of the other.

Scotty stood for a minute and gazed in silence. Then, "Wal, ole Krag, ye kin see the skull and cross-bones on my gun. I'm Death on yer track; ye can't shake me off. At any price, I mean to have them horns. And here's for luck." Then he raised the rifle and fired; but the distance was great. The Ram stood till he saw the puff of smoke, then moved quickly to one side, and the snow was tossed by the ball not far from his former stand.

The Ram turned and made eastward, skirting the rugged southern shore of the lake, making for the main divide; and Scotty, left far behind for a time, trudged steadily, surely, behind him. For added to his tireless strength was the Saxon understreak of brutish grit, of senseless, pig-dogged pertinacity—the inflexible determination that still sticks to its purpose long after sense, reason, and honor have abandoned the attempt, that blinds its owner to its own defeat, and makes him, even when he is downed, still feebly strike—yes, spend his final mite of strength in madly girding at his conqueror, whose quick response, he knows, will be to wipe him out.

It was on, on, all day; then camp for the night, and up again in the morning. Sometimes the trail was easy to follow, sometimes blotted out by new-fallen snow. But day after day they went. Sometimes Scotty was in sight of the prize that he pertinaciously was hunting, but never very near. The Ram seemed to have learned that five hundred yards was the farthest range of the rifle, and allowed the man to come up to that, the safety limit. After a time it seemed as though he much preferred to have him there, for then he knew where he was. One time Scotty stole a march, and would have had a close shot had not the fateful West Wind borne the taint, and Krag was warned in time; but this was in the first month of that dogged, fearful following. After a while the Ram was never out of sight.

Why did he not fly far away, and baffle the hunter by his speed?

Because he must feed. The man had his dried venison and chocolate, enough for many days; and when they were gone he could shoot a hare or a grouse, hastily cook it, and travel all day on that. But the Ram required hours to seek the scanty grass under the snow. The long pursuit was telling on him. His eyes were blazing bright as ever, his shapely corded limbs as certain in their stride; but his belly was pinching up, and hunger, weakening hunger, was joining with his other foe.

For five long weeks the chase went on, and the only respite to the Gunder Ram was when some snow-storm from the west would interpose its veil.

Then came two weeks when they were daily in sight of each other. In the morning Scotty, rising wolf-like from his frosty lair, would call out, "Come, Krag; time we wuz a-movin'." And the Ram on the distant ridge would stamp defiantly, then, setting his nose to the wind, move on, now fast, now slow, but keeping ever the safe five hundred yards or more ahead. When Scotty sat down to rest the Ram would graze. If Scotty hid, the Ram would run in alarm to some place where near approach unseen would be impossible. If Scotty remained still for some time, the Ram would watch him intently and as still as himself. Thus they went on, day after day, till ten eventless weeks dragged slowly by. A singular feeling had grown up between the two. The Ram became so used to the sleuth-hound on his track that he accepted him as an inevitable, almost a necessary evil; and one day, when Scotty rose and scanned the northern distance for the Ram, he heard the long snort far behind, and turning, he saw old Krag impatiently waiting. The wind had changed, and Krag had changed his route to suit. One day after their morning's start Scotty had a difficult two hours in crossing a stream over which old Krag had leaped. When he did reach the other side he heard a snort, and looked around to find that the Ram had come back to see what was keeping him.

Oh, Krag! Oh, Gunder Ram! Why do you make terms with such a foe implacable? Why play with Death? Have all the hundred warnings of the Mother Wind been in vain? Keep on, keep on; do your best, that she may save you yet; but make no terms. Remember that the snow, which ought to save, may yet betray.

* * *

Thus in the winter all the Chief Mountain was traversed; the Kootenay Rockies, spur by spur, right up to the Crow's Nest Pass; then westward, in the face of the White Wind, the indomitable pair turned

their steps, west and south to the McDonald Range; and onward still, till the Galtom Range was reached. Day by day the same old mechanical following—two dark moving specks on the great expanse of snow. Many a time their trail was crossed by that of other Sheep and other game. Once they met a party of miners who knew of Scotty and his hunt, and they chaffed him now; but he stared blankly, heeded them not, and went on. Many a time the Ram sought to hide his fateful footprints in the wake of some passing herd. But Scotty was not to be balked; his purpose had become his nature. All puzzles he worked out, and now there were fewer interruptions of the chase, for the snow-storms seemed to cease, the White Wind held aloof, and Nature offered no rebuke.

On and on, still the same scant half-mile apart; and on them both the hands of Time and Death seemed laid. Both were growing hollow-eyed and were gaunter every day. The man's hair had bleached since he set out on this insane pursuit, and the head and shoulders of the Ram were grizzling; only his jewel eyes and his splendid sweeping horns were the same, and borne as proudly as when first the chase began.

Each morning the man would rise,—stiff, half frozen, and gaunt, but dogged as a very Hound infernal,—and sneak along, trying for a close shot. But always Krag was warned in time, and springing into view from his own couch, would lead the chase as before. Till in the third month they crossed again from Galtom to Tobacco Range, then eastward back to Gunder Peak—the Ram, and the sleuth inexorable upon his trail behind him. Here, on the birthplace of the Ram, they sat one morning, at rest—the Ram on one ridge, Scotty six hundred yards away on the next. For twelve long weeks the Ram had led him through the snow, over ten long mountain-ranges—five hundred rugged miles.

And now they were back to their starting-point, each with his lifetime wasted by one half in that brief span. Scotty sat down, and lit his pipe. The Ram made haste to graze. As long as the man stayed there in view the Ram would keep that ridge. Scotty knew this well; a hundred times he had proved it. Then, as he sat and smoked, some evil spirit entered in and sketched a cunning plot. He emptied his pipe deliberately, put it away, then cut some rods of the low-creeping birch behind him; he gathered some stones; and the great Ram watched afar. The man moved to the edge of the ridge, and with sticks, some stones, and what clothing he could spare, he made a dummy of himself. Then, keeping exactly behind it, he crawled backward over the ledge and disappeared. After an hour of crawling and stalking he came up on a ridge behind the Ram.

There he stood, majestic as a bull, graceful as a deer, with horns that rolled around his brow like thunder-clouds about a peak. He was gazing intently on the dummy, wondering why his follower was so long still. Scotty was nearly three hundred yards away. Behind the Ram were some low rocks, but between was open snow. Scotty lay down and threw snow on his own back till he was all whitened, then set out to crawl two hundred yards, watching the great Ram's head, and coming on as fast as he dared. Still old Krag stared at the dummy, sometimes impatiently stamping. Once he looked about sharply, and once he would have seen that deadly crawler in the snow, but that his horn itself, his great right horn, must interpose its breadth between his eye and his foe, and so his last small chance of escape was gone. Nearer, nearer to the sheltering rocks crawled the Evil One. Then, safely reaching them at last, he rested, a scant half-hundred yards away. For the first time in his life he saw the famous horns quite close. He saw the great, broad shoulders, the curving neck, still massive, though the mark of famine was on all; he saw this splendid fellow-creature blow the hot breath of life from his nostrils, vibrant in the sun; and he even got a glimpse of the life-light in those glowing amber eyes: but he slowly raised the gun.

Oh, Mother White Wind, only blow! Let not this be. Is all your power offset? Are not a million idle tons of snow on every peak awaiting? And one, just one, will do; a single flying wreath of snow will save him yet. The noblest living thing on all these hills, must he be stricken down to glut the basest lust of man? Because he erred but once, must he be doomed?

But never day was calmer. Sometimes the Mountain Magpies warn their friends, but not a Bird was anywhere in view; and still the Gunder Ram was spellbound, watching that enemy, immovable, across the dip.

Up went the gun that never failed—directed by the eye that never erred. But the hand that had never trembled taking twenty human lives now shook as though in fear.

Two natures? Yes.

But the hand grew steady; the hunter's face was calm and hard. The rifle rang, and Scotty—hid his head; for the familiar "crack!" had sounded as it never did before. He heard a rattling on the distant stones, then a long-drawn *snoof!* But he neither looked nor moved. Two minutes later all was still, and he timidly raised his head. Was he gone? or what?

There on the snow lay a great gray-brown form, and at one end, like a twin-necked hydra coiling, were the horns, the wonderful horns, the sculptured record of the splendid life of a splendid creature, his fifteen years of life made visible at once. There were the points, much

worn now, that once had won his Lamb-days' fight. There were the years of robust growth, each long in measure of that growth. Here was that year of sickness, there the splinter on the fifth year's ring, which notched his first love-fight. The points had now come round, and on them, could we but have seen, were the lives of many Gray Wolves that had sought his life. And so the rings read on, the living record of a life whose very preciousness had brought it to a sudden end.

The golden chain across the web of white was broken for its gold.

Scotty walked slowly over, and gazed in sullen silence, not at the dear-won horns, but at the calm yellow eyes, unclosed, and yet undimmed by death. Stone-cold was he. He did not understand himself. He did not know that this was the sudden drop after the long, long slope up which he had been forcing himself for months. He sat down twenty yards away, with his back to the horns. He put a quid of tobacco in his mouth. But his mouth was dry; he spat it out again. He did not know what he himself felt. Words played but little part in his life, and his lips uttered only a torrent of horrid blasphemies, his one emotional outburst.

A long silence; then, "I'd give it back to him if I could."

He stared at the distance. His eyes fell on the coat he had left, and realizing that he was cold, he walked across and gathered up his things. Then he returned to the horns, and over him came the wild, inhuman lusting for his victim's body that he had heard his comrades speak of, but had never before understood—the reactionary lust that makes the panther fondle and caress the deer he has stricken down. He made a fire; then, feeling more like himself, he skinned the Ram's neck and cut off the head. This was familiar work, and he followed it up mechanically, cutting meat enough to satisfy his hunger. Then, bowing his shoulders beneath the weight of his massive trophy,—a weight he would scarcely have noticed three months ago,—he turned from the chase, old, emaciated, grizzled, and haggard, and toiled slowly down to the shanty he had left twelve weeks before.

* * *

"No! Money couldn't buy it"; and Scotty turned sullenly away to end discussion. He waited a time till the taxidermist had done his best, then he retraversed three hundred miles of mountain to his lonely home. He removed the cover, and hung the head where it got the best light. The work was well done: the horns were unchanged; the wonderful golden eyes were there, and when a glint of light gave to them a semblance of regard, the mountaineer felt once more some of the feelings of that day on the ridge. He covered up the head again.

Those who knew him best say he kept it covered and never spoke about it. But one man said: "Yes; I saw him uncover it once, and look kind o' queer." The only remark he ever made about it was: "Them's my horns, but he'll get even with me yet."

Four years went by. Scotty, now known as Old Man Scotty, had never hunted since. He had broken himself down in that long madness. He lived now entirely by his gold-pan, was quite alone, and was believed to have something on his mind. One day, late in the winter, an old partner stopped at his shanty. Their hours of conversation did not amount to as many paragraphs.

"I heared about ye killin' the Gunder Ram."

Scotty nodded.

"Let's see him, Scotty."

"Suit yourself"; and the old man jerked his head toward the draped thing on the wall. The stranger pulled off the cloth, and then followed the usual commonplace exclamations of wonder. Scotty received them in silence; but he turned to look. The firelight reflected in the glassy eyes lent a red and angry glare.

"Kivver him up when you're through," said Scotty, and turned to his smoking.

"Say, Scotty, why don't ye sell him if he bothers ye that-a-way? That there New-Yorker told me to tell ye that he'd give—"

"To h—l with yer New-Yorker! I'll niver sell him—I'll niver part with him. I stayed by him till I done him up, an' he'll stay by me till he gits even. He's been a-gittin' back at me these four years. He broke me down on that trip. He's made an old man o' me. He's left me half luny. He's sucking my life out now. But he ain't through with me yet. Thar's more o' him round than that head. I tell ye, when that old Chinook comes a-blowin' up the Ter-bak-ker Crik, I've heared noises that the wind don't make. I've heared him just the same as I done that day when he blowed his life out through his nose, an' me a-layin' on my face afore him. I'm up ag'in' it, an' I'm a-goin' to face it out—right—here—on—Ter-bak-ker—Crik."

The White Wind rose high that night, and hissed and wailed about Scotty's shanty. Ordinarily the stranger might not have noticed it; but once or twice there came in over the door a long *snoof* that jarred the latch and rustled violently the drapery of the head. Scotty glanced at his friend with a wild, scared look. No need for a word; the stranger's face was white.

In the morning it was snowing, but the stranger went his way. All that day the White Wind blew, and the snow came down harder and harder. Deeper and deeper it piled on everything. All the smaller peaks were rounded off with snow, and all the hollows of the higher ridges levelled. Still it came down, not drifting, but piling up, heavy, soft, adhesive—all day long, deeper, heavier, rounder. As night came on, the Chinook blew yet harder. It skipped from peak to peak like a living thing—no puff of air, but a living thing, as Greek and Indian both alike have taught, a being who creates, then loves and guards its own. It came like a mighty goddess, like an angry angel with a bugle-horn, with a dreadful message from the far-off western sea—a message of war; for it sang a wild, triumphant battle-song, and the strain of the song was:

> I am the mothering White Wind;
>   This is my hour of might.
> The hills and the snow are my children;
>   My service they do to-night.

And here and there, at the word received, there were mighty doings among the peaks. Here new effects were carven with a stroke;

here lakes were made or unmade; here messengers of life and death despatched. An avalanche from Purcell's Peak went down to gash the sides and show long veins of gold; another hurried, by the White Wind sent, to block a stream and turn its wasted waters to a thirsty land—a messenger of mercy. But down the Gunder Peak there whirled a monstrous mass, charged with a mission of revenge. Down, down, down, loud *snoofing* as it went, and sliding on from shoulder, ledge, and long incline, now wiping out a forest that would bar its path, then crashing, leaping, rolling, smashing over cliff and steep descent, still gaining as it sped. Down, down, faster, fiercer, in one fell and fearful rush, and Scotty's shanty, in its track, with all that it contained, was crushed and swiftly blotted out. The hunter had forefelt his doom. The Ram's own Mother White Wind, from the western sea, had come—had long delayed, but still had come at last.

Over the rocky upland dawned the spring, over the level plain of Tobacco Creek. Gently the rains from the westward washed the great white pile of the snow-slide. Slowly the broken shanty came to light; and there in the middle, quite unharmed, was the head of the Gunder Ram. His amber eyes were gleaming bright as of old, under cover of those wonderful horns; and below him were some broken bones, with rags and grizzled human hair.

Old Scotty is forgotten, but the Ram's head hangs enshrined on a palace wall to-day, a treasure among kingly treasures; and men, when they gaze on those marvellous horns, still talk of the glorious Gunder Ram who grew them far away on the heights of the Kootenay.

Krag

A Street Troubadour

Being the Adventures of a Cock Sparrow

Such a chirruping, such a twittering, and such a squirming, fluttering mass! Half a dozen English Sparrows rolling over and chattering around one another in the Fifth Avenue gutter, and in the middle of the mob, when it scattered somewhat, could be seen the cause of it all—a little Hen Sparrow, vigorously, indignantly defending herself against her crowd of noisy suitors. They seemed to be making love to her, but their methods were so rough they might have been a lynching party. They plucked, worried, and harried the indignant little lady in a manner utterly disgraceful, except that it was noticeable they did her no serious harm. She, however, laid about her with a will. Under no compulsion to spare her tormentors, apparently she would have slaughtered them all if she could.

It seemed clear that they were making love to her, but it seemed equally clear that she wanted none of them, and having partly convinced them of this at the point of her beak, she took advantage of a brief scattering of the assailants to fly up to the nearest eaves, displaying in one wing, as she went, some white feathers that afforded a mark to know her by, and may have been one of her chief charms.

* * *

A Cock Sparrow, in the pride of his black cravat and white collar-points, was hard at work building in a bird-house that some children had set on a pole in the garden for such as he. He was a singular Bird in several respects. The building-material that he selected was all twigs, that must have been brought from Madison or Union Square, and in the early morning he sometimes stopped work for a minute to utter a loud sweet song, much like that of a Canary.

It is not usual for a Cock Sparrow to build alone. But then this was an unusual Bird. After a week he had apparently finished the nest, for the bird-house was crammed to the very door with twigs purloined from the municipal shade-trees. He had now more leisure for music,

164

and astonished the people about by frequent rendering of his long, unsparrow-like ditty; and he might have gone down to history as an unaccountable mystery, but that a barber bird-fancier on Sixth Avenue supplied the missing chapters of his early life.

This man, it seems, had put a Sparrow's egg into the wicker basket-nest of his Canaries. The youngster had duly hatched, and had been trained by the foster-parents. Their specialty was song. He had the lungs and robustness of his own race. The Canaries had trained him well, and the result was a songster who made up in energy what he lacked in native talent. Strong and pugnacious, as well as musical, this vociferous roustabout had soon made himself master of the cage. He had no hesitation in hammering into silence a Canary that he could not put down by musical superiority, and after one of these little victories his strains were so unusually good that the barber had a stuffed Canary provided for the boisterous musician to vanquish whenever he wished to favor some visitor with Randy's exultant pæans of victory. He worried into silent subjection all of the Canaries he was caged with, and when finally kept by himself nothing angered him more than to be near some voluble songster that he could neither silence nor get at. On these occasions he forgot his music, and his own Sparrow nature showed in the harsh *chirrup, chirrup* that has apparently been developed to make itself appreciated in the din of street traffic.

By the time his black bib had appeared he had made himself one of the chief characters and quite the chief attraction of the barber-shop. But one day the shelf on which the bird-cages stood gave way, all the cages were dashed to the floor, and in the general smash many of the Birds escaped. Among them was Randy, or, more properly, Bertrand, as this pugnacious songster was named after the famous Troubadour. The Canaries had voluntarily returned to their cages, or permitted themselves to be caught. But Randy hopped out of a back window, chirruped a few times, sang a defiant answer to the elevated railway-whistle, and keeping just out of reach of all attempts to capture him, he began to explore the brick wilderness about. He had not been a prisoner for generations. He readily accepted the new condition of freedom, and within a week was almost as wild as any of his kin, and had degenerated into a little street rowdy like the others, squabbling among them in the gutter, giving them blow for blow, or surprising all hearers with occasional bursts of Canary music delivered with Sparrow energy.

* * *

This, then, was Randy, who had selected the bird-house for a nesting-place, and the reason for his intemperance in the matter of twigs is now clear. The only nest he had ever known was of basket-work; therefore a proper nest is made of twigs.

Within a few days Randy appeared with a mate. I might have forgotten the riot scene in the gutter, as such things are common, but

that I now recognized in Randy's bride the little white-winged Biddy Sparrow that had caused it.

She had apparently accepted Randy, but she was still putting on airs, pecking at him when he came near. He was squirming around with drooping wings and tilted tail, chirping like any other ardent Cock Sparrow, but occasionally stopping to show off his Canary accomplishment.

Any objections she may have had were apparently overcome, possibly by this astonishing display of genius, and he escorted her to the ready-made nest, running in ahead to show the way, and hopping proudly, noisily, officiously about her. She followed him, but came out again quickly, with Randy after her chirping and beseeching. He chattered a long time before he could persuade her to reënter, but again she came out immediately, this time sputtering and scolding. Again he seemed to exert his power of persuasion, and finally she went in chattering, reappeared with a twig in her bill, dropped it, and flew away out of sight. Randy came out. All his joy and pride in his house were gone. This was a staggering blow, when he had looked for unmitigated commendation. He sat disconsolately on the door-step for a minute, and chirruped in a way that probably meant, "Come back, come back!" But his bride did not come. He turned into the house. There was a scratching sound, and he came out at once with a large stick and flung it from the door to the ground. He returned for another, sent that flying after the first, and so went on, dragging out and hurling down all the sticks he had so carefully and laboriously carried in. That wonderful forked one that had given so much trouble to get here from Union Square, and those two smooth ones, just like the ones in his foster-mother's nest—all, all must go. For over an hour he toiled away in silence and alone. Then, apparently, he had ended his task, for on the ground below was a pile of sticks, as big as a bonfire, the labor of a week undone. Randy glared fiercely at them and at the empty house, gave a short, harsh chirp, probably a Sparrow bad word, then flew away.

Next day he reappeared with Biddy, fussing about her in passerine exuberance once more, and chirping as he led her to the door again. She hopped in, then out, looked aslant at the twigs below, went back in, reappeared with a very small twig that had been overlooked, dropped it, and with evident satisfaction watched it fall on the pile below. After running in and out a dozen times they set off together, and presently returned, Biddy with her bill full of hay, Randy with one straw. These were carried in and presumably arranged satisfactorily. Then they went for more hay, and having got Randy set right, she remained in the box to arrange the hay as he brought it, only occasionally going for a load when he was long in coming. It was marvellous to see how the chivalry in this aggressive musician was reducing him to subjection. It seemed a good opportunity to try their tastes. I put out thirty short strings and ribbons in a row on a balcony near. Fifteen were common strips, eight were gaudy strips, and seven were bright silk ribbons. Every other one in the row was a dull string.

Biddy was the first to see this array of material. She flew down, looked over it, around it, left eye, right eye; then decided to let it alone. But Randy came closer; he was not unfamiliar with threads. He hopped this way, then that, pulled at a thread, started back, but came nearer, nibbled at one or two, then made a dart at a string and bore it away. Next time Biddy came, and each bore off a string. They took only the dull ones, but after these were gone Biddy selected some of the brighter material, though even she did not venture on the gaudiest ribbons, and Randy would have no hand in bringing home any but the soberest and most stick-like materials. The nest was now half done. Randy once more ventured to carry in a stick, but a moment later it was whirling down to the pile below, with Biddy triumphantly gazing after it. Poor Randy! no toleration for *his* hobby—all those splendid sticks wasted. His mother had had a stick nest,—a beautiful nest it was,—but he was overruled. Nothing but straw now; then, not sticks, but softer material. He submitted—liberty had brought daily lessons of submission. He used to think that the barber-shop was the whole world and himself the most important living being. But of late both these ideas had been badly shaken. Biddy found that his education had been sadly neglected in all useful matters, and in each new kind of material she had to instruct him anew.

When the nest was two thirds finished, Biddy, whose ideas were quite luxurious, began to carry in large soft feathers. But now Randy thought this was going too far. He must draw the line somewhere. He drew it at feather beds. His earliest cradle had had no such lining. He proceeded to bundle out the objectionable feather bedding, and Biddy, returning with a new load, was just in time to see the first lot float downward from the door to join the stick pile below. She fluttered after them, seized them in the air, and returned to meet her lord coming out of the door with more of the obnoxious plumes, and there they stood, glaring at each other, chattering their loudest, their mouths full of feathers, and their hearts full of indignation.

How is it that when it is a question of home furnishing we sympathize with the female? I felt that Biddy had first right, and in the end she got her way. First there was a stormy time in which quantities of feathers were carried in and out of the house, or wind-borne about the garden. Then there was a lull, and next day all the feathers were

Randy drew the line at feather beds

carried back to the nest. Just how they arranged the matter will never be known, but it is sure that Randy himself did the greater part of the work, and never stopped till the box was crammed with the largest and softest of feathers. During all this they were usually together, but one day Biddy went off and stayed for some time. Randy looked about, chirruped, got no answer, looked up, then down, and far below he saw the pile of sticks that he had toiled to bring. Those dear sticks, just like the home of his early days! Randy fluttered down. There was the curious forked one still. The temptation was irresistible. Randy picked it up and hurried to the nest, then in. It had always been a difficult twig to manage—that side prong would catch at the door; but he had carried it so often now that he knew how. After half a minute's delay inside, while he was placing it, I suppose, he came out again, looked perkily about, preened and shook himself, then sang his Canary song from beginning to end several times, tried some new bars, and seemed extremely happy. When Biddy came with more feathers, he assiduously helped her to place them inside, and then the nest was finished. Two days later I got up to the nest, and in it found one egg. The Sparrows saw me go up, but did not fly chattering about my head, as do most Birds. They flew away to a distance, and watched anxiously from the shelter of some chimneys.

The third day there was a great commotion in the box, a muffled scuffling and chattering, and once or twice a tail appeared at the door as though the owner were trying to back out. Then it seemed that something was being dragged about. At length the owner of the tail came out far enough to show that it was Biddy; but, apparently, she was pulled in again. Evidently a disgraceful family brawl was on. It was quite unaccountable, until finally Biddy struggled out of the door, dragging Randy's pet twig to throw it contemptuously on the ground below. She had discovered it in the bedding where he had hidden it; hence the row. But I do not see how she could drag it out when he was resisting. I suspect that he really weakened for the sake of peace. In the scuffle and general upset the egg—their first arrival—was unfortunately tumbled out with the stick, and fell down to lie below, in porcelain fragments, on a wet yellow background. The Sparrows did not seem to trouble about the remains. Having dropped from the nest, it had dropped out of their world.

* * *

After this the pair got along peaceably for several days. Egg after egg was added to the nest. In a week there were five, and the two seemed now to be quite happy together. Randy sang to the astonishment of all the neighborhood, and Biddy carried in more feathers as though preparing to set and anticipating a blizzard. But about this time it occurred to me to try a little experiment with the pair. Watching my chance, late one evening, I dropped a marble into the luxurious nest. What happened at once I do not know, but early the next morning I was out on Fifth Avenue near the corner of Twenty-first Street. It was Sunday. The street was very quiet, but a ring of perhaps a dozen people were standing gazing at something in the gutter. As I came near I heard occasional chirruping, and getting a view into the ring, I saw two Sparrows locked in fierce combat, chirruping a little, but hammering and pecking away in deadly earnest. They scuffled around, regardless of the bystanders, for some time; but when at length they paused for breath, and sat back on their tails and heels to gasp, I was quite shocked to recognize Biddy and Randy. After another round they were shooed away by one of the onlookers, who evidently disapproved of Sunday brawling. They then flew to the nearest roof to go on as before. That afternoon I found below the nest not only the intrusive marble, but also the remains of the five eggs, all alike thrown out, and I suspect that the presence of that curious hard round egg in the nest, and the obvious implication, were the cause of the brawl.

Whether Biddy had been able to explain it or not I do not know, but it seemed that the couple decided to forget the past and begin again. There was evidently neither luck nor peace in that bird-box, so they abandoned it, feathers and all; and Biddy, whose ideas were distinctly original, selected the site this time, nothing less than the top of an electric lamp in the middle of Madison Square. All week they labored, and in spite of a high wind most of the time, they finished the nest. It is hard to see how the Birds could sleep at night with that great glaring buzzing light under their noses. Still, Biddy seemed pleased, Randy was learning to suppress his own opinion, and all would have gone well but that before the first egg was laid the carbon-points of the light burned out, and the man who put in the new ones thought proper to consign remorselessly the whole of the Biddy-Randy mansion to the garbage-can. A Robin or a Swallow might have felt this a crushing blow, but there is no limit to a Sparrow's energy and hopefulness. Evidently it was the wrong kind of a nest. Probably the material was at fault. At any rate, a radical change would be much better. After embezzling some long straws from the nest of an absent neighbor, Biddy laid them in the high fork of an elm-tree in Madison Square Park, by way of letting Randy know that this was the place now selected; and Randy, having learned by this time that it was less trouble to accept her decision than to offer an opinion of his own, sang a Canary trill on two chirps, and set about rummaging in the garbage-heaps for choice building-material, winking hard and looking the other way when a nice twig presented itself.

*   *   *

On the other side of the Square was the nest of a pair of very unpopular Sparrows. The male bird in particular had made himself thoroughly disliked. He was a big, handsome fellow with an enormous black cravat, but an out-and-out bully. Might is right in Sparrow world. Their causes for quarrel are food, mates, quarters, and nesting-material—pretty much as with ourselves. This arrogant little Bird, by reason of his strength, had the mate of his choice and the best nesting-site, and was adding to it all the most-admired material in the Square. My Sparrows had avoided the gaudy ribbons I offered. They were not educated up to that pitch, but they certainly had their esthetic preferences. A few Guinea-fowl feathers that originally came from Central Park Menagerie had been stolen from one nest to another, till now they rested in the sumptuous home with which Cravat and his wife had embellished one of the marble capitals of the new bank. The Bully did much as he pleased in the Park, and one day, on hearing Randy's song, flew at him. Randy had been a terror among Canaries, but against Cravat he had but little chance. He did his best, but was

Drove off the bully

defeated, and took refuge in flight. Puffed up by his victory, the Bully flew to Randy's new nest, and after a more or less scornful scrutiny proceeded to drag out some strings that he thought he might use at home. Randy had been worsted, but the sight of this pillage roused the doughty Troubadour again, and he flew at the Bully as before. From the branches they tumbled to the ground. Other Sparrows joined in, and, shame to tell! they joined with the big fellow against the comparative stranger. Randy was getting very roughly handled, feathers began to float away, when into the ring flashed a little Hen Sparrow with white wing-feathers, chirrup, chirrup, wallop, wallop, she went into it. Oh, how she did lay about her! The Sparrows that had joined in for fun now went off: there was no longer any fun in it, nothing but hard pecks, and the tables were completely turned on Cravat. He quickly lost heart, then, and fled toward his own quarter of the Square, with Biddy holding on to his tail like a little bulldog; and there she continued to hang till the feather came out by the roots, and she afterward had the satisfaction of working it into the coarser make-up of her nest along with the rescued material. It is hardly possible that Sparrows have refined ideas of justice and retribution, but it is sure that things which look like it do crop up among them. Within two days the Guinea-fowl feathers that had so long been the chief glory of the Cravat's nest now formed part of the furnishing of Biddy's new abode, and none had the temerity to dispute her claim.

It was now late in the season, feathers were scarce, and Biddy could not find enough for the lining that she was so particular about. But she found a substitute that appealed to her love of the novel. In the Square was the cab-stand, and scattering near were usually more or less horsehairs. These seemed to be good and original linings. A most happy thought, and with appropriate enthusiasm the ever-hopeful couple set about gathering horsehairs, two or three at a time. Possibly the nest of a Chipping Sparrow in one of the parks gave them the idea. The Chippy always lines with horsehair, and gets an admirable spring-mattress effect by curling the hair round and round the inside of the nest. The result is good, but one must know how to get it. It would have been well had the Sparrows learned how to handle the hair. When a Chippy picks up a horsehair to bring home it takes only one at a time, and is careful to lift it by the end, for the harmless-looking hair is not without its dangers. The Sparrows had no notion of handling it except as they did the straw. Biddy seized a hair near the middle, found it somewhat long, so took a second hold, several inches away. In most cases this made a great loop in the hair over her head or beyond her beak. But it was a convenient way to manage, and at first no mischief came, though Chippy, had she seen, might well have shuddered at the idea of that threatening noose.

It was the last day of the lining. Biddy had in some way given Randy to understand that no more hair was needed, and, proud and bustling, she was adding a few finishing touches and a final hair while he was trying some new variations of his finest bars on top of Farragut's head, when a loud alarm chirrup from Biddy caught his ear.

He looked toward the new home to see her struggling up and down without apparent reason, and yet unable to get more than her length away from the nest. She had at last put her head through one of those dangerous hair nooses, made by herself, and by mischance had tightened and twisted it so that she was caught. The more she struggled and twisted the tighter became the noose. Randy now discovered that he was deeply attached to this wilful little termagant. He became greatly excited, and flew about chattering. He tried to release her by pulling at her foot, but that only made matters worse. All their efforts were in vain. Several new kinks were added to the hair. Other hairs from the nest seemed to join in the plot, and, tangled and intermeshed, they tightened even more, till the group of wondering, upturned child faces in the Park below were centred on a tousled feathery form hanging still and silent in the place of the bustling, noisy, energetic Biddy Sparrow.

Poor Randy seemed deeply distressed. The neighbor Sparrows had come at the danger-call note, and joined their cries with his, but had not been able to help the victim. Now they went off to their own squabbles and troubles, and Randy hopped about chirping or sat still with drooping wings. It was long before he realized that she was dead, and all that day he exerted himself to interest her and make her join in their usual life. At night he rested alone in one of the trees, and at gray dawn was bustling about, singing occasionally and chirruping around the nest, from whose rim, in the fateful horsehair, hung Biddy, stiff and silent now.

* * *

Randy had never been an alert Sparrow. His Canary training had really handicapped him. He was venturesome and heedless with carriages as well as with children. This peculiarity was greatly increased by his present preoccupation, and while foraging somewhat listlessly on Madison Avenue, that afternoon, a messenger-boy on a wheel came silently up, and before Randy realized his danger, the wheel was on his tail. As he struggled to get away, even at the price of his tail, his right wing flashed under the hind wheel, and then he was crippled. The boy rode on, and Randy managed to flutter and hop away toward the sheltering trees. A little girl, assisted by her small dog, captured the cripple, after an exciting chase among the benches. She took him home, and moved by what her brothers considered sadly misplaced tenderness, she caged and nursed him. When he began to recover, he one day surprised them by singing his Canary song.

This created quite a stir in the household. In time a newspaper reporter heard of it. The inevitable write-up followed, and this met the eye of the Sixth Avenue barber. He came with many witnesses to claim his bird, and at length his claim was allowed.

So Randy is once more in a cage, carefully watched and fed, the central figure in a small world, and not at all unhappy. After all, he was

never a truly wild Bird. It was an accident that set him free originally.
An accident had mated him with Biddy. Their brief life together had
been a succession of storms and accidents. An accident had taken her
away, and another accident had renewed his cage life. This life,
comparatively calm and uneventful, has given him an opportunity to
cultivate his musical gifts, for he is in a very conservatory of music, and
close at hand are his old tutors and foster-parents.

Sometimes when left alone he amuses himself by beginning a rude
nest of sticks, but he looks guilty, and leaves that corner of the cage
when any one comes near. If a few feathers are given him they are
worked into the nest at first, but next morning are invariably found on
the floor below. These persistent attempts at nesting suggested that he
wanted a mate, and several were furnished on approval, but the result
was not happy. Prompt interference was needed each time to prevent
bloodshed and to rescue the intended bride. So the attempt was given
up. Evidently this Troubadour wants no new lady-love. His songs seem
to be rather of war, for the barber has discovered that when he wishes
to provoke Randy into his most rapturous musical expression it is only
necessary to let him demolish, not the effigy of a Canary, but a stuffed
Cock Sparrow. And on these occasions Randy develops an enthusiasm
almost amounting to inspiration if the dummy have a very well marked
black patch on the throat.

This, however, is mere by-play. All his best energies are devoted to
song. And if you stumble on the right barber-shop you may see this
energetic recluse, forgetting the cares, joys, and sorrows of active life in
his devotion to music, like some monk who has tried the world, found
it too hard for him, and has gladly returned to his cell, there to devote
the rest of his days to purely spiritual pleasures.

Biddy and Randy

JOHNNY BEAR

Johnny was a queer little Bear cub that lived with Grumpy, his mother, in the Yellowstone Park. They were among the many Bears that found a desirable home in the country about the Fountain Hotel.

The steward of the Hotel had ordered the kitchen garbage to be dumped in an open glade of the surrounding forest, thus providing, throughout the season, a daily feast for the Bears, and their numbers have increased each year since the law of the land has made the Park a haven of refuge where no wild thing may be harmed. They have accepted man's peace-offering, and many of them have become so well known to the Hotel men that they have received names suggested by their looks or ways. Slim Jim was a very long-legged thin Blackbear; Snuffy was a Blackbear that looked as though he had been singed; Fatty was a very fat, lazy Bear that always lay down to eat; the Twins were two half-grown, ragged specimens that always came and went together. But Grumpy and Little Johnny were the best known of them all.

Grumpy was the biggest and fiercest of the Blackbears, and Johnny, apparently her only son, was a peculiarly tiresome little cub, for he seemed never to cease either grumbling or whining. This probably meant that he was sick, for a healthy little Bear does not grumble all the time, any more than a healthy child. And indeed Johnny

175

looked sick; he was the most miserable specimen in the Park. His whole appearance suggested dyspepsia; and this I quite understood when I saw the awful mixtures he would eat at that garbage-heap. Anything at all that he fancied he would try. And his mother allowed him to do as he pleased; so, after all, it was chiefly her fault, for she should not have permitted such things.

Johnny had only three good legs, his coat was faded and mangy, his limbs were thin, and his ears and paunch were disproportionately large. Yet his mother thought the world of him. She was evidently convinced that he was a little beauty and the Prince of all Bears, so, of course, she quite spoiled him. She was always ready to get into trouble on his account, and he was always delighted to lead her there. Although such a wretched little failure, Johnny was far from being a fool, for he usually knew just what he wanted and how to get it, if teasing his mother could carry the point.

His whole appearance suggested dyspepsia

* * *

It was in the summer of 1897 that I made their acquaintance. I was in the Park to study the home life of the animals, and had been told that in the woods, near the Fountain Hotel, I could see Bears at any time, which, of course, I scarcely believed. But on stepping out of the back door five minutes after arriving, I came face to face with a large Blackbear and her two cubs.

I stopped short, not a little startled. The Bears also stopped and sat up to look at me. Then Mother Bear made a curious short *Koff Koff*, and looked toward a near pine-tree. The cubs seemed to know what she meant, for they ran to this tree and scrambled up like two little monkeys, and when safely aloft they sat like small boys, holding on with their hands, while their little black legs dangled in the air, and waited to see what was to happen down below.

The Mother Bear, still on her hind legs, came slowly toward me, and I began to feel very uncomfortable indeed, for she stood about six feet high in her stockings and had apparently never heard of the magical power of the human eye.

I had not even a stick to defend myself with, and when she gave a low growl, I was about to retreat to the Hotel, although previously assured that the Bears have always kept their truce with man. However, just at this turning-point the old one stopped, now but thirty feet away, and continued to survey me calmly. She seemed in doubt for a minute, but evidently made up her mind that, "although that human thing might be all right, she would take no chances for her little ones."

She looked up to her two hopefuls, and gave a peculiar whining *Er-r-r Er-r*, whereupon they, like obedient children, jumped, as at the word of command. There was nothing about them heavy or bear-like as commonly understood; lightly they swung from bough to bough till they dropped to the ground, and all went off together into the woods. I was much tickled by the prompt obedience of the little Bears. As soon as their mother told them to do something they did it. They did not even offer a suggestion. But I also found out that there was a good reason for it, for had they not done as she had told them they would have got such a spanking as would have made them howl.

This was a delightful peep into Bear home life, and would have been well worth coming for, if the insight had ended there. But my friends in the Hotel said that that was not the best place for Bears. I should go to the garbage-heap, a quarter-mile off in the forest. There, they said, I surely could see as many Bears as I wished (which was absurd of them).

Early the next morning I went to this Bears' Banqueting Hall in the pines, and hid in the nearest bushes.

Before very long a large Blackbear came quietly out of the woods to the pile, and began turning over the garbage and feeding. He was very nervous, sitting up and looking about at each slight sound, or running away a few yards when startled by some trifle. At length he cocked his ears and galloped off into the pines, as another Blackbear appeared. He also behaved in the same timid manner, and at last ran away when I shook the bushes in trying to get a better view.

At the outset I myself had been very nervous, for of course no man is allowed to carry weapons in the Park; but the timidity of these Bears reassured me, and thenceforth I forgot everything in the interest of seeing the great, shaggy creatures in their home life.

Soon I realized I could not get the close insight I wished from that bush, as it was seventy-five yards from the garbage-pile. There was none nearer; so I did the only thing left to do: I went to the garbage-pile itself, and, digging a hole big enough to hide in, remained there all day long, with cabbage-stalks, old potato-peelings, tomato-cans, and carrion piled up in odorous heaps around me. Notwithstanding the opinions of countless flies, it was not an attractive place. Indeed, it was so unfragrant that at night, when I returned to the Hotel, I was not allowed to come in until after I had changed my clothes in the woods.

It had been a trying ordeal, but I surely did see Bears that day. If I may reckon it a new Bear each time one came, I must have seen over forty. But of course it was not, for the Bears were coming and going. And yet I am certain of this: there were at least thirteen Bears, for I had thirteen about me at one time.

All that day I used my sketch-book and journal. Every Bear that came was duly noted; and this process soon began to give the desired insight into their ways and personalities.

Many unobservant persons think and say that all Negroes, or all Chinamen, as well as all animals of a kind, look alike. But just as surely as each human being differs from the next, so surely each animal is different from its fellow; otherwise how would the old ones know their mates or the little ones their mother, as they certainly do? These feasting Bears gave a good illustration of this, for each had its individuality; no two were quite alike in appearance or in character.

This curious fact also appeared: I could hear the Woodpeckers pecking over one hundred yards away in the woods, as well as the Chickadees chichadeeing, the Blue-jays blue-jaying, and even the Squirrels scampering across the leafy forest floor; and yet I *did not hear one of these Bears come*. Their huge, padded feet always went down in exactly the right spot to break no stick, to rustle no leaf, showing how perfectly they had learned the art of going in silence through the woods.

* * *

All morning the Bears came and went or wandered near my hiding-place without discovering me; and, except for one or two brief quarrels, there was nothing very exciting to note. But about three in the afternoon it became more lively.

There were then four large Bears feeding on the heap. In the middle was Fatty, sprawling at full length as he feasted, a picture of placid ursine content, puffing just a little at times as he strove to save himself the trouble of moving by darting out his tongue like a long red serpent, farther and farther, in quest of the tidbits just beyond claw reach.

Behind him Slim Jim was puzzling over the anatomy and attributes of an ancient lobster. It was something outside his experience, but the principle, "In case of doubt take the trick," is well known in Bearland, and settled the difficulty.

The other two were clearing out fruit-tins with marvellous dexterity. One supple paw would hold the tin while the long tongue would dart again and again through the narrow opening, avoiding the sharp edges, yet cleaning out the can to the last taste of its sweetness.

This pastoral scene lasted long enough to be sketched, but was ended abruptly. My eye caught a movement on the hilltop whence all the Bears had come, and out stalked a very large Blackbear with a tiny cub. It was Grumpy and Little Johnny.

The old Bear stalked down the slope toward the feast, and Johnny hitched alongside, grumbling as he came, his mother watching him as

Old Grumpy stalked down the slope, and Johnny hitched alongside

But Johnny wanted to see

solitously as ever a hen did her single chick. When they were within
thirty yards of the garbage-heap, Grumpy turned to her son and said
something which, judging from its effect, must have meant: "Johnny,
my child, I think you had better stay here while I go and chase those
fellows away."

Johnny obediently waited; but he wanted to *see*, so he sat up on his
hind legs with eyes agog and ears acock.

Grumpy came striding along with dignity, uttering warning growls
as she approached the four Bears. They were too much engrossed to
pay any heed to the fact that yet another one of them was coming, till
Grumpy, now within fifteen feet, let out a succession of loud coughing
sounds, and charged into them. Strange to say, they did not pretend to
face her, but, as soon as they saw who it was, scattered and all fled for
the woods.

Slim Jim could safely trust his heels, and the other two were not far
behind; but poor Fatty, puffing hard and waddling like any other very
fat creature, got along but slowly, and, unluckily for him, he fled in the
direction of Johnny, so that Grumpy overtook him in a few bounds and

gave him a couple of sound slaps in the rear which, if they did not accelerate his pace, at least made him bawl, and saved him by changing his direction. Grumpy, now left alone in possession of the feast, turned toward her son and uttered the whining *Er-r-r Er-r-r Er-r-r-r.* Johnny responded eagerly. He came "hopity-hop" on his three good legs as fast as he could, and, joining her on the garbage, they began to have such a good time that Johnny actually ceased grumbling.

He had evidently been there before now, for he seemed to know quite well the staple kinds of canned goods. One might almost have supposed that he had learned the brands, for a lobster-tin had no charm for him as long as he could find those that once were filled with jam. Some of the tins gave him much trouble, as he was too greedy or too clumsy to escape being scratched by the sharp edges. One seductive fruit-tin had a hole so large that he found he could force his head into it,

A sirup-tin kept him happy for a long time

and for a few minutes his joy was full as he licked into all the farthest corners. But when he tried to draw his head out, his sorrows began, for he found himself caught. He could not get out, and he scratched and screamed like any other spoiled child, giving his mother no end of concern, although she seemed not to know how to help him. When at length he got the tin off his head, he revenged himself by hammering it with his paws till it was perfectly flat.

A large sirup-can made him happy for a long time. It had had a lid, so that the hole was round and smooth; but it was not big enough to admit his head, and he could not touch its riches with his tongue stretched out its longest. He soon hit on a plan, however. Putting in his little black arm, he churned it around, then drew out and licked it clean; and while he licked one he got the other one ready; and he did this again and again, until the can was as clean inside as when first it had left the factory.

A broken mouse-trap seemed to puzzle him. He clutched it between his fore paws, their strong inturn being sympathetically reflected in his hind feet, and held it firmly for study. The cheesy smell about it was decidedly good, but the thing responded in such an uncanny way, when he slapped it, that he kept back a cry for help only by the exercise of unusual self-control. After gravely inspecting it, with his head first on this side and then on that, and his lips puckered into a little tube, he submitted it to the same punishment as that meted out to the refractory fruit-tin, and was rewarded by discovering a nice little bit of cheese in the very heart of the culprit.

Johnny had evidently never heard of ptomaïne-poisoning, for nothing came amiss. After the jams and fruits gave out he turned his attention to the lobster- and sardine-cans, and was not appalled by even the army beef. His paunch grew quite balloon-like, and from much licking his arms looked thin and shiny, as though he was wearing black silk gloves.

* * *

It occurred to me that I might now be in a really dangerous place. For it is one thing surprising a Bear that has no family responsibilities, and another stirring up a bad-tempered old mother by frightening her cub.

"Supposing," I thought, "that cranky Little Johnny should wander over to this end of the garbage and find me in the hole; he will at once set up a squall, and his mother, of course, will think I am hurting him, and, without giving me a chance to explain, may forget the rules of the Park and make things very unpleasant."

Luckily, all the jam-pots were at Johnny's end; he stayed by them, and Grumpy stayed by him. At length he noticed that his mother had a better tin than any he could find, and as he ran whining to take it from her he chanced to glance away up the slope. There he saw something that made him sit up and utter a curious little *Koff Koff Koff Koff.*

His mother turned quickly, and sat up to see "what the child was

Johnny got behind his mother

looking at." I followed their gaze, and there, oh, horrors! was an enormous Grizzly Bear. He was a monster; he looked like a fur-clad omnibus coming through the trees.

Johnny set up a whine at once and got behind his mother. She uttered a deep growl, and all her back hair stood on end. Mine did too, but I kept as still as possible.

With stately tread the Grizzly came on. His vast shoulders sliding along his sides, and his silvery robe swaying at each tread, like the trappings on an elephant, gave an impression of power that was appalling.

Johnny began to whine more loudly, and I fully sympathized with him now, though I did not join in. After a moment's hesitation Grumpy turned to her noisy cub and said something that sounded to me like two or three short coughs—*Koff Koff Koff.* But I imagine that she really said: "My child, I think you had better get up that tree, while I go and drive the brute away."

At any rate, that was what Johnny did, and this what she set out to do. But Johnny had no notion of missing any fun. He wanted to *see*

what was going to happen. So he did not rest contented where he was hidden in the thick branches of the pine, but combined safety with view by climbing to the topmost branch that would bear him, and there, sharp against the sky, he squirmed about and squealed aloud in his excitement. The branch was so small that it bent under his weight, swaying this way and that as he shifted about, and every moment I expected to see it snap off. If it had been broken when swaying my way, Johnny would certainly have fallen on me, and this would probably have resulted in bad feelings between myself and his mother; but the limb was tougher than it looked, or perhaps Johnny had had plenty of experience, for he neither lost his hold nor broke the branch.

Meanwhile, Grumpy stalked out to meet the Grizzly. She stood as high as she could and set all her bristles on end; then, growling and chopping her teeth, she faced him.

The Grizzly, so far as I could see, took no notice of her. He came striding toward the feast as though alone. But when Grumpy got within twelve feet of him she uttered a succession of short, coughy roars, and, charging, gave him a tremendous blow on the ear. The Grizzly was

Then they clinched

surprised; but he replied with a left-hander that knocked her over like a sack of hay.

Nothing daunted, but doubly furious, she jumped up and rushed at him.

Then they clinched and rolled over and over, whacking and pounding, snorting and growling, and making no end of dust and rumpus. But above all their noise I could clearly hear Little Johnny, yelling at the top of his voice, and evidently encouraging his mother to go right in and finish the Grizzly at once.

Why the Grizzly did not break her in two I could not understand. After a few minutes' struggle, during which I could see nothing but dust and dim flying legs, the two separated as by mutual consent,—perhaps the regulation time was up,—and for a while they stood glaring at each other, Grumpy at least much winded.

The Grizzly would have dropped the matter right there. He did not wish to fight. He had no idea of troubling himself about Johnny. All he wanted was a quiet meal. But no! The moment he took one step toward the garbage-pile, that is, as Grumpy thought, toward Johnny, she went at him again. But this time the Grizzly was ready for her. With one blow he knocked her off her feet and sent her crashing on to a huge upturned pine-root. She was fairly staggered this time. The force of the blow, and the rude reception of the rooty antlers, seemed to take all the fight out of her. She scrambled over and tried to escape. But the Grizzly was mad now. He meant to punish her, and dashed around the root. For a minute they kept up a dodging chase about it; but Grumpy was quicker of foot, and somehow always managed to keep the root between herself and her foe, while Johnny, safe in the tree, continued to take an intense and uproarious interest.

At length, seeing he could not catch her that way, the Grizzly sat up on his haunches; and while he doubtless was planning a new move, old Grumpy saw her chance, and making a dash, got away from the root and up to the top of tree where Johnny was perched.

Johnny came down a little way to meet her, or perhaps so that the tree might not break off with the additional weight. Having photographed this interesting group from my hiding-place, I thought I must get a closer picture at any price, and for the first time in the day's proceedings I jumped out of the hole and ran under the tree. This move proved a great mistake, for here the thick lower boughs came between, and I could see nothing at all of the Bears at the top.

I was close to the trunk, and was peering about and seeking for a chance to use the camera, when old Grumpy began to come down, chopping her teeth and uttering her threatening cough at me. While I stood in doubt, I heard a voice far behind me calling:

"Say, Mister! You better look out; that ole B'ar is liable to hurt you."

I turned to see the cow-boy of the Hotel on his Horse. He had been riding after the cattle, and chanced to pass near just as events were moving quickly.

"Do you know these Bears?" said I, as he rode up.

"Wall, I reckon I do," said he. "That there little one up top is Johnny; he's a little crank. An' the big un is Grumpy; she's a big crank. She's mighty onreliable gen'relly, but she's always strictly ugly when Johnny hollers like that."

"I should much like to get her picture when she comes down," said I.

"Tell ye what I'll do: I'll stay by on the pony, an' if she goes to bother you I reckon I can keep her off," said the man.

He accordingly stood by as Grumpy slowly came down from branch to branch, growling and threatening. But when she neared the ground she kept on the far side of the trunk, and finally slipped down and ran into the woods, without the slightest pretence of carrying out any of her dreadful threats. Thus Johnny was again left alone. He climbed up to his old perch and resumed his monotonous whining:

Wah! Wah! Wah! ("Oh, dear! Oh, dear! Oh, dear!")

I got the camera ready, and was arranging deliberately to take his picture in his favorite and peculiar attitude for threnodic song, when all at once he began craning his neck and yelling, as he had done during the fight.

I looked where his nose pointed, and here was the Grizzly coming on straight toward me—not charging, but striding along, as though he meant to come the whole distance.

I said to my cow-boy friend: "Do you know this Bear?"

He replied: "Wall! I reckon I do. That's the ole Grizzly. He's the biggest B'ar in the Park. He gen'relly minds his own business, but he ain' scared o' nothin'; an' to-day, ye see, he's been scrappin', so he's liable to be ugly."

"I would like to take his picture," said I; "and if you will help me, I am willing to take some chances on it."

"All right," said he, with a grin. "I'll stand by on the Horse, an' if he charges you I'll charge him; an' I kin knock him down once, but I can't do it twice. You better have your tree picked out."

As there was only one tree to pick out, and that was the one that Johnny was in, the prospect was not alluring. I imagined myself scrambling up there next to Johnny, and then Johnny's mother coming up after me, with the Grizzly below to catch me when Grumpy should throw me down.

The Grizzly came on, and I snapped him at forty yards, then again at twenty yards; and still he came quietly toward me. I sat down on the garbage and made ready. Eighteen yards—sixteen yards—twelve yards—eight yards, and still he came, while the pitch of Johnny's protests kept rising proportionately. Finally at five yards he stopped, and swung his huge bearded head to one side, to see what was making that aggravating row in the tree-top, giving me a profile view, and I snapped the camera. At the click he turned on me with a thunderous

G—R—O—W—L!

and I sat still and trembling, wondering if my last moment had come. For a second he glared at me, and I could note the little green electric lamp in each of his eyes. Then he slowly turned and picked up—a large tomato-can.

"Goodness!" I thought, "Is he going to throw that at me?" But he deliberately licked it out, dropped it, and took another, paying thenceforth no heed whatever either to me or to Johnny, evidently considering us equally beneath his notice.

I backed slowly and respectfully out of his royal presence, leaving him in possession of the garbage, while Johnny kept on caterwauling from his safety-perch.

What became of Grumpy the rest of that day I do not know. Johnny, after bewailing for a time, realized that there was no sympathetic hearer of his cries, and therefore very sagaciously stopped them. Having no mother now to plan for him, he began to plan for himself, and at once proved that he was better stuff than he seemed. After watching, with a look of profound cunning on his little black face, and waiting till the Grizzly was some distance away, he silently slipped down behind the trunk, and, despite his three-leggedness, ran like a hare to the next tree, never stopping to breathe till he was on its topmost bough. For he was thoroughly convinced that the only object that the Grizzly had in life was to kill him, and he seemed quite aware that his enemy could not climb a tree.

Another long and safe survey of the Grizzly, who really paid no heed to him whatever, was followed by another dash for the next tree, varied occasionally by a cunning feint to mislead the foe. So he went dashing from tree to tree and climbing each to its very top, although it might be but ten feet from the last, till he disappeared in the woods. After, perhaps, ten minutes, his voice again came floating on the

breeze, the habitual querulous whining which told me he had found his
mother and had resumed his customary appeal to her sympathy.

* * *

It is quite a common thing for Bears to spank their cubs when they
need it, and if Grumpy had disciplined Johnny this way, it would have
saved them both a deal of worry.

Perhaps not a day passed, that summer, without Grumpy getting
into trouble on Johnny's account. But of all these numerous occasions
the most ignominious was shortly after the affair with the Grizzly.

I first heard the story from three bronzed mountaineers. As they
were very sensitive about having their word doubted, and very good
shots with the revolver, I believed every word they told me, especially
when afterward fully indorsed by the Park authorities.

It seemed that of all the tinned goods on the pile the nearest to
Johnny's taste were marked with a large purple plum. This conclusion
he had arrived at only after most exhaustive study. The very odor of
those plums in Johnny's nostrils was the equivalent of ecstasy. So
when it came about one day that the cook of the Hotel baked a huge
batch of plum-tarts, the telltale wind took the story afar into the woods,
where it was wafted by way of Johnny's nostrils to his very soul.

Of course Johnny was whimpering at the time. His mother was
busy "washing his face and combing his hair," so he had double cause
for whimpering. But the smell of the tarts thrilled him; he jumped up,
and when his mother tried to hold him he squalled, and I am afraid—he
bit her. She should have cuffed him, but she did not. She only gave a
disapproving growl, and followed to see that he came to no harm.

With his little black nose in the wind, Johnny led straight for the
kitchen. He took the precaution, however, of climbing from time to
time to the very top of a pine-tree lookout to take an observation, while
Grumpy stayed below.

Thus they came close to the kitchen, and there, in the last tree,
Johnny's courage as a leader gave out, so he remained aloft and
expressed his hankering for tarts in a woe-begone wail.

It is not likely that Grumpy knew exactly what her son was crying
for. But it is sure that as soon as she showed an inclination to go back
into the pines, Johnny protested in such an outrageous and heart-
rending screeching that his mother simply could not leave him, and he
showed no sign of coming down to be led away.

Grumpy herself was fond of plum-jam. The odor was now, of

course, very strong and proportionately alluring; so Grumpy followed it somewhat cautiously up to the kitchen door.

There was nothing surprising about this. The rule of "live and let live" is so strictly enforced in the Park that the Bears often come to the kitchen door for pickings, and on getting something, they go quietly back to the woods. Doubtless Johnny and Grumpy would each have gotten their tart but that a new factor appeared in the case.

That week the Hotel people had brought a new Cat from the East. She was not much more than a kitten, but still had a litter of her own, and at the moment that Grumpy reached the door, the Cat and her family were sunning themselves on the top step. Pussy opened her eyes to see this huge, shaggy monster towering above her.

The Cat had never before seen a Bear—she had not been there long enough; she did not know even what a Bear was. She knew what a Dog

"Stop!" shrieked the cat

was, and here was a bigger, more awful bobtailed black dog than ever she had dreamed of coming right at her. Her first thought was to fly for her life. But her next was for the kittens. She must take care of them. She must at least cover their retreat. So, like a brave little mother, she braced herself on that door-step, and spreading her back, her claws, her tail, and everything she had to spread, she screamed out at that Bear an unmistakable order to

STOP!

The language must have been "Cat," but the meaning was clear to the Bear; for those who saw it maintain stoutly that Grumpy not only stopped, but she also conformed to the custom of the country and in token of surrender held up her hands.

However, the position she thus took made her so high that the Cat seemed tiny in the distance below. Old Grumpy had faced a Grizzly once, and was she now to be held up by a miserable little spike-tailed skunk no bigger than a mouthful? She was ashamed of herself, especially when a wail from Johnny smote on her ear and reminded her of her plain duty, as well as supplied his usual moral support.

So she dropped down on her front feet to proceed.

Again the Cat shrieked, "STOP!"

But Grumpy ignored the command. A scared mew from a kitten nerved the Cat, and she launched her ultimatum, which ultimatum was herself. Eighteen sharp claws, a mouthful of keen teeth, had Pussy, and she worked them all with a desperate will when she landed on Grumpy's bare, bald, sensitive nose, just the spot of all where the Bear could not stand it, and then worked backward to a point outside the sweep of Grumpy's claws. After one or two vain attempts to shake the spotted fury off, old Grumpy did just as most creatures would have done under the circumstances: she turned tail and bolted out of the enemy's country into her own woods.

But Puss's fighting blood was up. She was not content with repelling the enemy; she wanted to inflict a crushing defeat, to achieve an absolute and final rout. And however fast old Grumpy might go, it did not count, for the Cat was still on top, working her teeth and claws like a little demon. Grumpy, always erratic, now became panic-stricken. The trail of the pair was flecked with tufts of long black hair, and there was even bloodshed (in the fiftieth degree). Honor surely was satisfied, but Pussy was not. Round and round they had gone in the mad race. Grumpy was frantic, absolutely humiliated, and ready to make any terms; but Pussy seemed deaf to her cough-like yelps, and no one knows how far the Cat might have ridden that day had not Johnny unwittingly put a new idea into his mother's head by bawling in his best style from the top of his last tree, which tree Grumpy made for and scrambled up.

This was so clearly the enemy's country and in view of his reinforcements that the Cat wisely decided to follow no farther. She jumped from the climbing Bear to the ground, and then mounted

Then Pussy launched her ultimatum

sentry-guard below, marching around with tail in the air, daring that Bear to come down. Then the kittens came out and sat around, and enjoyed it all hugely. And the mountaineers assured me that the Bears would have been kept up the tree till they were starved, had not the cook of the Hotel come out and called off his Cat—although this statement was not among those vouched for by the officers of the Park.

* * *

The last time I saw Johnny he was in the top of a tree, bewailing his unhappy lot as usual, while his mother was dashing about among the pines, "with a chip on her shoulder," seeking for some one—any one— that she could punish for Johnny's sake, provided, of course, that it was not a big Grizzly or a Mother Cat.

This was early in August, but there were not lacking symptoms of change in old Grumpy. She was always reckoned "onsartain," and her devotion to Johnny seemed subject to her characteristic. This perhaps accounted for the fact that when the end of the month was near, Johnny would sometimes spend half a day in the top of some tree, alone, miserable, and utterly unheeded.

The last chapter of his history came to pass after I had left the region. One day at gray dawn he was tagging along behind his mother as she prowled in the rear of the Hotel. A newly hired Irish girl was already astir in the kitchen. On looking out, she saw, as she thought, a Calf where it should not be, and ran to shoo it away. That open kitchen door still held unmeasured terrors for Grumpy, and she ran in such alarm that Johnny caught the infection, and not being able to keep up with her, he made for the nearest tree, which unfortunately turned out to be a post, and soon—too soon—he arrived at its top, some seven feet from the ground, and there poured forth his woes on the chilly morning air, while Grumpy apparently felt justified in continuing her flight alone. When the girl came near and saw that she had treed some wild animal, she was as much frightened as her victim. But others of the kitchen staff appeared, and recognizing the vociferous Johnny, they decided to make him a prisoner.

A collar and chain were brought, and after a struggle, during which several of the men got well scratched, the collar was buckled on Johnny's neck and the chain made fast to the post.

When he found that he was held, Johnny was simply too mad to scream. He bit and scratched and tore till he was tired out. Then he lifted up his voice again to call his mother. She did appear once or twice in the distance, but could not make up her mind to face that Cat, so disappeared, and Johnny was left to his fate.

He put in the most of that day in alternate struggling and crying.

Toward evening he was worn out, and glad to accept the meal that was brought by Norah, who felt herself called on to play mother, since she had chased his own mother away.

When night came it was very cold; but Johnny nearly froze at the top of the post before he would come down and accept the warm bed provided at the bottom.

During the days that followed, Grumpy came often to the garbage-heap, but soon apparently succeeded in forgetting all about her son. He was daily tended by Norah, and received all his meals from her. He also received something else; for one day he scratched her when she brought his food, and she very properly spanked him till he squealed. For a few hours he sulked; he was not used to such treatment. But hunger subdued him, and thenceforth he held his new guardian in wholesome respect. She, too, began to take an interest in the poor motherless little wretch, and within a fortnight Johnny showed signs of developing a new character. He was much less noisy. He still expressed his hunger in a whining *Er-r-r Er-r-r Er-r-r*, but he rarely squealed now, and his unruly outbursts entirely ceased.

By the third week of September the change was still more marked. Utterly abandoned by his own mother, all his interest had centred in Norah, and she had fed and spanked him into an exceedingly well-behaved little Bear. Sometimes she would allow him a taste of freedom, and he then showed his bias by making, not for the woods, but for the kitchen where she was, and following her around on his hind legs. Here also he made the acquaintance of that dreadful Cat; but Johnny had a powerful friend now, and Pussy finally became reconciled to the black, woolly interloper.

As the Hotel was to be closed in October, there was talk of turning Johnny loose or of sending him to the Washington Zoo; but Norah had claims that she would not forego.

When the frosty nights of late September came, Johnny had greatly improved in his manners, but he had also developed a bad cough. An examination of his lame leg had shown that the weakness was not in the foot, but much more deeply seated, perhaps in the hip, and that meant a feeble and tottering constitution.

He did not get fat, as do most Bears in fall; indeed, he continued to fail. His little round belly shrank in, his cough became worse, and one

morning he was found very sick and shivering in his bed by the post. Norah brought him indoors, where the warmth helped him so much that thenceforth he lived in the kitchen.

For a few days he seemed better, and his old-time pleasure in *seeing things* revived. The great blazing fire in the range particularly appealed to him, and made him sit up in his old attitude when the opening of the door brought the wonder to view. After a week he lost interest even in that, and drooped more and more each day. Finally not the most exciting noises or scenes around him could stir up his old fondness for seeing what was going on.

He coughed a good deal, too, and seemed wretched, except when in Norah's lap. Here he would cuddle up contentedly, and whine most miserably when she had to set him down again in his basket.

A few days before the closing of the Hotel, he refused his usual breakfast, and whined softly till Norah took him in her lap; then he feebly snuggled up to her, and his soft *Er-r-r Er-r-r* grew fainter, till it ceased. Half an hour later, when she laid him down to go about her work, Little Johnny had lost the last trace of his anxiety to see and know what was going on.

THE MOTHER TEAL AND THE OVERLAND ROUTE

A green-winged Teal had made her nest in the sedge by one of the grass-edged pools that fleck the sunny slope of the Riding Mountain. The passing half-breed, driving his creaking ox-wagon, saw only a pond with the usual fringe of coarse grass, beyond which was a belt of willow scrub and an old poplar-tree. But the little Teal in the rushes, and her neighbors, the Flickers, on the near-by poplar, saw in the nestling pool a kingdom, a perfect paradise, for this was home. Now was the ripeness of the love-moon, with the mother-moon at hand in its fulness of promise. Indeed, the little Flickers had almost chipped their glassy shells, and the eggs, the ten treasures of the Teal, had lost the look of mere interesting things, and were putting on, each, an air of sleeping personality, warm, sentient, pulsatory, and almost vocal.

The little Teal had lost her mate early in the season. At least, he had disappeared, and as the land abounded in deadly foes, it was fair to suppose him dead. But her attention was fully taken up with her nest and her brood.

All through the latter part of June she tended them carefully, leaving but a little while each day to seek food, and then covering them carefully with a dummy foster-mother that she had made of down from her own breast.

One morning, as she flew away, leaving the dummy in charge, she heard an ominous crackling in the thick willows near at hand, but she wisely went on. When she returned, her neighbor, the Flicker, was still uttering a note of alarm, and down by her own nest were the fresh tracks of a man. The dummy mother had been disturbed, but, strange to tell, the eggs were all there and unharmed.

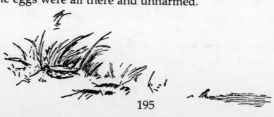

The enemy, though so near, had been baffled after all. As the days went by, and the grand finish of her task drew near, the little Greenwing felt the mother-love growing in her heart to be ready for the ten little prisoners that her devotion was to set free. They were no longer mere eggs, she felt, and sometimes she would talk to them in low raucous tones, and they would seem to answer from within in whispered "peepings," or perhaps in sounds that have no human name because too fine for human ear. So there is small wonder that when they do come out they have already learned many of the few simple words that make up Teal-talk.

The many hazards of the early nesting-time were rapidly passed, but a new one came. The growing springtime had turned into a drought. No rain had fallen for many, many days, and as the greatest day of all drew near, the mother saw with dismay that the pond was shrinking, quickly shrinking. Already it was rimmed about by a great stretch of bare mud, and unless the rains came soon, the first experience of the little ones would be a perilous overland journey.

It was just as impossible to hurry up the hatching as it was to bring rain, and the last few days of the mother's task were, as she had feared, in view of a wide mud-flat where once had been the pond.

They all came out at last. The little china tombs were broken one by one, disclosing each a little Teal: ten little balls of mottled down, ten little cushions of yellow plush, ten little golden caskets with jewel eyes, enshrining each a priceless spark of life.

But fate had been so harsh. It was now a matter of life and death to reach a pond. Oh, why did not Old Sol give the downlings three days of paddling to strengthen on before enforcing this dreadful journey overland? The mother must face the problem and face it now, or lose them all.

The Ducklings do not need to eat for several hours after they are hatched. Their bodies are yet sustained by the provender of their last abode. But once that is used they must eat. The nearest pond was half a mile away. And the great questions were: Can these baby Ducks hold out that long? Can they escape the countless dangers of the road? For not a Harrier, Falcon, Hawk, Fox, Weasel, Coyote, Gopher, Ground-squirrel, or Snake but would count them his lawful prey.

All this the mother felt instinctively, even if she did not set it forth in clear expression; and as soon as the ten were warmed and lively she led them into the grass. Such a scrambling and peeping and tumbling about as they tried to get through and over the grass-stalks that, like a bamboo forest, barred their way! Their mother had to watch the ten with one eye and the whole world with the other, for not a friend had she or they outside of themselves. The countless living things about were either foes or neutral.

* * *

After a long scramble through the grass they climbed a bank and got among the poplar scrub, and here sat down to rest. One little fellow that had struggled along bravely with the others was so weak that there seemed no chance of his reaching that far-away Happyland, the pond.

When they were rested, their mother gave a low, gentle *quack* that doubtless meant, "Come along, children," and they set off again, scrambling over and around the twigs, each peeping softly when he was getting along nicely, or plaintively when he found himself caught in some thicket.

At last they came to a wide open place. It was easy to travel here, but there was great danger of Hawks. The mother rested long in the edge of the thicket, and scanned the sky in every direction before she ventured into the open. Then, when all was clear, she marshalled her little army for a dash over this great desert of nearly one hundred yards.

The little fellows bravely struggled after her, their small yellow bodies raised at an angle, and their tiny wings held out like arms as they pushed along after "mother."

She was anxious to finish it all at one dash, but soon saw that that was hopeless. The strongest of her brood could keep up with her, but the others dragged in order of weakness. The brood now formed a little procession over twenty feet long, and the weakling was nearly ten feet behind that again.

A dangerous rest in the open was now enforced. The peepers came panting up to their mother, and full of anxiety, she lay there beside them till they were able to go on. Then she led them as before, quacking gently, "Courage, my darlings!"

They were not half-way to the pond yet, and the journey was telling on them long before they reached this last friendly thicket. The brood strung out into another procession, with a wide gap to the runtie in the rear, when a great Marsh Hawk suddenly appeared skimming low over the ground.

"Squat!" gasped Mother Greenwing, and the little things all lay flat, except the last one. Too far off to hear the low warning, he struggled on. The great Hawk swooped, seized him in his claws, and bore him peeping away over the bushes. All the poor mother could do was gaze in dumb sorrow as the bloodthirsty pirate bore off the downling, unresisted and unpunished. Yet, no; not entirely; for, as he flew straight to the bank of the pond where lodged his crew of young marauders, he heedlessly passed over the home bush of a Kingbird, and that fearless little warrior screamed out his battle-cry as he launched in air to give chase. Away went the pirate, and away went the King, the one huge, heavy, and cowardly, the other small, swift, and fearless as a hero, away and away, out of sight, the Kingbird gaining at every stroke, till his voice was lost in the distance.

The sorrow of the Mother Greenwing, if less deep than that of the human mother, was yet very real. But she had now the nine to guard. They needed her every thought. She led them as quickly as possible into the bushes, and for a time they breathed more freely.

Thenceforth she managed to have the journey lie through the cover. An hour or more passed by in slight alarms and in many rests, and the pond was very near; and well it was, for the Ducklings were almost worn out, their little paddles were scratched and bleeding, and their strength was all but gone. For a time they gasped under shadow of the last tall bush before again setting out in a compact flock to cross the next bare place, a rough opening through the poplars.

And they never knew that death in another form had hovered on their track. A Red Fox crossed the trail of the little Duck army. His keen nose told him at once that here was a feast awaiting, and all he had to do was follow it up and eat. So he sneaked softly and swiftly along their well-marked trail. He was already in sight of them. In the ordinary course he soon would have them, mother and all, but the ordinary course may go askew. He was near enough to count the little marchers, if count he could, when the wind brought something which made him stop, crouch low, then, at a surer whiff, he slunk away, fled as swiftly as he could without being seen. And the realest danger, surest death of all that had threatened, was thwarted by an unseen power, and not even the watchful Mother Duck had the slightest hint of it.

* * *

The little ones now toddled along after their mother, who led them quickly to cross the opening. To her delight, a long arm of the pond was quite close, just across that treeless lane. She made straight for it, joyfully calling, "Come, my darlings!"

But alas! the treeless opening was one of the man-made things called a "cart-trail." On each side of it were two deep-worn, endless cañons that man calls "wheel-ruts," and into the first of these fell four of her brood. Five managed to scramble across, but the other rut was yet deeper and wider, and the five were there engulfed.

Oh, dear, this was terrible! The little ones were too weak now to climb out. The ruts seemed endless in both directions, and the mother did not know how to help them. She and they were in despair, and as she ran about calling and urging them to put forth all their strength, there came up suddenly the very thing she most feared,—the deadliest enemy of Ducks,—a great tall man.

Mother Greenwing flung herself at his feet and flopped on the grass. Not begging for mercy! Oh, no! She was only trying to trick the man into thinking she was wounded, so that he would follow her, and she could lead him away.

But this man knew the trick, and he would not follow. Instead of that he looked about, and found the nine little bright-eyed downlings deep in the ruts, vainly trying to hide.

He stooped gently, and gathered them all into his hat. Poor little things, how they did *peep*! Poor little mother, how she did cry in bitterness for her brood! Now she knew that they all were to be destroyed before her very eyes, and she beat her breast on the ground before the terrible giant in agony of sorrow.

Then the heartless monster went to the edge of the pond, no doubt for a drink to wash the Ducklings down his throat. He bent down, and

Three times did she drench him

a moment later the Ducklings were spattering free over the water. The mother flew out on the glassy surface. She called, and they all came skurrying to her. She did not know that this man was really her friend; she never knew that he was the divinity whose mere presence had been enough to drive the Fox away and to save them in their direst strait,— his race has persecuted hers too long,—and she went on hating him to the end.

She tried to lead her brood far away from him. She took them right across the open pond. This was a mistake, for it exposed them to other, to real, enemies. That great Marsh Hawk saw them, and he came swooping along, sure of getting one in each claw.

"Run for the rushes!" called out the Mother Greenwing; and run they all did, pattering over the surface as fast as their tired little legs could go.

"Run! run!" cried the mother. But the Hawk was close at hand now. In spite of all their running he would be upon them in another second. They were too young to dive. There seemed no escape, when, just as he pounced, the bright little mother gave a great splash with all her strength, and using both feet and wings, dashed the water all over the Hawk. He was astonished. He sprang back into the air to shake himself dry. The mother urged the little ones to "keep on." Keep on they did. But down came the Hawk again, again to be repelled with a shower of spray. Three times did he pounce, three times did she drench him, till at last all the downlings were safe in the friendly rushes. The angry Hawk now made a lunge at the mother; but she could dive, and giving a good-by splash, she easily disappeared.

Far in the rushes she came up, and called a gentle *quack, quack*! The nine tired little ones came to her, and safely they rested at last.

But that was not all. Just as they began to feast on the teeming insect life, a far-away faint peep was heard. Mother Greenwing called again her mothering *qu-a-a-a-a-c-c—k*. And through the sedge demurely paddling, like an old-timer, came their missing one that the Hawk had carried off.

He had not been hurt by the claws. The valiant Kingbird had overtaken the Hawk over the pond. At the first blow of his bill the Hawk had shrieked and dropped his prey; the little Duck fell unharmed into the water, and escaped into the rushes till his mother and brothers came, then he rejoined them, and they lived happily in the great pond till they all grew up and flew away on wings of their own.

CHINK: THE DEVELOPMENT
OF A PUP

Chink was just old enough to think himself a very remarkable little Dog; and so he was, but not in the way he fondly imagined. He was neither fierce nor dreadful, strong nor swift, but he was one of the noisiest, best-natured, silliest Pups that ever chewed his master's boots to bits. His master, Bill Aubrey, was an old mountaineer who was camped below Garnet Peak in the Yellowstone Park. This is in a very quiet corner, far from the usual line of travel, and Bill's camp, before ours came, would have been a very lonely place but for his companion, this irrepressible, woolly-coated little Dog.

Chink was never still for five minutes. Indeed, he would do anything he was told to do except keep still. He was always trying to do some absurd and impossible thing, or, if he did attempt the possible, he usually spoiled his best effort by his way of going about it. He once spent a whole morning trying to run up a tall, straight pine-tree in whose branches was a snickering Pine Squirrel.

The darling ambition of his life for some weeks was to catch one of the Picket-pin Gophers that swarmed on the prairie about the camp. These little animals have a trick of sitting bolt upright on their hind legs, with their paws held close in, so that at a distance they look exactly like picket-pins. Often when we went out to picket our horses for the night we would go toward a Gopher, thinking it was a picket-pin already driven in, and would find out the mistake only when it dived into the ground with a defiant chirrup.

Chink had determined to catch one of these Gophers the very first day he came into the valley. Of course he went about it in his own original way, doing everything wrong end first, as usual. This, his master said, was due to a streak of Irish in his make-up. So Chink would begin a most elaborate stalk a quarter of a mile from the Gopher. After crawling on his breast from tussock to tussock for a hundred yards or so, the nervous strain became too great, and Chink, getting too much excited to crawl, would rise on his feet and walk straight toward the Gopher, which would now be sitting up by his hole, fully alive to the situation.

After a minute or two of this very open approach, Chink's excitement would overpower all caution. He would begin running, and at the last, just as he should have done his finest stalking, he would go bounding and barking toward the Gopher, which would sit like a peg of wood till the proper moment, then dive below with a derisive chirrup, throwing with its hind feet a lot of sand right into Chink's eager, open mouth.

Day after day this went on with level sameness, and still Chink did not give up. Perseverance, he seemed to believe, must surely win in the end, as indeed it did. For one day he made an unusually elaborate stalk after an unusually fine Gopher, carried out all his absurd tactics, finishing with the grand, boisterous charge, and actually caught his victim; but this time it happened to be a wooden picket-pin. Any one who doubts that a Dog knows when he has made a fool of himself should have seen Chink that day as he sheepishly sneaked out of sight behind the tent.

But failure had no lasting effect on Chink. There was a streak of grit as well as Irish in him that carried him through every reverse, and nothing could dash his good nature. He was into everything with the maximum of energy and the minimum of discretion, delighted as long as he could be always up and doing.

Every passing wagon and horseman and grazing Calf had to be chivvied, and if the Cat from the guard-house strayed by, Chink felt that it was a solemn duty he owed to the soldiers, the Cat, and himself to chase her home at frightful speed. He would dash twenty times a day after an old hat that Bill used deliberately to throw into a Wasps' nest with the order, "Fetch it!"

It took time, but countless disasters began to tell. Chink slowly realized that there were long whips and big, fierce Dogs with wagons; that Horses have teeth in their heels; that Calves have relatives with clubs on their heads; that a slow Cat may turn out a Skunk; and that Wasps are not Butterflies. Yes, it took an uncommonly long time, but it all told in the end. Chink began to develop a grain—a little one, but a living, growing grain—of good Dog sense.

* * *

It seemed as if all his blunders were the rough, unsymmetrical stones of an arch, and the keystone was added, the structure, his character, made strong and complete, by his crowning blunder in the matter of a large Coyote.

This Coyote lived not far from our camp, and he evidently realized, as all the animals there do, that no man is allowed to shoot, trap, hunt, or in any way molest the wild creatures in the Park; above all, in this part, close to the military patrol, with soldiers always on watch. Secure in the knowledge of this, the Coyote used to come about the camp each night for scraps. At first I found only his tracks in the dust, as though he had circled the camp but feared to come very near. Then we began to hear his weird evening song just after sundown, or about sun-up. At length his track was plain in the dust about the scrap-bucket each morning when I went out to learn from the trail what animals had been there during the night. Then growing bolder, he came about the camp occasionally in the daytime. Shyly at first, but with increasing assurance, as he was satisfied of his immunity, until finally he was not only there every night, but seemed to hang around nearly all day, sneaking in to steal whatever was eatable, or sitting in plain view on some rising ground at a distance.

One morning, as he sat on a bank some fifty yards away, one of us, in a spirit of mischief, said to Chink: "Chink, do you see that Coyote over there grinning at you? Go and chase him out of that."

Chink always did as he was told, and burning to distinguish himself, he dashed after the Coyote, who loped lightly away, and there was a pretty good race for a quarter of a mile; but it was nothing to the race which began when the Coyote turned on his pursuer.

Chink realized all at once that he had been lured into the power of a Tartar, and strained every muscle to get back to camp. The Coyote was swifter, and soon overtook the Dog, nipping him first on one side, then on the other, with manifest glee, as if he were cracking a series of good jokes at Chink's expense.

Chink yelped and howled and ran his hardest, but had no respite from his tormentor till he dashed right into camp; and we, I am afraid, laughed with the Coyote, and the Puppy did not get the sympathy he deserved for his trouble in doing as he was told.

One more experience like this, on a smaller scale, was enough to dampen even Chink's enthusiasm. He decided to let that Coyote very much alone in future.

Not so the Coyote, however. He had discovered a new and delightful amusement. He came daily now and hung about the camp, knowing perfectly well that no one would dare to shoot him. Indeed, the lock of every gun in the party was sealed up by the government officials, and soldiers were everywhere on watch to enforce the laws.

Thenceforth that Coyote lay in wait for poor Chink, and sought every opportunity to tease him. The little Dog learned that if he went a hundred yards from camp alone, the Coyote would go after him, and bite and chase him right back to his master's tent.

Day after day this went on, until at last Chink's life was made a misery to him. He did not dare now to go fifty yards from the tent alone; and even if he went with us when we rode, that fierce and impudent Coyote was sure to turn up and come along, trotting close beside or behind, watching for a chance to worry poor Chink and spoiling all his pleasure in the ramble, but keeping just out of reach of our quirts, or a little farther off when we stopped to pick up some stones.

One day Aubrey moved his camp a mile up-stream, and we saw less of the Coyote, for the reason that he moved a mile up-stream too, and, like all bullies who are unopposed, grew more insolent and tyrannical every day, until poor little Chink's life became at last a veritable reign of terror, at which his master merely laughed.

Aubrey gave it out that he had moved camp to get better Horse-feed. It soon turned out, however, that he wanted to be alone while he enjoyed the contents of a whiskey-flask that he had obtained somewhere. But one flask was a mere starter for him. The second day he mounted his Horse, said, "Chink, you watch the tent," and rode away over the mountains to the nearest saloon, leaving Chink obediently curled up on some sacking.

* * *

Now, with all his puppyish silliness, Chink was a faithful watch-dog, and his master knew that he would take care of the tent as well as he could.

Late that afternoon a passing mountaineer came along. When he was within shouting distance he stopped, as is customary, and shouted: "Hello there, Bill! Oh, Bill!"

But getting no answer, he went up to the door, and there was met by "an odd-looking Purp with his bristles all on end"; and Chink, for of course it was he, warned him in many fierce growls to keep away.

The mountaineer understood the situation and went on. Evening came, and no master to relieve Chink, who was now getting very hungry.

There was some bacon in the tent wrapped in a bag, but that was sacred. His master had told him to "watch it," and Chink would have starved rather than touch it.

He ventured out on the flat in hope of finding a mouse or something to stay the pangs of hunger, when suddenly he was pounced on by that brute of a Coyote, and the old chase was repeated as Chink dashed back to the tent.

There a change came over him. The remembrance of his duty seemed suddenly to alter him and brace him up, just as the cry of her Kitten will turn a timid Cat into a Tigress.

He was a mere Puppy yet, and a little fool in many ways, but away back of all was a fibre of strength that would grow with his years. The moment that Coyote tried to follow into the tent,—his master's tent,—Chink forgot all his own fears, and turned on the enemy like a little demon.

The beasts feel the force of right and wrong. They know moral courage and cowardice. The moral force was all with the little scared Dog, and both animals seemed to know it. The Coyote backed off, growling savagely, and vowing, in Coyote fashion, to tear that Dog to ribbons very soon. All the same, he did not venture to enter the tent, as he clearly had intended doing.

Then began a literal siege; for the Coyote came back every little while, and walked round the tent, scratching contemptuously with his hind feet, or marching up to the open door, to be met at once, face to face, by poor little Chink, who, really half dead with fear, was brave again as soon as he saw any attempt to injure the things in his charge.

All this time Chink had nothing to eat. He could slip out and get a drink at the near-by stream once or twice a day, but he could not get a meal in that way. He could have torn a hole in the sack and eaten some bacon, but he would not, for that was in trust; or he could have watched his chance to desert his post, and sneaked off to our camp, where he would have been sure of a good meal. But no; adversity had developed the true Dog in him. He would not betray his master's trust in any way. He was ready to die at his post, if need be, while that master was away indulging in a drunken carouse.

For four days and four nights of misery did this heroic little Dog keep his place, and keep tent and stuff from the Coyote that he held in mortal terror.

On the fifth morning old Aubrey had awakened to the fact that he was not at home, and that his camp in the mountains was guarded only by a small Dog. He was tired of his spree now, and he got on his Horse and set out over the hills, sober but very shaky. When he was about half-way on the trail it suddenly dawned on his clouded brain that he had left Chink without any food.

"Hope the little beast hain't spoiled all my bacon," he thought, and he pressed on more briskly till he came to the ridge commanding a view of his tent. There it was, and there at the door, exchanging growls and snapping at each other, were the big, fierce Coyote and poor little Chink.

"Wal, I be darned!" exclaimed Aubrey. "I forgot all about that

Trembling with fear and weakness, he was making his last stand

blasted Coyote. Poor Chink! he must 'a' had a mighty tough time. Wonder he ain't all chawed up an' the camp in tatters.''

There he was, bravely making his last stand. His legs were tottering under him with fear and hunger, but he still put on his boldest face, and was clearly as ready as ever to die in defence of the camp.

The cold gray eyes of the mountaineer took in this part of the situation at the first glance, and when he galloped up and saw the untouched bacon, he realized that Chink had eaten nothing since he left. When the Puppy, trembling with fear and weakness, crawled up and looked in his face and licked his hand as much as to say, ''I've done what you told me,'' it was too much for old Aubrey. The tears stood in his eyes as he hastened to get food for the little hero.

Then he turned to him and said: ''Chink, old pard, I've treated you dirty, an' you always treated me white. I'll never go on another spree without takin' you along, Chink, an' I'll treat you as white as you treated me, if I know how. 'Tain't much more I kin do for you, pard, since ye don't drink, but I reckon I kin lift the biggest worry out o' yer life, an' I'll do it, too."

Then from the ridge-pole he took down the pride of his heart, his treasured repeating rifle, and, regardless of consequences, he broke the government seals, wax eagles, red tape, and all, and went to the door.

The Coyote was sitting off a little way with a Mephistophelian grin on his face, as usual; but the rifle rang, and Chink's reign of terror was at an end.

What matter if the soldiers did come out and find that the laws of the Park had been violated, that Aubrey had shot one of the animals of the Park?

What matter to Aubrey if his gun was taken from him and destroyed, and he and his outfit expelled from the Park, with a promise of being jailed if ever he returned? What did it all matter?

"It's all right," said old Aubrey. "I done the squar' thing by my pard—my pard, that always treated me white."

THE KANGAROO RAT

It was a rough, rock-built, squalid ranch-house that I lived in, on the Currumpaw. The plaster of the walls was mud, the roof and the walls were dry mud, the great river-flat around it was sandy mud, and the hills a mile away were piled-up mud, sculptured by frost and rain into the oddest of mud vagaries, with here and there a coping of lava to prevent the utter demolition of some necessary mud pinnacle by the indefatigable sculptors named.

The place seemed uninviting to a stranger from the lush and fertile prairies of Manitoba, but the more I saw of it the more it was revealed a paradise. For every cottonwood of the straggling belt that the river used to mark its doubtful course across the plain, and every dwarfed and spiny bush and weedy copse, was teeming with *life*. And every day and every night I made new friends, or learned new facts about the mudland denizens.

Man and the Birds are understood to possess the earth during the daylight, therefore the night has become the time for the four-footed ones to be about, and in order that I might set a sleepless watch on their movements I was careful each night before going to bed to sweep smooth the dust about the shanty and along the two pathways, one to the spring and one to the corral by way of the former corn-patch, still called the "garden."

Each morning I went out with all the feelings of a child meeting the Christmas postman, or of a fisherman hauling in his largest net, eager to know what there was for me.

Not a morning passed without a message from the beasts. Nearly every night a Skunk or two would come and gather up table-scraps, prying into all sorts of forbidden places in their search. Once or twice a

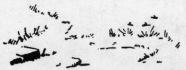
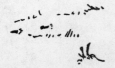

Bobcat came. And one morning the faithful dust reported in grate detail how the Bobcat and the Skunk had differed. There was evidence, too, that the Bobcat quickly said (in Bobcat, of course), "I beg pardon, I mistook you for a rabbit, but will never again make such a mistake."

More than once the sinister trail of the "Hydrophoby-cat" was recorded. And on one occasion the great broad track of the King Wolf of the region came right up the pathway, nearly to the door, the tracks getting closer together as he neared it. Then stopping, he had exactly retraced his steps and gone elsewhere about his business. Jack-rabbits, Coyotes, and Cotton-tails all passed, and wrote for me a few original lines commemorative of their visit—and all were faithfully delivered on call next morning.

But always over and through all other tracks was a curious, delicate, lace-like fabric of polkadots and interwoven sinuous lines. It was there each morning, fresh made the night before, whatever else was missing. But there was so much of its pattern that it was impossible to take any one line and follow it up.

At first it seemed to be made up of the trails of many small bipeds, each closely followed by its little one. Now, man and Birds are the only bipeds, but these were clearly not the tracks of any Bird. Trying to be judicial, I put together all the facts that the dust reported. First, here was proof that a number of tiny, two-legged, fur-slippered creatures came nightly to dance in the moonlight. Each one, as he pirouetted about, was closely followed by a much smaller one of the same kind, as though by his page. They came from nowhere and went again as they would. And they must have been invisible at will, or else how escape the ever-watchful Coyotes?

If only this had been in England or Ireland, any peasant could have explained it offhand—invisible pairs of tiny, furry boots, dancing in the moonlight—why, the veriest idiot knows that—*fairies*, of course.

But in New Mexico I had never heard of such a thing. In no work on this country, so far as I knew, was there any mention of their occurrence.

If only it could be! Would it not be delightful? I would gladly have believed. Christian Andersen would have insisted on believing in it, and then made others believe it, too. But for me, alas! it was impossible, for long ago, when my soul came to the fork in the trail marked on the left "To Arcadie," on the right "To Scientia," I took the flinty, upland right-hand path. I had given up my fayland eyes for—for I do not know what. And so I was puzzled, but the more puzzled, the more interested, of course; and remembering, from former experience, that it pays to offer a great deal of clear writing-space to the visitors who nightly favored me with their autographs, I made with unusual care a large extension of the clean-swept dust sheet, to which the sage-brush-scented evening wind added a still smoother finish, and which next day enabled me to follow out a single line of the point-lace pattern.

It went dimpling down the path, toward the six old corn-stumps called the garden, and then, leaving the clear written dust, it had turned aside, and seemed to end at a weed-covered mound, about which were

They came nightly to dance in the moonlight

several small holes that went in, not downward, but at a level. (Yes, of course, another pretty mystery nearly gone. How sharp the flints are on this upland path!) I set a trap by these holes, and next morning I had surely caught my "fairy." Just the loveliest, daintiest fawn-brown little creature that ever was seen in fur: large beautiful eyes like a Fawn's—no, not like a Fawn's, for no Fawn that ever lived had such wonderfully innocent orbs of liquid brown, ears like thinnest shells of the sea, showing the pink veins' flood of life. His hind feet were large and strong; but his fore feet—his hands, I mean—were the tiniest of the tiny, pinky white and rounded and dimpled, just like a baby's, only whiter and smaller than the tip of baby's smallest finger. His throat and breast were snowy white. However does he keep himself so sweetly clean in such a land of mud! Down the outside of his brown velvet knickerbockers was the cutest little silvery-white stripe, just like that on a trooper's breeches. His tail, the train that I suppose the page carried in dancing, was remarkably long, and was decorated to match the breeches with two long white stripes, and ended in a feather duster, which was very pretty but rather overdone, I thought, until I found out that it was designed for several important purposes.

His movements were just like what one might have expected from such an elegant creature. He had touched my heart before I had seen anything but his tracks, and now he won it wholly at first meeting.

"You little beauty! You have been so invisible and mysterious that I began to hope you were a fairy, but now I see I have heard of you before. You are *Perodipus ordi*, that is sometimes called the Kangaroo Rat. I am much obliged to you for all the lace designs you have sketched and for the pretty verses you have written for me, although I could not read them all; but I am eager to have you translate them, and, in fact, am ready to sit at those microscopic and beautiful feet of yours and learn."

* * *

It is of course well known that the daintiest flowers grow out of the dirt, so I was not surprised to find that the Perodipus's home is in a cave underground. No doubt those wonderful eyes and long feelers were to help him in the unlighted corridors of his subterranean house.

It may seem a ruthless deed, but I was so eager to know him better that I determined to open his nest to the light of day as well as keep him a prisoner for a time, to act as my professor in Natural History.

I transferred the plush-clad atom of life to a large box that was lined with tin and half full of loose earth. Then I went out with a spade, carefully to follow and pry into the secrets of the Brownie world of which my captive was a native.

First I made a scaled diagram of the landscape concerned, for science is measurement, and exact knowledge was what I had sought since I made my choice of trails. Then I sketched the plants on the low

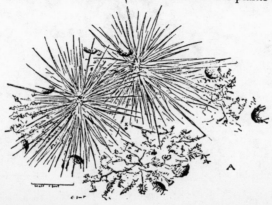

mound. There were three large, prickly thistles, and two vigorous Spanish bayonets, or soapweeds, all of them dangerous to an unwary intruder. Next, I noticed there were nine gateways. Nine—I wonder why nine. Nine Muses? Nine lives? No, nothing of that sort (Perodipus does not live in the clouds). There were nine simply because in this case there happened to be nine direct approaches to this Perodipus's citadel. Another might have had three, or yet another twenty-three entries, according to the needs of its owner or the locality.

Over each of the nine holes was a strong, spine-armed sentinel

A ferocious-looking reptile

forever on guard and absolutely unbuyable, so that if at any time the Coyote—the Satan of the little prairie-folk—should appear among the moonlight dancers, each could dash homeward and enter by a handy door, sure that there would be standing by that door a fearless, well-armed warden, who would say to the Coyote, in a language he would well understand, "Stop! Keep off, or I'll spear you!"

And I feel very sure now that if an accident had opened a new approach, say in the direction of A, the wise little creature would also have made a handy door there for his own use. The Spanish bayonet could also keep the cattle and other heavy animals from trampling the mound, and when at night the Perodipus was making a dash for home with some fleet foe behind him, the tall, dark form of the friendly bayonet would be his landmark in the uncertain light. In summer-time, I now remembered, when other plants were not dead, as at present, the bayonet, in its sombre evergreen, would be a poor landmark by night; but it meets the new necessity in a splendid way. Out of its bristling topmost serried spears it sends far up into the purple night a wondrous candelabrum on a towering pole, with flowers of shining white, that must loom up afar, like some new constellation in the sky. And so the Perodipus's safety port is lighthoused day and night.

I began carefully to open up the main gallery to the home of my moonlight dancer, and had not gone very far when I came on something that made me jump; nothing less than a ferocious-looking reptile—the *Huajalote*, that the Mexicans hold in superstitious and mortal dread, the *Amblystoma* of scientists. It was only a small one, but it gave me the creeps to see him lashing his venomous-looking tail and oozing all over with a poisonous slime. If he could affect me so much, what might he be like to the gentle little Perodipus, whose home he seemed trying to raid? But for some reason that I did not understand then, the reptile was boring his nose into a solid bank of sand that was the end of the gallery he had entered by. Since we were all playing "fairy-tale," I, the Giant, did not hesitate to put the Dragon where he could harm the fairies no longer.

After hours of patient digging and measuring I got a map of the underground world where the Perodipus passes the daytime.

The central chamber could be *nearly* reached by any of the entrances, but one not knowing the secret would have passed by and come out into the air again at another door. No matter how often he went in, he never would have found the nest or any of the real treasure of the home, for the road to the nest was plugged with earth each time the owner left it.

And this is exactly what happened to the Huajalote; for he seemed to have an idea that there was a secret passage if he only could find it, and no doubt thought it was somewhere through the bank of earth he was boring into, though really he was not anywhere near to the spot.

I think the chamber was not shut off from the air, for the small round hole X (see page 214) was, I suspect, its air-shaft, though I am not sure of this, for the roof caved in before I could examine it fully.

The chamber itself was very large, being twelve inches long and

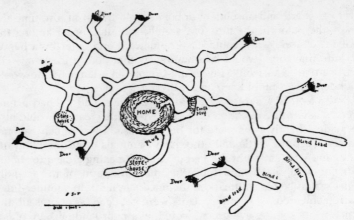

eight inches wide, with a high vaulted roof at least over five inches from the floor, and ribbed with the living roots of the grand old bayonet-trees at the door. Having discovered the entry to it, I thought I was in the nest; but not so. I was stopped now by a mass of interlaced, spiny grasses that would probably have turned the Huajalote had he gotten so far. After I had forced my way through this I found that the real entrance was cleverly hidden near a corner. Then there was a thick felting of fine grass and weed silk, and inside of all a lining of softest feathers. I think that every gay little Bird on the plains must have contributed one of its finest feathers to that nest, for it was as soft and pretty and warm as it should have been for the cradle of those pinky-white seed-pearls that the Perodipus's babies are when first they come from the land of the Stars and the Stork into their underground home.

Down in one corner of this Great Hall I found signs of another secret passage. It was like exploring a mediæval castle. This passage went down at a slant when I got fairly into it, and before long it opened out into a large store-house that was filled with over a pint of seeds of the prairie sunflower. This room was sunken deepest of all in the ground, and was also in the shadiest part of the mound, so that the seed would be in no danger of heating or sprouting. At one end of this chamber was another blind lead that possibly was used in filling the warehouse and afterward sealed up for safety. There were many of these blind alleys. They appeared to be either entrances plugged up or else deliberate plans to mislead an intruder who did not have the key to the secret door.

Yet one more chamber was found, and that was a second storehouse, a reserve supply of carefully selected helianthus seeds, about half a gill of them, and yet not a bad one or a shrivelled one was to be found in the lot.

But I did not find any of the Perodipus family, and think it possible that when they heard my rude approach they all escaped by some other secret passage that I failed to discover.

This was the home of my nightly visitor, planned and carried out with wisdom for all the straits of his daily life and near future.

* * *

Its owner in the cage I now watched with double interest. He was the embodiment of restless energy, palpitating with life from the tip of his translucent nose and ears to the end of his vibrant tail. He could cross the box at a single bound, and I now saw the purpose of his huge tail. In the extraordinary long flying leaps that Perodipus makes, the tuft on the end does for him what the feathers do for an arrow. It keeps him straight in the air on his trajectory. But it does more, for it enables him slightly to change his course if he finds it wiser after he has leaped. And the tail itself has other uses. The Perodipus has no pocket in his striped trousers to carry home his winter supplies, but he has capacious pockets, one in each cheek, which he can fill till they bulge out wider than himself—so wide that he must turn his head sidewise to enter his own front gate. Such a load added to his head totally displaces his centre of gravity, which is adjusted for leaping with empty pockets. But here is where the tail comes in. Its great length and size make it a powerful lever, and by raising it to different angles he accommodates himself to his load and leaps along in perfect poise in spite of a week's provision in his cheeks.

He was the most indefatigable little miner that I ever saw. Those pinky-white paws, not much larger than a pencil-point, seemed never weary of digging, and would send the earth out between his hind legs in little jets like a steam-shovel. He seemed tireless at his work. He first tunnelled the whole mass through and through, and, I doubt not, made and unmade several ideal underground residences, and solved many problems of rapid underground transit. Then he embarked in some landscape-gardening schemes and made it his nightly business to change entirely the geography of his whole country, laboriously making hills and cañons wheresoever seemed unto him good.

There was one landscape effect that he seemed very fond of. That was a sort of Colorado Cañon with the San Francisco Mountain on its edge. He tried a long time to use a certain large stone for a peak to his mountain, but it was past his strength, and he resented, rather than profited by, any help I gave him. This stone gave him endless trouble for a time. He could not use it, nor even get rid of it, until he discovered that he could at least dig the earth from under it, and so keep it going down, until finally it settled at the bottom of the box and troubled him no more.

He used to take a lot of comfort out of jumping clear from the top of the Frisco Peak across the Grand Cañon into Utah (two hundred

miles), at the other side of the box, and back home again to the Peak
(six thousand feet).

I watched, sketched, and studied him as well as I could,
considering his shyness and nocturnal habits, and I learned daily to
admire him more. His untiring devotion to his nightly geographical
lesson was marvellous. His talent for heaving up new mountain-ranges
was astonishing, positively volcanic. When first I suspected his
existence, I had been willing to call him a fairy. When I saw him I said,
"Why, it's only a Kangroo Rat." But after I had watched him a couple
of weeks in the cage I realized fully that millions of little creatures with
such energy, working for thousands of years, could not but change the
whole surface of a country, by letting in the frost and rain, as well as by
their own work. Then I was obliged to concede that Perodipus was
more than Rat or Brownie; he was nothing less than a Geological
Epoch.

* * *

There was one more lesson, a great surprise, in store for me. It is well
known to scientists that the common House-mouse has a song not
unlike that of some Birds. Occasionally gifted individuals are found that
fill our closet or cellar with midnight music that a Canary might be
proud of. Further investigations have shown that the common Deer-
mouse of the Eastern woods also is a gifted vocalist.

Now, any cow-boy on the upland plains will tell you that at night,
when sleeping out, he has often heard the most curious strains of birdy
music in his half-awakening hours,—a soft, sweet twittering song with
trills and deeper notes,—and if he thought about it at all he set it down
to some small Bird singing in its dreams, or accepted his comrade's
unexplanatory explanation that it was one of those "prairie night-
ingales." But what that was he did not trouble himself to know.

I have often heard the strange night song, but not being able to
trace it home, I set it down to some little Bird that was too happy to
express it all in daylight hours.

Several times at night I overheard from my captive a long-drawn
note, before it dawned on me that this was the same voice as that

which often sings to the rising moon. I did not hear him really sing, I am sorry to say. I have no final proof. My captive was not seeking to amuse me. Indeed, his attitude toward me from first to last was one of unbending scorn. I can only say I *think* (and hope) that it was the same voice. But my allegiance is due to exact science. Oh, why did I not take the other trail? For then I should have been able to announce here, as now I do not dare to, that the sweet night singer of the plains and the plush-clad fairy that nightly danced about my door *are the same.*

Shooting across the open like an arrow

But one night there was a fresh upheaval of Nature, and my Immeasurable Force tried a new experiment in terrestrial convulsions. He started his mountain, not in the middle of his kingdom, as aforetime, but afar to the south-west, in one corner of the box, and a notable mountain he made. He simply ruined the Grand Cañon to use the material of its walls.

Higher and higher those tiny pink pawlets piled the beetling crags, and the dizzy peak arose above the sinking plain as it never had before.

It went up fast, too, for it was in the angle of the box, and it was rapidly nearing the heaven of heavens represented by the lid, when an accident turned the current of the Perodipus's ambitions. He was now at an altitude that he had never before reached since his imprisonment, so high that he could touch the narrow strip of the wooden walls that was unprotected by the tin. The new substance tempted his teeth. Oh, new-found joy! it was easy to cut. He set to work with his usual energy, and in a very short time cut his way through the half-inch pine, then escaped from the tin-clad kingdom that had been forced upon him, and its Geological Epoch was gone. My professor had quit his chair. I had been willing to find an impossible mystery, but I had found a delightful story from Nature's wonderland.

* * *

And now he is once more skimming merrily over the mud and sands of the upland plains; shooting across the open like a living, feathered arrow; tempting the rash Coyote to thrust his unfortunate nose into those awful cactus brakes, or teaching the Prairie Owls that if they do not let him alone they will surely come to grief on a Spanish bayonet; coming out by night again to scribble his lacework designs on the smooth places, to write verses of measured rhythm, or to sing and play hop-scotch in the moonlight with his merry crew.

Soft as a shadow, swift as an arrow, dainty as thistle-down, bright-eyed and beautiful, with a secret way to an underground world where he finds safety from his foes—my first impression was not so very far astray. I had surely found the Little Folk, and nearer, better, and more human Little Folk than any in the nursery books. My chosen flinty track had led me on the Upper Arcadie at last. And now, when I hear certain purblind folk talk of Fairies and Brownies as a race peculiar to the romantic parts of England, Ireland, or India, I think:

"*You* have been wasting your time reading books. You have never been on the shifting Currumpaw when the moon of the Mesas comes up to glint the river at its every bend, and bathe the hills in green and veil the shades in blue. You have not heard the moonlight music. You have not seen these moonbeams skip from thistle-top and bayonet-spear to rest in peace at last, as by appointment, on the smooth-swept dancing-floor of a tiny race that visits this earth each night, coming from nowhere, and disappearing without a sound of falling feet.

"You have never seen this, for you have not found the key to the

Tempting the rash coyote

secret chamber; and if you did, you still might doubt, for the dainty
moonlight revellers have coats of darkness and become invisible at will.

"Indeed, I believe you would say the whole thing was a dream. But
what about the lace traceries in the dust? They are there when the sun
comes up next morning."

TITO

The Story of the Coyote that Learned How

A raindrop may deflect a thunderbolt, or a hair may ruin an empire, as surely as a spider-web once turned the history of Scotland; and if it had not been for one little pebble, this history of Tito might never have happened.

That pebble was lying on a trail in the Dakota Badlands, and one hot, dark night it lodged in the foot of a Horse that was ridden by a tipsy cow-boy. The man got off, as a matter of habit, to know what was laming his Horse. But he left the reins on its neck instead of on the ground, and the Horse, taking advantage of this technicality, ran off in the darkness. Then the cow-boy, realizing that he was afoot, lay down in a hollow under some buffalo-bushes and slept the loggish sleep of the befuddled.

The golden beams of the early summer sun were leaping from top to top of the wonderful Badland Buttes, when an old Coyote might have been seen trotting homeward along the Garner's Creek Trail with a Rabbit in her jaws to supply her family's breakfast.

Fierce war had for a long time been waged against the Coyote kind by the cattlemen of Billings County. Traps, guns, poison, and Hounds had reduced their number nearly to zero, and the few survivors had learned the bitter need of caution at every step. But the destructive ingenuity of man knew no bounds, and their numbers continued to dwindle.

The old Coyote quit the trail very soon, for nothing that man had made is friendly. She skirted along a low ridge, then across a little hollow where grew a few buffalo-bushes, and, after a careful sniff at a very stale human trail-scent, she crossed another near ridge on whose sunny side was the home of her brood. Again she cautiously circled, peered about, and sniffed, but, finding no sign of danger, went down to the doorway and uttered a low *woof-woof*. Out of the den, beside a sage-bush, there poured a procession of little Coyotes, merrily tumbling over one another. Then, barking little barks and growling little puppy growls, they fell upon the feast that their mother had brought, and gobbled and tussled while she looked on and enjoyed their joy.

Wolver Jake, the cow-boy, had awakened from his chilly sleep about sunrise, in time to catch a glimpse of the Coyote passing over the ridge. As soon as she was out of sight he got on his feet and went to the edge, there to witness the interesting scene of the family breakfasting and frisking about within a few yards of him, utterly unconscious of any danger.

But the only appeal the scene had to him lay in the fact that the county had set a price on every one of these Coyotes' lives. So he got out his big .45 navy revolver, and nothwithstanding his shaky condition, he managed somehow to get a sight on the mother as she was caressing one of the little ones that had finished its breakfast, and shot her dead on the spot.

The terrified cubs fled into the den, and Jake, failing to kill another with his revolver, came forward, blocked up the hole with stones, and leaving the seven little prisoners quaking at the far end, set off on foot for the nearest ranch, cursing his faithless Horse as he went.

In the afternoon he returned with his pard and tools for digging. The little ones had cowered all day in the darkened hole, wondering why their mother did not come to feed them, wondering at the darkness and the change. But late that day they heard sounds at the door. Then light was again let in. Some of the less cautious young ones ran forward to meet their mother, but their mother was not there—only two great rough brutes that began tearing open their home.

After an hour or more the diggers came to the end of the den, and here were the woolly, bright-eyed, little ones, all huddled in a pile at the farthest corner. Their innocent puppy faces and ways were not noticed by the huge enemy. One by one they were seized. A sharp blow, and each quivering, limp form was thrown into a sack to be carried to the nearest magistrate who was empowered to pay the bounties.

Even at this age there was a certain individuality of character among the puppies. Some of them squealed and some of them growled when dragged out to die. One or two tried to bite. The one that had been slowest to comprehend the danger, had been the last to retreat, and so was on top of the pile, and therefore the first killed. The one that had first realized the peril had retreated first, and now crouched at the bottom of the pile. Coolly and remorselessly the others were killed one by one, and then this prudent little puppy was seen to be the last of the family. It lay perfectly still, even when touched, its eyes being half closed, as, guided by instinct, it tried to "play possum." One of the men picked it up. It neither squealed nor resisted. Then Jake, realizing ever the importance of "standing in with the boss," said: "Say, let's keep that 'un for the children." So the last of the family was thrown alive into the same bag with its dead brothers, and, bruised and frightened, lay there very still, understanding nothing, knowing only that after a long time of great noise and cruel jolting it was again half strangled by a grip on its neck and dragged out, where were a lot of creatures like the diggers.

These were really the inhabitants of the Chimney-pot Ranch, whose brand is the Broad-arrow; and among them were the children for whom the cub had been brought. The boss had no difficulty in getting Jake to accept the dollar that the cub Coyote would have brought in bounty-money, and his present was turned over to the children. In answer to their question, "What is it?" a Mexican cow-hand present said it was a Coyotito,—that is, a "little Coyote,"—and this, afterward shortened to "Tito," became the captive's name.

* * *

Tito was a pretty little creature, with woolly body, a puppy-like expression, and a head that was singularly broad between the ears.

But, as a children's pet, she—for it proved to be female—was not a success. She was distant and distrustful. She ate her food and seemed healthy, but never responded to friendly advances; never even learned to come out of the box when called. This probably was due to the fact that the kindness of the small children was offset by the roughness of the men and boys, who did not hesitate to drag her out by the chain when they wished to see her. On these occasions she would suffer in silence, playing possum, shamming dead, for she seemed to know that that was the best thing to do. But as soon as released she would once more retire into the darkest corner of her box, and watch her tormentors with eyes that, at the proper angle, showed a telling glint of green.

Among the children of the ranchmen was a thirteen-year-old boy. The fact that he grew up to be like his father, a kind, strong, and thoughtful man, did not prevent him being, at this age, a shameless little brute.

Like all boys in that country, he practised lasso-throwing, with a view to being a cow-boy. Posts and stumps are uninteresting things to catch. His little brothers and sisters were under special protection of the Home Government. The Dogs ran far away whenever they saw him

Coyotito, the captive

coming with the rope in his hands. So he must needs practise on the unfortunate Coyotito. She soon learned that her only hope for peace was to hide in the kennel, or, if thrown at when outside, to dodge the rope by lying as flat as possible on the ground. Thus Lincoln unwittingly taught the Coyote the dangers and limitations of a rope, and so he proved a blessing in disguise—a very perfect disguise. When the Coyote had thoroughly learned how to baffle the lasso, the boy  terror devised a new amusement. He got a large trap of the kind known as "Fox-size." This he set in the dust as he had seen Jake set a Wolf-trap, close to the kennel, and over it he scattered scraps of meat, in the most approved style for Wolf-trapping. After a while Tito, drawn by the smell of the meat, came hungrily sneaking out toward it, and almost immediately was caught in the trap by one foot. The boy terror was watching from a near hiding-place. He gave a wild Indian whoop of delight, then rushed forward to drag the Coyote out of the box into which she had retreated. After some more delightful thrills of excitement and struggle he got his lasso on Tito's body, and, helped by a younger brother, a most promising pupil, he succeeded in setting the Coyote free from the trap before the grown-ups had discovered his amusement. One or two experiences like this taught her a mortal terror of traps. She soon learned the smell of the steel, and could detect and avoid it, no matter how cleverly Master Lincoln might bury it in the dust, while the younger brother screened the operation from the intended victim by holding his coat over the door of Tito's kennel.

One day the fastening of her chain gave way, and Tito went off in an uncertain fashion, trailing her chain behind her. But she was seen by one of the men, who fired a charge of bird-shot at her. The burning, stinging, and surprise of it all caused her to retreat to the one place she knew, her own kennel. The chain was fastened again, and Tito added to her ideas this, a horror of guns and the smell of gunpowder; and this also, that the one safety from them is to "lay low."

There were yet other rude experiences in store for the captive.

Poisoning Wolves was a topic of daily talk at the Ranch, so it was not surprising that Lincoln should privately experiment on Coyotito. The deadly strychnine was too well guarded to be available. So Lincoln hid some Rough on Rats in a piece of meat, threw it to the captive, and sat by to watch, as blithe and conscience-clear as any professor of chemistry trying a new combination.

Tito smelled the meat—everything had to be passed on by her nose. Her nose was in doubt. There was a good smell of meat, a familiar but unpleasant smell of human hands, and a strange new odor, but not the odor of the trap; so she bolted the morsel. Within a few minutes she began to have fearful pains in her stomach, followed by cramps. Now in all the Wolf tribe there is the instinctive habit to throw up anything that disagrees with them, and after a minute or two of suffering the Coyote sought relief in this way; and to make it doubly sure she hastily gobbled some blades of grass, and in less than an hour was quite well again.

Lincoln had put in poison enough for a dozen Coyotes. Had he put in less she could not have felt the pang till too late, but she recovered and never forgot that peculiar smell that means such awful after-pains. More than that, she was ready thenceforth to fly at once to the herbal cure that Nature had everywhere provided. An instinct of this kind grows quickly, once followed. It had taken minutes of suffering in the first place to drive her to the easement. Thenceforth, having learned, it was her first thought on feeling pain. The little miscreant did indeed succeed in having her swallow another bait with a small dose of poison, but she knew what to do now and had almost no suffering.

Later on, a relative sent Lincoln a Bull-terrier, and the new combination was a fresh source of spectacular interest for the boy, and of tribulation for the Coyote. It all emphasized for her that old idea to "lay low"—that is, to be quiet, unobtrusive, and hide when danger is in sight. The grown-ups of the household at length forbade these persecutions, and the Terrier was kept away from the little yard where the Coyote was chained up.

It must not be supposed that, in all this, Tito was a sweet, innocent victim. She had learned to bite. She had caught and killed several chickens by shamming sleep while they ventured to forage within the radius of her chain. And she had an inborn hankering to sing a morning and evening hymn, which procured for her many beatings. But she learned to shut up, the moment her opening notes were followed by a rattle of doors or windows, for these sounds of human nearness had frequently been followed by a *"bang"* and a charge of bird-shot, which somehow did no serious harm, though it severely stung her hide. And these experiences all helped to deepen her terror of guns and of those who used them. The object of these musical outpourings was not clear. They happened usually at dawn or dusk, but sometimes a loud noise at high noon would set her going. The song consisted of a volley of short barks, mixed with doleful squalls that never failed to set the Dogs astir in a responsive uproar, and once or twice had begotten a far-away answer from some wild Coyote in the hills.

There was one little trick that she had developed which was purely instinctive—that is, an inherited habit. In the back end of her kennel she had a little *cache* of bones, and knew exactly where one or two lumps of unsavory meat were buried within the radius of her chain, for a time of famine which never came. If any one approached these hidden treasures she watched with anxious eyes, but made no other demonstration. If she saw that the meddler knew the exact place, she took an early opportunity to secrete them elsewhere.

After a year of this life Tito had grown to full size, and had learned many things that her wild kinsmen could not have learned without losing their lives in doing it. She knew and feared traps. She had learned to avoid poison baits, and knew what to do at once if, by some mistake, she should take one. She knew what guns are. She had learned to cut her morning and evening song very short. She had some acquaintance with Dogs, enough to make her hate and distrust them all. But, above all, she had this idea: whenever danger is near, the very best move possible is to lay low, be very quiet, do nothing to attract notice. Perhaps the little brain that looked out of those changing yellow eyes was the storehouse of much other knowledge about men, but what it was did not appear.

The Coyote was fully grown when the boss of the outfit bought a couple of thoroughbred Greyhounds, wonderful runners, to see whether he could not entirely extirpate the remnant of the Coyotes that still destroyed occasional Sheep and Calves on the range, and at the same time find amusement in the sport. He was tired of seeing that Coyote in the yard; so, deciding to use her for training the Dogs, he had her roughly thrown into a bag, then carried a quarter of a mile away and dumped out. At the same time the Greyhounds were slipped and chivvied on. Away they went bounding at their matchless pace, that nothing else on four legs could equal, and away went the Coyote, frightened by the noise of the men, frightened even to find herself free. Her quarter-mile start quickly shrank to one hundred yards, the one hundred to fifty, and on sped the flying Dogs. Clearly there was no chance for her. On and nearer they came. In another minute she would have been stretched out—not a doubt of it. But on a sudden she stopped, turned, and walked toward the Dogs with her tail serenely waving in the air and a friendly cock to her ears. Greyhounds are peculiar Dogs. Anything that runs away, they are going to catch and kill if they can. Anything that is calmly facing them becomes at once a non-combatant. They bounded over and past the Coyote before they could curb their own impetuosity, and returned completely nonplussed. Possibly they recognized the Coyote of the house-yard as she stood there wagging her tail. The ranchmen were nonplussed too. Every one was utterly taken aback, had a sense of failure, and the real victor in the situation was felt to be the audacious little Coyote.

The Greyhounds refused to attack an animal that wagged its tail and would not run; and the men, on seeing that the Coyote could *walk* far enough away to avoid being caught by hand, took their ropes (lassoes), and soon made her a prisoner once more.

The next day they decided to try again, but this time they added the white Bull-terrier to the chasers. The Coyote did as before. The Greyhounds declined to be party to any attack on such a mild and friendly aquaintance. But the Bull-terrier, who came puffing and panting on the scene three minutes later, had no such scruples. He was not so tall, but he was heavier than the Coyote, and, seizing her by her wool-protected neck, he shook her till, in a surprisingly short time, she lay limp and lifeless, at which all the men seemed pleased, and congratulated the Terrier, while the Greyhounds pottered around in restless perplexity.

A stranger in the party, a newly arrived Englishman, asked if he might have the brush,—the tail, he explained,—and on being told to help himself, he picked up the victim by the tail, and with one awkward chop of his knife he cut it off at the middle, and the Coyote dropped, but gave a shrill yelp of pain. She was not dead, only playing possum, and now she leaped up and vanished into a near-by thicket of cactus and sage.

With Greyhounds a running animal is the signal for a run, so the two long-legged Dogs and the white, broad-chested Dog dashed after the Coyote. But right across their path, by happy chance, there flashed a brown streak ridden by a snowy powder-puff, the visible but evanescent sign for Cottontail Rabbit. The Coyote was not in sight now. The Rabbit was, so the Greyhounds dashed after the Cottontail, who took advantage of a Prairie-dog's hole to seek safety in the bosom of Mother Earth, and the Coyote made good her escape.

She had been a good deal jarred by the rude treatment of the Terrier, and her mutilated tail gave her some pain. But otherwise she was all right, and she loped lightly away, keeping out of sight in the hollows, and so escaped among the fantastic buttes of the Badlands, to be eventually the founder of a new life among the Coyotes of the Little Missouri.

Moses was preserved by the Egyptians till he had outlived the dangerous period, and learned from them wisdom enough to be the savior of his people against those same Egyptians. So the bobtailed Coyote was not only saved by man and carried over the dangerous period of puppyhood: she was also unwittingly taught by him how to baffle the traps, poisons, lassos, guns, and Dogs that had so long waged a war of extermination against her race.

* * *

Thus Tito escaped from man, and for the first time found herself face to face with the whole problem of life; for now she had her own living to get.

A wild animal has three sources of wisdom:

First, *the experience of its ancestors,* in the form of instinct, which is inborn learning, hammered into the race by ages of selection and tribulation. This is the most important to begin with, because it guards him from the moment he is born.

Second, *the experience of his parents and comrades,* learned chiefly by example. This becomes most important as soon as the young can run.

Third, *the personal experience* of the animal itself. This grows in importance as the animal ages.

The weakness of the first is its fixity; it cannot change to meet quickly changing conditions. The weakness of the second is the animal's inability freely to exchange ideas by language. The weakness of the third is the danger in acquiring it. But the three together are a strong arch.

Now, Tito was in a new case. Perhaps never before had a Coyote faced life with unusual advantages in the third kind of knowledge, none at all in the second, and with the first dormant. She travelled rapidly away from the ranchmen, keeping out of sight, and sitting down once in a while to lick her wounded tail-stump. She came at last to a Prairie-dog town. Many of the inhabitants were out, and they barked at the intruder, but all dodged down as soon as she came near. Her instinct taught her to try and catch one, but she ran about in vain for some time, and then gave it up. She would have gone hungry that night but that she found a couple of Mice in the long grass by the river. Her mother had not taught her to hunt, but her instinct did, and the accident that she had an unusual brain made her profit very quickly by her experience.

In the days that followed she quickly learned how to make a living; for Mice, Ground Squirrels, Prairie-dogs, Rabbits, and Lizards were abundant, and many of these could be captured in open chase. But open chase, and sneaking as near as possible before beginning the open chase, lead naturally to stalking for a final spring. And before the moon had changed the Coyote had learned how to make a comfortable living.

Once or twice she saw the men with the Greyhounds coming her way. Most Coyotes would, perhaps, have barked in bravado, or would have gone up to some high place whence they could watch the enemy; but Tito did no such foolish thing. Had she run, her moving form would have caught the eyes of the Dogs, and then nothing could have saved her. She dropped where she was, and lay flat until the danger had passed. Thus her ranch training to lay low began to stand her in good stead, and so it came about that her weakness was her strength. The Coyote kind had so long been famous for their speed, had so long learned to trust in their legs, that they never dreamed of a creature that could run them down. They were accustomed to play with their pursuers, and so rarely bestirred themselves to run from Greyhounds, till it was too late. But Tito, brought up at the end of a chain, was a poor runner. She had no reason to trust her legs. She rather trusted her wits, and so lived.

During that summer she stayed about the Little Missouri, learning the tricks of small-game hunting that she should have learned before she shed her milk-teeth, and gaining in strength and speed. She kept far away from all of the ranches, and always hid on seeing a man or a strange beast, and so passed the summer alone. During the daytime she was not lonely, but when the sun went down she would feel the impulse to sing that wild song of the West which means so much to the Coyotes.

It is not the invention of an individual nor of the present, but was slowly built out of the feelings of all Coyotes in all ages. It expresses their nature and the Plains that made their nature. When one begins it, it takes hold of the rest, as the fife and drum do with soldiers, or the ki-yi war-song with Indian braves. They respond to it as a bell-glass does to a certain note the moment that note is struck, ignoring other sounds. So the Coyote, no matter how brought up, must vibrate at the night song of the Plains, for it touches something in himself.

They sing it after sundown, when it becomes the rallying-cry of their race and the friendly call to a neighbor; and they sing it as one boy in the woods holloas to another to say, "All's well! Here am I. Where are you?" A form of it they sing to the rising moon, for this is the time for good hunting to begin. They sing when they see the new camp-fire, for the same reason that a Dog barks at a stranger. Yet another weird chant they have for the dawning before they steal quietly away from the offing of the camp—a wild, weird, squalling refrain:

Wow-wow-wow-wow-wow-w-o-o-o-o-o-w,

again and again; and doubtless with many another change that man cannot distinguish any more than the Coyote can distinguish the words in the cow-boy's anathemas.

Tito instinctively uttered her music at the proper times. But sad experiences had taught her to cut it short and keep it low. Once or twice she had got a far-away reply from one of her own race, whereupon she had quickly ceased and timidly quit the neighborhood.

One day, when on the Upper Garner's Creek, she found the trail where a piece of meat had been dragged along. It was a singularly inviting odor, and she followed it, partly out of curiosity. Presently she came on a piece of the meat itself. She was hungry; she was always hungry now. It was tempting, and although it had a peculiar odor, she swallowed it. Within a few minutes she felt a terrific pain. The memory of the poisoned meat the boy had given her, was fresh. With trembling, foaming jaws she seized some blades of grass, and her stomach threw off the meat; but she fell in convulsions on the ground.

The trail of meat dragged along and the poison baits had been laid the day before by Wolver Jake. This morning he was riding the drag, and on coming up from the draw he saw, far ahead, the Coyote struggling. He knew, of course, that it was poisoned, and rode quickly up; but the convulsions passed as he neared. By a mighty effort, at the sound of the Horses' hoofs the Coyote arose to her front feet. Jake drew his revolver and fired, but the only effect was fully to alarm her. She tried to run, but her hind legs were paralyzed. She put forth all her strength, dragging her hind legs. Now, when the poison was no longer in the stomach, will-power could do a great deal. Had she been allowed to lie down then she would have been dead in five minutes; but the revolver-shots and the man coming stirred her to strenuous action. Madly she struggled again and again to get her hind legs to work. All the force of desperate intent she brought to bear. It was like putting forth tenfold power to force the nervous fluids through their blocked-up channels as she dragged herself with marvellous speed downhill. What is nerve but will? The dead wires of her legs were hot with this fresh power, multiplied, injected, blasted into them. They had to give in. She felt them thrill with life again. Each wild shot from the gun lent vital help. Another fierce attempt, and one hind leg obeyed the call to duty. A few more bounds, and the other, too, fell in. Then lightly she loped away among the broken buttes, defying the agonizing gripe that still kept on inside.

Had Jake held off then she would yet have laid down and died; but he followed, and fired and fired, till in another mile she bounded free from pain, saved from her enemy by himself. He had compelled her to take the only cure, so she escaped.

And these were the ideas that she harvested that day: That curious smell on the meat stands for mortal agony. Let it alone! And she never forgot it; thenceforth she knew strychnine.

Fortunately, Dogs, traps, and strychnine do not wage war at once, for the Dogs are as apt to be caught or poisoned as the Coyotes. Had there been a single Dog in the hunt that day Tito's history would have ended.

* * *

When the weather grew cooler toward the end of autumn Tito had gone far toward repairing the defects in her early training. She was more like an ordinary Coyote in her habits now, and she was more disposed to sing the sundown song.

One night, when she got a response, she yielded to the impulse again to call, and soon afterwards a large, dark Coyote appeared. The fact that he was there at all was a guarantee of unusual gifts, for the war against his race was raged relentlessly by the cattlemen. He approached with caution. Tito's mane bristled with mixed feelings at the sight of one of her own kind. She crouched flat on the ground and waited. The newcomer came stiffly forward, nosing the wind; then up the wind nearly to her. Then he walked around so that she should wind him, and raising his tail, gently waved it. The first acts meant armed neutrality, but the last was a distinctly friendly signal. Then he approached, and she rose up suddenly and stood as high as she could to be smelled. Then she wagged the stump of her tail, and they considered themselves acquainted.

The newcomer was a very large Coyote, half as tall again as Tito, and the dark patch on his shoulders was so large and black that the cow-boys, when they came to know him, called him Saddleback. From that time these two continued more or less together. They were not always close together, often were miles apart during the day, but toward night one or the other would get on some high, open place and sing the loud

Yap-yap-yap-yow-wow-wow-wow-wow,

They considered themselves acquainted

and they would forgather for some foray on hand.

The physical advantages were with Saddleback, but the greater cunning was Tito's, so that she in time became the leader. Before a month a third Coyote had appeared on the scene and become also a member of this loose-bound fraternity, and later two more appeared. Nothing succeeds like success. The little bob-tailed Coyote had had rare advantages of training just where the others were lacking: she knew the devices of man. She could not tell about these in words, but she could by the aid of a few signs and a great deal of example. It soon became evident that her methods of hunting were successful, whereas, when they went without her, they often had hard luck. A man at Boxelder Ranch had twenty Sheep. The rules of the county did not allow any one to own more, as this was a Cattle-range. The Sheep were guarded by a large and fierce Collie. One day in winter two of the Coyotes tried to raid this flock by a bold dash, and all they got was a mauling from the Collie. A few days later the band returned at dusk. Just how Tito arranged it, man cannot tell. We can only guess how she taught them their parts, but we know that she surely did. The Coyotes hid in the willows. Then Saddleback, the bold and swift, walked openly toward the Sheep and barked a loud defiance. The Collie jumped up with bristling mane and furious growl, then, seeing the foe, dashed straight at him. Now was the time for the steady nerve and the unfailing limbs. Saddleback let the Dog come near enough *almost* to catch him, and so beguiled him far and away into the woods, while the other Coyotes, led by Tito, stampeded the Sheep in twenty directions; then following the farthest, they killed several and left them in the snow.

In the gloom of descending night the Dog and his master labored till they had gathered the bleating survivors; but next morning they found that four had been driven far away and killed, and the Coyotes had had a banquet royal.

The shepherd poisoned the carcasses and left them. Next night the Coyotes returned. Tito sniffed the now frozen meat, detected the poison, gave a warning growl, and scattered filth over the meat, so that none of the band should touch it. One, however, who was fast and foolish, persisted in feeding in spite of Tito's warning, and when they came away he was lying poisoned and dead in the snow.

* * *

Jake now heard on all sides that the Coyotes were getting worse. So he set to work with many traps and much poison to destroy those on the Garner's Creek, and every little while he would go with the Hounds and scour the Little Missouri south and east of the Chimney-pot Ranch; for it was understood that he must never run the Dogs in country where traps and poison were laid. He worked in his erratic way all

winter, and certainly did have some success. He killed a couple of gray Wolves, said to be the last of their race, and several Coyotes, some of which, no doubt, were of the Bobtailed pack, which thereby lost those members which were lacking in wisdom.

Yet that winter was marked by a series of Coyote raids and exploits; and usually the track in the snow or the testimony of eye-witnesses told that the master spirit of it all was a little Bobtailed Coyote.

One of these adventures was the cause of much talk. The Coyote challenge sounded close to the Chimney-pot Ranch after sundown. A dozen Dogs responded with the usual clamor. But only the Bull-terrier dashed away toward the place whence the Coyotes had called, for the reason that he only was loose. His chase was fruitless, and he came back growling. Twenty minutes later there was another Coyote yell close at hand. Off dashed the Terrier as before. In a minute his excited yapping told that he had sighted his game and was in full chase. Away he went, furiously barking, until his voice was lost afar, and nevermore was heard. In the morning the men read in the snow the tale of the night. The first cry of the Coyotes was to find out if all the Dogs were loose; then, having found that only one was free, they laid a plan. Five Coyotes hid along the side of the trail; one went forward and called till it had decoyed the rash Terrier, and then led him right into the ambush. What chance had he with six? They tore him limb from limb, and devoured him, too, at the very spot where once he had worried Coyotito. And next morning, when the men came, they saw by the signs that the whole thing had been planned, and that the leader whose cunning had made it a success was a little Bobtailed Coyote.

The men were angry, and Lincoln was furious; but Jake remarked: "Well, I guess that Bobtail came back and got even with that Terrier."

* * *

When spring was near, the annual love-season of the Coyotes came on. Saddleback and Tito had been together merely as companions all winter, but now a new feeling was born. There was not much courting. Saddleback simply showed his teeth to possible rivals. There was no ceremony. They had been friends for months, and now, in the light of the new feeling, they naturally took to each other and were mated. Coyotes do not give each other names as do mankind, but have one sound like a growl and short howl, which stands for "mate" or "husband" or "wife." This they use in calling to each other, and it is by recognizing the tone of the voice that they know who is calling.

The loose rambling brotherhood of the Coyotes was broken up

Their evening song

now, for the others also paired off, and since the returning warm weather was bringing out the Prairie-dogs and small game, there was less need to combine for hunting. Ordinarily Coyotes do not sleep in dens or in any fixed place. They move about all night while it is cool, then during the daytime they get a few hours' sleep in the sun, on some quiet hillside that also gives a chance to watch out. But the mating season changes this habit somewhat.

As the weather grew warm Tito and Saddleback set about preparing a den for the expected family. In a warm little hollow, an old Badger abode was cleaned out, enlarged, and deepened. A quantity of leaves and grass was carried into it and arranged in a comfortable nest. The place selected for it was a dry, sunny nook among the hills, half a mile west of the Little Missouri. Thirty yards from it was a ridge which commanded a wide view of the grassy slopes and cottonwood groves by the river. Men would have called the spot very beautiful, but it is tolerably certain that that side of it never touched the Coyotes at all.

Tito began to be much preoccupied with her impending duties. She stayed quietly in the neighborhood of the den, and lived on such food as Saddleback brought her, or she herself could easily catch, and also on the little stores that she had buried at other times. She knew every Prairie-dog town in the region, as well as all the best places for Mice and Rabbits.

Not far from the den was the very Dog-town that first she had crossed the day she had gained her liberty and lost her tail. If she were capable of such retrospect, she must have laughed to herself to think what a fool she was then. The change in her methods was now shown. Somewhat removed from the others, a Prairie-dog had made his den in the most approved style, and now when Tito peered over he was feeding on the grass ten yards from his own door. A Prairie-dog away from the others is, of course, easier to catch than one in the middle of the town, for he has but one pair of eyes to guard him; so Tito set about stalking this one. How was she to do it when there was no cover, nothing but short grass and a few low weeds? The Whitebear knows how to approach the Seal on the flat ice, and the Indian how to get within striking distance of the grazing Deer. Tito knew how to do the same trick, and although one of the town Owls flew over with a warning chuckle, Tito set about her plan. A Prairie-dog cannot see well unless he is sitting up on his hind legs; his eyes are of little use when he is nosing in the grass; and Tito knew this. Further, a yellowish-gray animal on a yellowish-gray landscape is invisible till it moves. Tito seemed to know that. So, without any attempt to crawl or hide, she walked gently up-wind toward the Prairie-dog. Up-wind, not in order to prevent the Prairie-dog smelling her, but so that she could smell him, which came to the same thing. As soon as the Prairie-dog sat up with some food in his hand she froze into a statue. As soon as he dropped again to nose in the grass, she walked steadily nearer, watching his every move so that she might be motionless each time he sat up to see what his distant brothers were barking at. Once or twice he seemed alarmed by the calls of his friends, but he saw nothing and resumed his

Fair game

feeding. She soon cut the fifty yards down to ten, and the ten to five, and still was undiscovered. Then, when again the Prairie-dog dropped down to seek more fodder, she made a quick dash, and bore him off kicking and squealing. Thus does the angel of the pruning-knife lop off those that are heedless and foolishly indifferent to the advantages of society.

* * *

Tito had many adventures in which she did not come out so well. Once she nearly caught an Antelope fawn, but the hunt was spoiled by the sudden appearance of the mother, who gave Tito a stinging blow on the side of the head and ended her hunt for that day. She never again made that mistake—she had sense. Once or twice she had to jump to escape the strike of a Rattlesnake. Several times she had been fired at by hunters with long-range rifles. And more and more she had to look out for the terrible Gray Wolves. The Gray Wolf, of course, is much larger and stronger than the Coyote, but the Coyote has the advantage of speed, and can always escape in the open. All it must beware of is being caught in a corner. Usually when a Gray Wolf howls the Coyotes go quietly about their business elsewhere.

Tito had a curious fad, occasionally seen among the Wolves and Coyotes, of carrying in her mouth, for miles, such things as seemed to be interesting and yet were not tempting as eatables. Many a time had she trotted a mile or two with an old Buffalo-horn or a cast-off shoe, only to drop it when something else attracted her attention. The cowboys who remark these things have various odd explanations to offer: one, that it is done to stretch the jaws, or keep them in practice, just as a man in training carries weights. Coyotes have, in common with Dogs and Wolves, the habit of calling at certain stations along their line of travel, to leave a record of their visit. These stations may be a stone, a tree, a post, or an old Buffalo-skull, and the Coyote calling there can learn, by the odor and track of the last comer, just who the caller was, whence he came, and whither he went. The whole country is marked out by these intelligence depots. Now it often happens that a Coyote that has not much else to do will carry a dry bone or some other useless object in its mouth, but sighting the signal-post, will go toward it to get the news, lay down the bone, and afterward forget to take it along, so that the signal-posts in time become further marked with a curious collection of odds and ends.

This singular habit was the cause of a disaster to the Chimney-pot Wolf-hounds, and a corresponding advantage to the Coyotes in the war. Jake had laid a line of poison baits on the western bluffs. Tito knew what they were, and spurned them as usual; but finding more later, she gathered up three or four and crossed the Little Missouri toward the ranch-house. This she circled at a safe distance; but when something made the pack of Dogs break out into clamor, Tito dropped the baits, and next day, when the Dogs were taken out for exercise, they found and devoured these scraps of meat, so that in ten minutes there were four hundred dollars' worth of Greyhounds lying dead. This led to an edict against poisoning in that district, and thus was a great boon to the Coyotes.

Tito quickly learned that not only each kind of game must be hunted in a special way, but different ones of each kind may require quite different treatment. The Prairie-dog with the outlying den was really an easy prey, but the town was quite compact now that he was gone. Near the centre of it was a fine, big, fat Prairie-dog, a perfect alderman, that she had made several vain attempts to capture. On one occasion she had crawled almost within leaping distance, when the angry *bizz* of a Rattlesnake just ahead warned her that she was in danger. Not that the Rattler cared anything about the Prairie-dog, but he did not wish to be disturbed; and Tito, who had an instinctive fear of the Snake, was forced to abandon the hunt. The open stalk proved an utter failure with the Alderman, for the situation of his den made every Dog in the town his sentinel; but he was too good to lose, and Tito waited until circumstances made a new plan.

All Coyotes have a trick of watching from a high lookout whatever passes along the roads. After it has passed they go down and examine its track. Tito had this habit, except that she was always careful to keep out of sight herself.

One day a wagon passed from the town to the southward. Tito lay low and watched it. Something dropped on the road. When the wagon was out of sight Tito sneaked down, first to smell the trail as a matter of habit, second to see what it was that had dropped. The object was really an apple, but Tito saw only an unattractive round green thing like a cactus-leaf without spines, and of a peculiar smell. She snuffed it, spurned it, and was about to pass on; but the sun shone on it so brightly, and it rolled so curiously when she pawed, that she picked it up in a mechanical way and trotted back over the rise, where she found herself at the Dog-town. Just then two great Prairie-hawks came skimming like pirates over the plain. As soon as they were in sight the Prairie-dogs all barked, jerking their tails at each bark, and hid below. When all were gone Tito walked on toward the hole of the big fat fellow whose body she coveted, and dropping the apple on the ground a couple of feet from the rim of the crater that formed his home, she put her nose down to enjoy the delicious smell of Dog-fat. Even his den smelled more fragrant than those of the rest. Then she went quietly behind a greasewood-bush, in a lower place some twenty yards away, and lay flat. After a few seconds some venturesome Prairie-dog looked out, and seeing nothing, gave the "all's well" bark. One by one they came out, and in twenty minutes the town was alive as before. One of the last to come out was the fat old Alderman. He always took good care of his own precious self. He peered out cautiously a few times, then climbed to the top of his lookout. A Prairie-dog hole is shaped like a funnel, going straight down. Around the top of this is built a high ridge which serves as a lookout, and also makes sure that, no matter how they may slip in their hurry, they are certain to drop into the funnel and be swallowed up by the all-protecting earth. On the outside the ground slopes away gently from the funnel. Now, when the

Alderman saw that strange round thing at his threshold he was afriad. Second inspection led him to believe that it was not dangerous, but was probably interesting. He went cautiously toward it, smelled it, and tried to nibble it; but the apple rolled away, for it was round, and the ground was smooth as well as sloping. The Prairie-dog followed and gave it a nip which satisfied him that the strange object would make good eating. But each time he nibbled, it rolled farther away. The coast seemed clear, all the other Prairie-dogs were out, so the fat Alderman did not hesitate to follow up the dodging, shifting apple.

This way and that it wriggled, and he followed. Of course it worked toward the low place where grew the greasewood-bush. The little tastes of apple that he got only whetted his appetite. The Alderman saw that strange round thing at his threshold he was afraid. his hole toward that old, familiar bush, and had no thought of anything but the joy of eating. And Tito curled herself and braced her sinewy legs, and measured the distance between, until it dwindled to not more than three good jumps; then up and like an arrow she went, and grabbed and bore him off at last.

Now it will never be known whether it was accident or design that led to the placing of that apple, but it proved important, and if such a thing were to happen once or twice to a smart Coyote,—and it is usually clever ones that get such chances,—it might easily grow into a new trick of hunting.

After a hearty meal Tito buried the rest in a cold place, not to get rid of it, but to hide it for future use; and a little later, when she was too weak to hunt much, her various hoards of this sort came in very useful.

The Alderman and the apple

True, the meat had turned very strong; but Tito was not critical, and she had no fears of theories of microbes, so suffered no ill effects.

* * *

The lovely Hiawathan spring was touching all things in the fairy Badlands. Oh, why are they called Badlands? If Nature sat down deliberately on the eighth day of creation and said, "Now work is done, let's play; let's make a place that shall combine everything that is finished and wonderful and beautiful—a paradise for man and bird and beast," it was surely then that she made these wild, fantastic hills, teeming with life, radiant with gayest flowers, varied with sylvan groves, bright with prairie sweeps and brimming lakes and streams. In foreground, offing, and distant hills that change at every step, we find some proof that Nature squandered here the riches that in other lands she used as sparingly as gold, with colorful sky above and colorful land below, and the distance blocked by sculptured buttes that are built of precious stones and ores, and tinged as by a lasting and unspeakable sunset. And yet, for all this ten times gorgeous wonderland enchanted, blind man has found no better name than one which says, *the road to it is hard.*

The little hollow west of Chimney Butte was freshly grassed. The dangerous-looking Spanish bayonets, that through the bygone winter had waged war with all things, now sent out their contribution to the peaceful triumph of the spring, in flowers that have stirred even the chilly scientists to name then *Gloriosa*; and the cactus, poisonous, most reptilian of herbs, surprised the world with a splendid bloom as little like itself as the pearl is like its mother shell-fish. The sage and the greasewood lent their gold, and the sand-anemone tinged the Badland hills like bluish snow; and in the air and earth and hills on every hand was felt the fecund promise of the spring. This was the end of the winter famine, the beginning of the summer feast, and this was the time by the All-mother ordained when first the little Coyotes should see the light of day.

A mother does not have to learn to love her helpless, squirming brood. They bring the love with them—not much or little, not measurable, but perfect love. And in that dimly lighted warm abode she fondled them and licked them and cuddled them with heartful warmth of tenderness that was as much a new epoch in her life as in theirs.

But the pleasure of loving them was measured in the same measure as anxiety for their safety. In bygone days her care had been mainly for herself. All she had learned in her strange puppyhood, all she had picked up since, was bent to the main idea of self-preservation. Now she was ousted from her own affections by her brood. Her chief care was to keep their home concealed, and this was not very hard at first, for she left them only when she must, to supply her own wants.

She came and went with great care, and only after spying well the land so that none should see and find the place of her treasure. If it were possible for the little ones' idea of their mother and the cow-boys' idea to be set side by side they would be found to have nothing in common, though both were right in their point of view. The ranchmen knew the Coyote only as a pair of despicable, cruel jaws, borne around on tireless legs, steered by incredible cunning, and leaving behind a track of destruction. The little ones knew her as a loving, gentle, all-powerful guardian. For them her breast was soft and warm and infinitely tender. She fed and warmed them, she was their wise and watchful keeper. She was always at hand with food when they hungered, with wisdom to foil the cunning of their foes, and with a heart of courage tried to crown her well-laid plans for them with uniform success.

A baby Coyote is a shapeless, senseless, wriggling, and—to every one but its mother—a most uninteresting little lump. But after its eyes are open, after it has developed its legs, after it has learned to play in the sun with its brothers, or run at the gentle call of its mother when she brings home game for it to feed on, the baby Coyote becomes one of the cutest, dearest little rascals on earth. And when the nine that made up Coyotito's brood had reached this stage, it did not require the glamour of motherhood to make them objects of the greatest interest.

The summer was now on. The little ones were beginning to eat flesh-meat, and Tito, with some assistance from Saddleback, was kept busy to supply both themselves and the brood. Sometimes she brought them a Prairie-dog, at other times she would come home with a whole bunch of Gophers and Mice in her jaws; and once or twice, by the clever trick of relay-chasing, she succeeded in getting one of the big Northern Jack-rabbits for the little folks at home.

After they had feasted they would lie around in the sun for a time. Tito would mount guard on a bank and scan the earth and air with her keen, brassy eye, lest any dangerous foe should find their happy valley; and the merry pups played little games of tag, or chased the Butterflies, or had apparently desperate encounters with each other, or tore and worried the bones and feathers that now lay about the threshold of the home. One, the least, for there is usually a runt, stayed near the mother and climbed on her back or pulled at her tail. They made a lovely picture as they played, and the wrestling group in the middle seemed the focus of it all at first; but a keener, later look would have rested on

Tito and her brood

the mother, quiet, watchful, not without anxiety, but, above all, with a
face full of motherly tenderness. Oh, she was so proud and happy, and
she would sit there and watch them and silently love them till it was
time to go home, or until some sign of distant danger showed. Then,
with a low growl, she gave the signal, and all disappeared from sight in
a twinkling, after which she would set off to meet and turn the danger,
or go on a fresh hunt for food.

* * *

Wolver Jake had several plans for making a fortune, but each in turn was abandoned as soon as he found that it meant work. At one time or other most men of this kind see the chance of their lives in a poultry-farm. They cherish the idea that somehow the poultry do all the work. And without troubling himself about the details, Jake devoted an unexpected windfall to the purchase of a dozen Turkeys for his latest scheme. The Turkeys were duly housed in one end of Jake's shanty, so as to be well guarded, and for a couple of days were the object of absorbing interest, and had the best of care—too much, really. But Jake's ardor waned about the third day; then the recurrent necessity for long celebrations at Medora, and the ancient allurements of idle hours spent lying on the tops of sunny buttes and of days spent sponging on the hospitality of distant ranches, swept away the last pretense of attention to his poultry-farm. The Turkeys were utterly neglected—left to forage for themselves; and each time that Jake returned to his uninviting shanty, after a few days' absence, he found fewer birds, till at last none but the old Gobbler was left.

Jake cared little about the loss, but was filled with indignation against the thief.

He was now installed as wolver to the Broad-arrow outfit. That is, he was supplied with poison, traps, and Horses, and was also entitled to all he could make out of Wolf bounties. A reliable man would have gotten pay in addition, for the ranchmen are generous, but Jake was not reliable.

Every wolver knows, of course, that his business naturally drops into several well-marked periods.

In the late winter and early spring—the love-season—the Hounds will not hunt a She-wolf. They will quit the trail of a He-wolf at this time to take up that of a She-wolf, but when they do overtake her, they, for some sentimental reason, invariably let her go in peace. In August and September the young Coyotes and Wolves are just beginning to run alone, and they are then easily trapped and poisoned. A month or so later the survivors have learned how to take care of themselves, but in the early summer the wolver knows that there are dens full of little ones all through the hills. Each den has from five to fifteen pups, and the only difficulty is to know the whereabouts of these family homes.

One way of finding the dens is to watch from some tall butte for a Coyote carrying food to its brood. As this kind of wolving involved much lying still, it suited Jake very well. So, equipped with a Broad-arrow Horse and the boss's field-glasses, he put in week after week at den-hunting—that is, lying asleep in some possible lookout, with an occasional glance over the country when it seemed easier to do that than to lie still.

The Coyotes had learned to avoid the open. They generally went homeward along the sheltered hollows; but this was not always possible, and one day, while exercising his arduous profession in the country west of Chimney Butte, Jake's glasses and glance fell by chance on a dark spot which moved along an open hillside. It was gray, and it looked like this: and even Jake knew that that meant Coyote. If it had been a gray Wolf it would have been so: with tail up. A Fox would have looked so: the large ears and tail and the yellow color would have marked it. And a Deer would have looked so: That dark shade from the front end meant something in his mouth,—probably something being carried home,—and that would mean a den of little ones.

He made careful note of the place, and returned there next day to watch, selecting a high butte near where he had seen the Coyote carrying the food. But all day passed, and he saw nothing. Next day, however, he descried a dark Coyote, old Saddleback, carrying a large Bird, and by the help of the glasses he made out that it was a Turkey, and then he knew that the yard at home was quite empty, and he also knew where the rest of them had gone, and vowed terrible vengeance when he should find the den. He followed Saddleback with his eyes as far as possible, and that was no great way, then went to the place to see if he could track him any farther; but he found no guiding signs, and he did not chance on the little hollow that was the playground of Tito's brood.

Meanwhile Saddleback came to the little hollow and gave the low call that always conjured from the earth the unruly procession of the nine riotous little pups, and they dashed at the Turkey and pulled and worried till it was torn up, and each that got a piece ran to one side alone and silently proceeded to eat, seizing his portion in his jaws when another came near, and growling his tiny growl as he showed the brownish whites of his eyes in his effort to watch the intruder. Those that got the softer parts to feed on were well fed. But the three that did not turned all their energies on the frame of the Gobbler, and over that there waged a battle royal. This way and that they tugged and tussled, getting off occasional scraps, but really hindering each other feeding, till Tito glided in and deftly cut the Turkey into three or four, when each dashed off with a prize, over which he sat and chewed and smacked his lips and jammed his head down sideways to bring the backmost teeth to bear, while the baby runt scrambled into the home den, carrying in triumph his share—the Gobbler's grotesque head and neck.

* * *

Jake felt that he had been grievously wronged, indeed ruined, by that Coyote that stole his Turkeys. He vowed he would skin them alive when he found the pups, and took pleasure in thinking about how he would do it. His attempt to follow Saddleback by trailing was a failure, and all his searching for the den was useless, but he had come prepared for any emergency. In case he found the den he had brought a pick and shovel; in case he did not he had brought a living white Hen.

The Hen he now took to a broad open place near where he had seen Saddleback, and there he tethered her to a stick of wood that she could barely drag. Then he made himself comfortable on a lookout that was near, and lay still to watch. The Hen, of course, ran to the end of the string, and then lay on the ground flopping stupidly. Presently the clog gave enough to ease the strain, she turned by mere chance in another direction, and so, for a time, stood up to look around.

The day went slowly by, and Jake lazily stretched himself on the blanket in his spying-place. Toward evening Tito came by on a hunt. This was not surprising, for the den was only half a mile away. Tito had learned, among other rules, this, "Never show yourself on the sky-line," In former days the Coyotes used to trot along the tops of the ridges for the sake of the chance to watch both sides. But men and guns had taught Tito that in this way you are sure to be seen. She therefore made a practice of running along near the top, and once in a while peeping over.

This was what she did that evening as she went out to hunt for the children's supper, and her keen eyes fell on the white Hen, stupidly stalking about and turning up its eyes in a wise way each time a harmless Turkey-buzzard came in sight against a huge white cloud.

Tito was puzzled. This was something new. It *looked* like game, but she feared to take any chances. She circled all around without showing herself, then decided that, whatever it might be, it was better let alone. As she passed on, a faint whiff of smoke caught her attention. She followed cautiously, and under a butte far from the Hen she found Jake's camp. His bed was there, his Horse was picketed, and on the remains of the fire was a pot which gave out a smell which she well knew about men's camps—the smell of coffee. Tito felt uneasy at this proof that a man was staying so near her home, but she went off quietly on her hunt, keeping out of sight, and Jake knew nothing of her visit.

About sundown he took in his decoy Hen, as Owls were abundant, and went back to his camp.

* * *

Next day the Hen was again put out, and late that afternoon Saddleback came trotting by. As soon as his eye fell on the white Hen he stopped short, his head on one side, and gazed. Then he circled to get the wind, and went cautiously sneaking nearer, very cautiously, somewhat puzzled, till he got a whiff that reminded him of the place where he had found those Turkeys. The Hen took alarm, and tried to run away; but Saddleback made a rush, seized the Hen so fiercely that the string was broken, and away he dashed toward the home valley.

Jake had fallen asleep, but the squawk of the Hen happened to awaken him, and he sat up in time to see her borne away in old Saddleback's jaws.

As soon as they were out of sight Jake took up the white-feather trail. At first it was easily followed, for the Hen had shed plenty of plumes in her struggles, but once she was dead in Saddleback's jaws,

very few feathers were dropped except where she was carried through
the brush. But Jake was following quietly and certainly, for Saddleback
had gone nearly in a straight line home to the little ones with the
dangerous telltale prize. Once or twice there was a puzzling delay
when the Coyote had changed his course or gone over an open place;
but one white feather was good for fifty yards, and when the daylight
was gone, Jack was not two hundred yards from the hollow, in which at
that very moment were the nine little pups, having a perfectly delightful time with the Hen, pulling it to pieces, feasting and growling, sneez-
ing the white feathers from their noses or coughing them from their
throats.

If a puff of wind had now blown from them toward Jake, it might
have carried a flurry of snowy plumes or even the merry cries of the
little revellers, and the den would have been discovered at once. But, as
luck would have it, the evening lull was on, and all distant sounds were
hidden by the crashing that Jake made in trying to trace his feather
guides through the last thicket.

About this time Tito was returning home with a Magpie that she
had captured by watching till it went to feed within the ribs of a dead
Horse, when she ran across Jake's trail. Now, a man on foot is always a
suspicious character in this country. She followed the trail for a little to
see where he was going, and that she knew at once from the scent.
How it tells her no one can say, yet all hunters know that it does. And
Tito marked that it was going straight toward her home. Thrilled with
new fear, she hid the Bird she was carrying, then followed the trail of
the man. Within a few minutes she could hear him in the thicket, and
Tito realized the terrible danger that was threatening. She went swiftly,
quietly around to the den hollow, came on the heedless little roisterers,
after giving the signal-call, which prevented them taking alarm at her
approach; but she must have had a shock when she saw how marked
the hollow and the den were now, all drifted over with feathers white
as snow. Then she gave the danger-call that sent them all to earth, and
the little glade was still.

Her own nose was so thoroughly and always her guide that it was
not likely she thought of the white feathers being the telltale. But now
she realized that a man, one she knew of old as a treacherous character,
one whose scent had always meant mischief to her, that had been
associated with all her own troubles and the cause of nearly all her
desperate danger, was close to her darlings; was tracking them down;
in a few minutes would surely have them in his merciless power.

Oh, the wrench to the mother's heart at the thought of what she
could foresee! But the warmth of the mother-love lent life to the
mother-wit. Having sent the little ones out of sight, and by a sign
conveyed to Saddleback her alarm, she swiftly came back to the man,
then she crossed before him, thinking, in her half-reasoning way, that
the man *must* be following a foot-scent just as she herself would do, but
would, of course, take the stronger line of tracks she was now laying.
She did not realize that the failing daylight made any difference. Then
she trotted to one side, and to make doubly sure of being followed, she

uttered the fiercest challenge she could, just as many a time she had done to make the Dogs pursue her:

Grrr-wow-wow-wa-a-a-h,

and stood still; then ran a little nearer and did it again, and then again much nearer, and repeated her bark, she was so determined that the wolver should follow her.

Of course the wolver could see nothing of the Coyote, for the shades were falling. He had to give up the hunt anyway. His understanding of the details was as different as possible from that the Mother Coyote had, and yet it came to the same thing. He recognized that the Coyote's bark was the voice of the distressed mother trying to call him away. So he knew the brood must be close at hand, and all he now had to do was return in the morning and complete his search. So he made his way back to his camp.

* * *

Saddleback thought they had won the victory. He felt secure, because the foot-scent that he might have supposed the man to be following would be stale by morning. Tito did not feel so safe. That two-legged beast was close to her home and her little ones; had barely been turned aside; might come back yet.

The wolver watered and repicketed his Horse, kindled the fire anew, made his coffee and ate his evening meal, then smoked awhile before lying down to sleep, thinking occasionally of the little woolly scalps he expected to gather in the morning.

He was about to roll up in his blanket when, out of the dark distance, there sounded the evening cry of the Coyote, the rolling challenge of more than one voice. Jake grinned in fiendish glee, and said: "There you are all right. Howl some more. I'll see you in the morning."

It was the ordinary, or rather *one* of the ordinary, camp-calls of the Coyote. It was sounded once, and then all was still. Jake soon forgot it in his loggish slumber.

The callers were Tito and Saddleback. The challenge was not an empty bluff. It had a distinct purpose behind it—to know for sure whether the enemy had any dogs with him; and because there was no responsive bark Tito knew that he had none.

Then Tito waited for an hour or so till the flickering fire had gone dead, and the only sound of life about the camp was the cropping of the grass by the picketed Horse. Tito crept near softly, so softly that the Horse did not see her till she was within twenty feet; then he gave a start that swung the tightened picket-rope up into the air, and snorted gently. Tito went quietly forward, and opening her wide gape, took the rope in, almost under her ears, between the great scissor-like back teeth, then chewed it for a few seconds. The fibres quickly frayed, and,

aided by the strain the nervous Horse still kept up, the last of the strands gave way, and the Horse was free. He was not much alarmed; he knew the smell of Coyote; and after jumping three steps and walking six, he stopped.

The sounding thumps of his hoofs on the ground awoke the sleeper. He looked up, but, seeing the Horse standing there, he went calmly off to sleep again, supposing that all went well.

Tito had sneaked away, but she now returned like a shadow, avoided the sleeper, but came around, sniffed doubtfully at the coffee, and then puzzled over a tin can, while Saddleback examined the frying-pan full of "camp-sinkers" and then defiled both cakes and pan with dirt. The bridle hung on a low bush; the Coyotes did not know what it was, but just for luck they cut it into several pieces, then, taking the sacks that held Jake's bacon and flour, they carried them far away and buried them in the sand.

Having done all the mischief she could, Tito, followed by her mate, now set off for a wooded gully some miles away, where was a hole that had been made first by a Chipmunk, but enlarged by several other animals, including a Fox that had tried to dig out its occupants. Tito stopped and looked at many possible places before she settled on this. Then she set to work to dig. Saddleback had followed in a half-comprehending way, till he saw what she was doing. Then when she, tired with digging, came out, he went into the hole, and after snuffing about went on with the work, throwing out the earth between his hind legs; and when it was piled up behind he would come out and push it yet farther away.

And so they worked for hours, not a word said, and yet with a sufficient comprehension of the object in view to work in relief of each other. And by the time the morning came they had a den big enough to do for their home, in case they must move, though it would not compare with the one in the grassy hollow.

* * *

It was nearly sunrise before the wolver awoke. With the true instinct of a plainsman he turned to look for the Horse. *It was gone*. What his ship is to the sailor, what wings are to the Bird, what money is to the merchant, the Horse is to the plainsman. Without it he is helpless, lost at sea, wing broken, crippled in business. Afoot on the plains is the sum of earthly terrors. Even Jake realized this, and ere his foggy wits had fully felt the shock he sighted the steed afar on a flat, grazing and stepping even farther from the camp. At a second glance Jake noticed that the Horse was trailing the rope. If the rope had been left behind Jake would have known that it was hopeless to try to catch him; he would have finished his den-hunt and found the little Coyotes. But with the trailing rope, there was a good chance of catching the Horse; so Jake set out to try.

Of all maddening things there is nothing worse than to be almost, but not quite, able to catch your Horse. Do what he might, Jake could not get quite near enough to seize that short rope, and the Horse led him on and on, until at last they were well on the homeward trail.

Now Jake was afoot anyhow, so seeing no better plan, he set out to follow that Horse right back to the Ranch.

But when about seven miles were covered Jake succeeded in catching him. He rigged up a rough *jáquima* with the rope and rode barebacked in fifteen minutes over the three miles that lay between him and the Sheep-ranch, giving vent all the way to his pent-up feelings in cruel abuse of that Horse. Of course it did not do any good, and he knew that, but he considered it was heaps of satisfaction.

Here Jake got a meal and borrowed a saddle and a mongrel Hound that could run a trail, and returned late in the afternoon to finish his den-hunt. Had he known it, he now could have found it without the aid of the cur, for it was really close at hand when he took up the feather-trail where last he had left it. Within one hundred yards he rose to the top of the little ridge; then just over it, almost face to face, he came on a Coyote, carrying in its mouth a large Rabbit. The Coyote leaped just at the same moment that Jake fired his revolver, and the Dog broke into a fierce yelling and dashed off in pursuit, while Jake blazed and blazed away, without effect, and wondered why the Coyote should still hang on to that Rabbit as she ran for her life with the Dog yelling at her heels. Jake followed as far as he could and fired at each chance, but scored no hit. So when they had vanished among the buttes he left the Dog to follow or come back as he pleased, while he returned to the den, which, of course, was plain enough now. Jake knew that the pups were there yet. Had he not seen the mother bringing a Rabbit for them?

So he set to work with pick and shovel all the rest of that day. There were plenty of signs that the den had inhabitants, and, duly encouraged, he dug on, and after several hours of the hardest work he had ever done, he came to the end of the den—*only to find it empty.* After cursing his luck at the first shock of disgust, he put on his strong leather glove and groped about in the nest. He felt something firm and drew it out. It was the head and neck of his own Turkey Gobbler, and that was all he got for his pains.

* * *

Tito had not been idle during the time that the enemy was Horse-hunting. Whatever Saddleback might have done, Tito would live in no fool's paradise. Having finished the new den, she trotted back to the little valley of feathers, and the first young one that came to meet her at the door of this home was a broad-headed one much like herself. She seized him by the neck and set off, carrying him across country toward the new den, a couple of miles away. Every little while she had to put her offspring down to rest and give it a chance to breathe. This made the moving slow, and the labor of transporting the pups occupied all that day, for Saddleback was not allowed to carry any of them, probably because he was too rough.

Beginning with the biggest and brightest, they were carried away one at a time, and late in the afternoon only the runt was left. Tito had not only worked at digging all night, she had also trotted over thirty miles, half of it with a heavy baby to carry. But she did not rest. She was just coming out of the den, carrying her youngest in her mouth, when over the very edge of this hollow appeared the mongrel Hound, and a little behind him Wolver Jake

Away went Tito, holding the baby tight, and away went the Dog behind her.

Bang! bang! bang! said the revolver.

But not a shot touched her. Then over the ridge they dashed, where the revolver could not reach her, and sped across a flat, the tired Coyote and her baby, and the big fierce Hound behind her, bounding his hardest. Had she been fresh and unweighted she could soon have left the clumsy cur that now was barking furiously on her track and rather gaining than losing in the race. But she put forth all her strength, careered along a slope, where she gained a little, then down across a brushy flat where the cruel bushes robbed her of all she had gained. But again into the open they came, and the wolver, laboring far behind, got sight of them and fired again and again with his revolver, and only stirred the dust, but still it made her dodge and lose time, and it also spurred the Dog. The hunter saw the Coyote, his old acquaintance of the bobtail, carrying still, as he thought, the Jack-rabbit she had been bringing to her brood, and wondered at her strange persistence. "Why doesn't she drop that weight when flying for her life?" But on she went and gamely bore her load over the hills, the man cursing his luck that he had not brought his Horse, and the mongrel bounding in deadly earnest but thirty feet behind her. Then suddenly in front of Tito yawned a little cut-bank gully. Tired and weighted, she dared not try the leap; she skirted around. But the Dog was fresh; he cleared it easily, and the mother's start was cut down by half. But on she went, straining to hold the little one high above the scratching brush and the dangerous bayonet-spikes; but straining too much, for the helpless cub was choking in his mother's grip. She must lay him down or strangle him; with such a weight she could not much longer keep out of reach. She tried to give the howl for help, but her voice was muffled by the

Tito's race for life

cub, now struggling for breath, and as she tried to ease her grip on him
a sudden wrench jerked him from her mouth into the grass—into the
power of the merciless Hound. Tito was far smaller than the Dog;
ordinarily she would have held him in fear; but her little one, her baby,
was the only thought now, and as the brute sprang forward to tear it in
his wicked jaws, she leaped between and stood facing him with all her
mane erect, her teeth exposed, and plainly showed her resolve to save
her young one at any price. The Dog was not brave, only confident that
he was bigger and had the man behind him. But the man was far away,
and balked in his first rush at the trembling little Coyote, that tried to
hide in the grass, the cur hesitated a moment, and Tito howled the long

howl for help—the muster-call:

Yap-yap-yap-yah-yah-yah-h-h-h-h
Yap-yap-yap-yah-yah-yah-h-h-h-h,

and made the buttes around reëcho so that Jake could not tell where it came from; but some one else there was that heard and did know whence it came. The Dog's courage revived on hearing something like a far-away shout. Again he sprang at the little one, but again the mother balked him with her own body, and then they closed in deadly struggle. "Oh, if Saddleback would only come!" But no one came, and now she had no further chance to call. Weight is everything in a closing fight, and Tito soon went down, bravely fighting to the last, but clearly worsted; and the Hound's courage grew with the sight of victory, and all he thought of now was to finish her and then kill her helpless baby in its turn. He had no ears or eyes for any other thing, till out of the nearest sage there flashed a streak of gray, and in a trice the big-voiced coward was hurled back by a foe almost as heavy as himself—hurled back with a crippled shoulder. Dash, chop, and stanch old Saddleback sprang on him again. Tito struggled to her feet, and they closed on him together. His courage fled at once when he saw the odds, and all he wanted now was safe escape—escape from Saddleback, whose speed was like the wind, escape from Tito, whose baby's life was at stake. Not twenty jumps away did he get; not breath enough had he to howl for help to his master in the distant hills; not fifteen yards away from her little one that he meant to tear, they tore him all to bits.

And Tito lifted the rescued young one, and travelling as slowly as she wished, they reached the new-made den. There the family safely reunited, far away from danger of further attack by Wolver Jake or his kind.

And there they lived in peace till their mother had finished their training, and every one of them grew up wise in the ancient learning of the plains, wise in the later wisdom that the ranchers' war has forced upon them, and not only they, but their children's children, too.

The Buffalo herds have gone; they have succumbed to the rifles of the hunters. The Antelope droves are nearly gone; Hound and lead were too much for them. The Blacktail bands have dwindled before axe and fence. The ancient dwellers of the Badlands have faded like snow under the new conditions, but the Coyotes are no more in fear of extinction. Their morning and evening song still sounds from the level buttes, as it did long years ago when every plain was a teeming land of game. They have learned the deadly secrets of traps and poisons, they know how to baffle the gunner and Hound, they have matched their wits with the hunter's wits. They have learned how to prosper in a land of man-made plenty, in spite of the worst that man can do, and it was Tito that taught them how.

WHY THE CHICKADEE GOES CRAZY ONCE A YEAR

Along time ago, when there was no winter in the north, the Chickadees lived merrily in the woods with their relatives, and cared for nothing but to get all the pleasure possible out of their daily life in the thickets. But at length Mother Carey sent them all a warning that they must move to the south, for hard frost and snow were coming on their domains, with starvation close behind.

The Nuthatches and other cousins of the Chickadees took this warning seriously, and set about learning how and when to go; but Tomtit, who led his brothers, only laughed and turned a dozen wheels around a twig that served him for a trapeze.

"Go to the south?" said he. "Not I; I am too well contented here; and as for frost and snow, I never saw any and have no faith in them."

But the Nuthatches and Kinglets were in such a state of bustle that at length the Chickadees did catch a little of the excitement, and left off play for a while to question their friends; and they were not pleased with what they learned, for it seemed that all of them were to make a journey that would last many days, and the little Kinglets were actually going as far as the Gulf of Mexico. Besides, they were to fly by night in order to avoid their enemies the Hawks, and the weather at this season was sure to be stormy. So the Chickadees said it was all nonsense, and went off in a band, singing and chasing one another through the woods.

253

But their cousins were in earnest. They bustled about making their preparations, and learned beforehand what it was necessary for them to know about the way. The great wide river running southward, the moon at height, and the trumpeting of the Geese were to be their guides, and they were to sing as they flew in the darkness, to keep from being scattered.

The noisy, rollicking Chickadees were noisier than ever as the preparations went on, and made sport of their relatives, who were now gathered in great numbers in the woods along the river; and at length, when the proper time of the moon came, the cousins arose in a body and flew away in the gloom. The Chickadees said that the cousins all were crazy, made some good jokes about the Gulf of Mexico, and then dashed away in a game of tag through the woods, which, by the by, seemed rather deserted now, while the weather, too, was certainly turning remarkably cool.

At length the frost and snow really did come, and the Chickadees were in a woful case. Indeed, they were frightened out of their wits, and dashed hither and thither, seeking in vain for some one to set them aright on the way to the south. They flew wildly about the woods, till they were truly crazy. I suppose there was not a Squirrel-hole or a hollow log in the neighborhood that some Chickadee did not enter to inquire if this was the Gulf of Mexico. But no one could tell anything about it, no one was going that way, and the great river was hidden under ice and snow.

About this time a messenger from Mother Carey was passing with a message to the Caribou in the far north; but all he could tell the Chickadees was that *he* could not be their guide, as he had no instructions, and, at any rate, he was going the other way. Besides, he told them they had had the same notice as their cousins whom they had called "crazy"; and from what he knew of Mother Carey, they would probably have to brave it out here all through the snow, not only now, but in all following winters; so they might as well make the best of it.

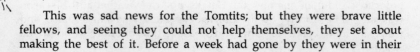

This was sad news for the Tomtits; but they were brave little fellows, and seeing they could not help themselves, they set about making the best of it. Before a week had gone by they were in their usual good spirits again, scrambling about the twigs or chasing one another as before. They had still the assurance that winter would end. So filled were they with this idea that even at its commencement, when a fresh blizzard came on, they would gleefully remark to one another that it was a "sign of spring," and one or another of the band would lift his voice in the sweet little chant that we all know so well:

another would take it up and reëcho:

and they would answer and repeat the song until the dreary woods rang again with the good news, and people learned to love the brave little Bird that sets his face so cheerfully to meet so hard a case.

But to this day, when the chill wind blows through the deserted woods, the Chickadees seem to lose their wits for a few days, and dart into all sorts of odd and dangerous places. They may then be found in great cities, or open prairies, cellars, chimneys, and hollow logs; and the next time you find one of the wanderers in any such place, be sure to remember that Tomtit goes crazy once a year, and probably went into his strange retreat in search of the Gulf of Mexico.

ANIMAL HEROES

CONTENTS

THE SLUM CAT

LIFE I

"M-e-a-t! M-e-a-t!" came shrilling down Scrimper's Alley. Surely the Pied Piper of Hamelin was there, for it seemed that all the Cats in the neighborhood were running toward the sound, though the Dogs, it must be confessed, looked scornfully indifferent.

"Meat! Meat!" and louder; then the centre of attraction came in view—a rough, dirty little man with a push-cart; while straggling behind him were a score of Cats that joined in his cry with a sound nearly the same as his own. Every fifty yards, that is, as soon as a goodly throng of Cats was gathered, the push-cart stopped. The man with the magic voice took out of the box in his cart a skewer on which were pieces of strong-smelling boiled liver. With a long stick he pushed the pieces off. Each Cat seized on one, and wheeling, with a slight depression of the ears and a little tiger growl and glare, she rushed away with her prize to devour it in some safe retreat.

"Meat! Meat!" And still they came to get their portions. All were well known to the meat-man. There was Castiglione's Tiger; this was Jones's Black; here was Pralitsky's "Torkershell," and this was Madame Danton's White; there sneaked Blenkinshoff's Maltee, and that climbing on the barrow was Sawyer's old Orange Billy, an impudent fraud that never had had any financial backing,—all to be remembered and kept in account. This one's owner was sure pay, a dime a week; that one's doubtful. There was John Washee's Cat, that got only a small piece

because John was in arrears. Then there was the saloon-keeper's collared and ribboned ratter, which got an extra lump because the 'barkeep' was liberal; and the roundsman's Cat, that brought no cash, but got unusual consideration because the meat-man did. But there were others. A black Cat with a white nose came rushing confidently with the rest, only to be repulsed savagely. Alas! Pussy did not understand. She had been a pensioner of the barrow for months. Why this unkind change? It was beyond her comprehension. But the meat-man knew. Her mistress had stopped payment. The meat-man kept no books but his memory, and it never was at fault.

Outside this patrician 'four hundred' about the barrow, were other Cats, keeping away from the push-cart because they were not on the list, the Social Register as it were, yet fascinated by the heavenly smell and the faint possibility of accidental good luck. Among these hangers-on was a thin gray Slummer, a homeless Cat that lived by her wits—slab-sided and not over-clean. One could see at a glance that she was doing her duty by a family in some out-of-the-way corner. She kept one eye on the barrow circle and the other on the possible Dogs. She saw a score of happy Cats slink off with their delicious 'daily' and their tiger-like air, but no opening for her, till a big Tom of her own class sprang on a little pensioner with intent to rob. The victim dropped the meat to defend herself against the enemy, and before the 'all-powerful' could intervene, the gray Slummer saw her chance, seized the prize, and was gone.

She went through the hole in Menzie's side door and over the wall at the back, then sat down and devoured the lump of liver, licked her chops, felt absolutely happy, and set out by devious ways to the rubbish-yard, where, in the bottom of an old cracker-box, her family was awaiting her. A plaintive mewing reached her ears. She went at speed and reached the box to see a huge Black Tom-cat calmly destroying her brood. He was twice as big as she, but she went at him with all her strength, and he did as most animals will do when caught wrong-doing, he turned and ran away. Only one was left, a little thing like its mother, but of more pronounced color—gray with black spots, and a white touch on nose, ears, and tail-tip. There can be no question of the mother's grief for a few days; but that wore off, and all her care was for the survivor. That benevolence was as far as possible from the motives of the murderous old Tom there can be no doubt; but he proved a blessing in deep disguise, for both mother and Kit were visibly bettered in a short time. The daily quest for food continued. The meat-man rarely proved a success, but the ash-cans were there, and if they did not afford a meat-supply, at least they were sure to produce potato-skins that could be used to allay the gripe of hunger for another day.

One night the mother Cat smelt a wonderful smell that came from the East River at the end of the alley. A new smell always needs investigating, and when it is attractive as well as new, there is but one course open. It led Pussy to the docks a block away, and then out on a wharf, away from any cover but the night. A sudden noise, a growl and a rush, were the first notice she had that she was cut off by her old enemy, the Wharf Dog. There was only one escape. She leaped from the wharf to the vessel from which the smell came. The Dog could not follow, so when the fish-boat sailed in the morning Pussy unwillingly went with her and she was seen no more.

* * *

The Slum Kitten waited in vain for her mother. The morning came and went. She became very hungry. Toward evening a deep-laid instinct drove her forth to seek food. She slunk out of the old box, and feeling her way silently among the rubbish, she smelt everything that seemed eatable, but without finding food. At length she reached the wooden steps leading down into Jap Malee's bird-store underground. The door was open a little. She wandered into a world of rank and curious smells and a number of living things in cages all about her. A negro was sitting idly on a box in a corner. He saw the little stranger enter and watched it curiously. It wandered past some Rabbits. They paid no heed. It came to a wide-barred cage in which was a Fox. The gentleman with the bushy tail was in a far corner. He crouched low; his eyes glowed. The Kitten wandered, sniffing, up to the bars, put its head in, sniffed again, then made toward the feed-pan, to be seized in a flash by the crouching Fox. It gave a frightened "mew", but a single shake cut that short and would have ended Kitty's nine lives at once, had not the negro come to the rescue. He had no weapon and could not get into the cage, but he spat with such copious vigor in the Fox's face that he dropped the Kitten and returned to the corner, there to sit blinking his eyes in sullen fear.

The negro pulled the Kitten out. The shake of the beast of prey seemed to have stunned the victim, really to have saved it much suffering. The Kitten seemed unharmed, but giddy. It tottered in a circle for a time, then slowly revived, and a few minutes later was purring in the negro's lap, apparently none the worse, when Jap Malee, the bird-man came home.

Jap was not an Oriental; he was a full-blooded Cockney, but his eyes were such little accidental slits aslant in his round, flat face, that his first name was forgotten in the highly descriptive title of "Jap." He was not especially unkind to the birds and beasts whose sales were supposed to furnish his living, but his eye was on the main chance; he knew what he wanted. He didn't want the Slum Kitten.

The negro gave it all the food it could eat, then carried it to a distant block and dropped it in a neighboring iron-yard.

One full meal is as much as any one needs in two or three days, and under the influence of this stored-up heat and power, Kitty was very lively. She walked around the piled-up rubbish, cast curious glances on far-away Canary-birds in cages that hung from high windows; she peeped over fences, discovered a large Dog, got quietly down again, and presently finding a sheltered place in full sunlight, she lay down and slept for an hour. A slight 'sniff' awakened her, and before her stood a large Black Cat with glowing green eyes, and the thick neck and square jaws that distinguish the Tom; a scar marked his cheek, and his left ear was torn. His look was far from friendly; his ears moved backward a little, his tail twitched, and a faint, deep sound came from his throat. The Kitten innocently walked toward him. She did not remember him. He rubbed the sides of his jaws on a post, and quietly, slowly turned and disappeared. The last that she saw of him was the end of his tail twitching from side to side; and the little Slummer had no idea that she had been as near death to-day, as she had been when she ventured into the fox-cage.

As night came on the Kitten began to feel hungry. She examined carefully the long invisible colored stream that the wind is made of. She selected the most interesting of its strands, and, nose-led, followed. In the corner of the iron-yard was a box of garbage. Among this she found something that answered fairly well for food; a bucket of water under a faucet offered a chance to quench her thirst.

The night was spent chiefly in prowling about and learning the main lines of the iron-yard. The next day she passed as before, sleeping in the sun. Thus the time wore on. Sometimes she found a good meal at the garbage-box, sometimes there was nothing. Once she found the big Black Tom there, but discreetly withdrew before he saw her. The water-bucket was usually at its place, or, failing that, there were some muddy little pools on the stone below. But the garbage-box was very unreliable. Once it left her for three days without food. She searched along the high fence, and seeing a small hole, crawled through that and found herself in the open street. This was a new world, but before she had ventured far, there was a noisy, rumbling rush—a large Dog came bounding, and Kitty had barely time to run back into the hole in the fence. She was dreadfully hungry, and glad to find some old potato-peelings, which gave a little respite from the hunger-pang. In the morning she did not sleep, but prowled for food. Some Sparrows chirruped in the yard. They were often there, but now they were viewed with new eyes. The steady pressure of hunger had roused the wild hunter in the Kitten; those Sparrows were game—were food. She crouched instinctively and stalked from cover to cover, but the chirpers were alert and flew in time. Not once, but many times, she tried without result except to confirm the Sparrows in the list of things to be eaten if obtainable.

On the fifth day of ill luck the Slum Kitty ventured forth into the street, desperately bent on finding food. When far from the haven hole some small boys opened fire at her with pieces of brick. She ran in fear. A Dog joined in the chase, and Kitty's position grew perilous; but an old-fashioned iron fence round a house-front was there, and she slipped in between the rails as the Dog overtook her. A woman in a window above shouted at the Dog. Then the boys dropped a piece of cat-meat down to the unfortunate; and Kitty had the most delicious meal of her life. The stoop afforded a refuge. Under this she sat patiently till nightfall came with quiet, then sneaked back like a shadow to her old iron-yard.

Thus the days went by for two months. She grew in size and strength and in an intimate knowledge of the immediate neighborhood. She made the acquaintance of Downey Street, where long rows of ash-cans were to be seen every morning. She formed her own ideas of their proprietors. The big house was to her, not a Roman Catholic mission, but a place whose garbage-tins abounded in choicest fish scrapings. She soon made the acquaintance of the meat-man, and joined in the shy fringe of Cats that formed the outer circle. She also met the Wharf Dog as well as two or three other horrors of the same class. She knew what to expect of them and how to avoid them; and she was happy in being the inventor of a new industry. Many thousand Cats have doubtless hung, in hope, about the tempting milk-cans that the early milk-man leaves on steps and window-ledges, and it was by the merest accident that Kitty found one with a broken lid, and so was taught to

raise it and have a satisfying drink. Bottles, of course, were beyond her, but many a can has a misfit lid, and Kitty was very painstaking in her efforts to discover the loose-jointed ones. Finally she extended her range by exploration till she achieved the heart of the next block, and farther, till once more among the barrels and boxes of the yard behind the bird-man's cellar.

The old iron-yard never had been home, she had always felt like a stranger there; but here she had a sense of ownership, and at once resented the presence of another small Cat. She approached this newcomer with threatening air. The two had got as far as snarling and spitting when a bucket of water from an upper window drenched them both and effectually cooled their wrath. They fled, the newcomer over the wall, Slum Kitty under the very box where she had been born. This whole back region appealed to her strongly, and here again she took up her abode. The yard had no more garbage food than the other and no water at all, but it was frequented by stray Rats and a few Mice of the finest quality; these were occasionally secured, and afforded not only a palatable meal, but were the cause of her winning a friend.

* * *

Kitty was now fully grown. She was a striking-looking Cat of the tiger type. Her marks were black on a very pale gray, and the four beauty-spots of white on nose, ears, and tail-tip lent a certain distinction. She was very expert at getting a living, and yet she had some days of starvation and failed in her ambition of catching a Sparrow. She was quite alone, but a new force was coming into her life.

She was lying in the sun one August day, when a large Black Cat came walking along the top of a wall in her direction. She recognized him at once by his torn ear. She slunk into her box and hid. He picked his way gingerly, bounded lightly to a shed that was at the end of the yard, and was crossing the roof when a Yellow Cat rose up. The Black Tom glared and growled, so did the Yellow Tom. Their tails lashed from side to side. Strong throats growled and yowled. They approached each other with ears laid back, with muscles a-tense.

"Yow—yow—ow!" said the Black One.

"Wow—w—w!" was the slightly deeper answer.

"Ya—wow—wow—wow!" said the Black One, edging up half an inch nearer.

"Yow—w—w!" was the Yellow answer, as the blond Cat rose to full height and stepped with vast dignity a whole inch forward. "Yow—w!" and he went another inch, while his tail went swish, thump, from one side to the other.

"Ya—wow—yow—w!" screamed the Black in a rising tone, and he backed the eighth of an inch, as he marked the broad, unshrinking breast before him.

Windows opened all around, human voices were heard, but the Cat scene went on.

"Yo-ow!" rumbled the Yellow One

"Yow—yow—ow!" rumbled the Yellow Peril, his voice deepening as the other's rose. "Yow!" and he advanced another step.

Now their noses were but three inches apart; they stood sidewise, both ready to clinch, but each waiting for the other. They glared for three minutes in silence and like statues, except that each tail-tip was twisting.

The Yellow began again. "Yow—ow—ow!" in deep tone.

"Ya—a—a—a!" screamed the Black, with intent to strike terror by his yell; but he retreated one sixteenth of an inch. The Yellow walked up a long half-inch; their whiskers were mixing now; another advance, and their noses almost touched.

"Yo—w—w!" said Yellow, like a deep moan.

"Y—a—a—a—a—a—a!" screamed the Black, but he retreated a thirty-second of an inch, and the Yellow Warrior closed and clinched like a demon.

Oh, how they rolled and bit and tore, especially the Yellow One!

How they pitched and gripped and hugged, but especially the Yellow One!

Over and over, sometimes one on top, sometimes another, but mostly the Yellow One; and farther till they rolled off the roof, amid cheers from all the windows. They lost not a second in that fall to the junk-yard; they tore and clawed all the way down, but especially the Yellow One. And when they struck the ground, still fighting, the one on top was chiefly the Yellow One; and before they separated both had had as much as they wanted, especially the Black One! He scaled a wall and, bleeding and growling, disappeared, while the news was passed from window to window that Cayley's Nig had been licked at last by Orange Billy.

Either the Yellow Cat was a very clever seeker, or else Slum Kitty did not hide very hard; but he discovered her among the boxes, and she made no attempt to get away, probably because she had witnessed the fight. There is nothing like success in warfare to win the female heart, and thereafter the Yellow Tom and Kitty became very goods friends, not sharing each other's lives or food,—Cats do not do that way much,—but recognizing each other as entitled to special friendly privileges.

* * *

September had gone. October's shortening days were on when an event took place in the old cracker-box. If Orange Billy had come he would have seen five little Kittens curled up in the embrace of their mother, the little Slum Cat. It was a wonderful thing for her. She felt all the elation an animal mother can feel, all the delight, and she loved them and licked them with a tenderness that must have been a surprise to herself, had she had the power to think of such things.

She had added a joy to her joyless life, but she had also added a care and a heavy weight to her heavy load. All her strength was taken now to find food. The burden increased as the offspring grew up big enough to scramble about the boxes, which they did daily during her absence after they were six weeks old. That troubles go in flocks and luck in streaks, is well known in Slumland. Kitty had had three encounters with Dogs, and had been stoned by Malee's negro during a two days' starve. Then the tide turned. The very next morning she found a full milk-can without a lid, successfully robbed a barrow pensioner, and found a big fish-head, all within two hours. She had just returned with that perfect peace which comes only of a full

stomach, when she saw a little brown creature in her junk-yard. Hunting memories came back in strength; she didn't know what it was, but she had killed and eaten several Mice, and this was evidently a big Mouse with bob-tail and large ears. Kitty stalked it with elaborate but unnecessary caution; the little Rabbit simply sat up and looked faintly amused. He did not try to run, and Kitty sprang on him and bore him off. As she was not hungry, she carried him to the cracker-box and dropped him among the Kittens. He was not much hurt. He got over his fright, and since he could not get out of the box, he snuggled among the Kittens, and when they began to take their evening meal he very soon decided to join them. The old Cat was puzzled. The hunter instinct had been dominant, but absence of hunger had saved the Rabbit and given the maternal instinct a chance to appear. The result was that the Rabbit became a member of the family, and was thenceforth guarded and fed with the Kittens.

Two weeks went by. The Kittens romped much among the boxes during their mother's absence. The Rabbit could not get out of the box. Jap Malee, seeing the Kittens about the back yard, told the negro to shoot them. This he was doing one morning with a 22-calibre rifle. He had shot one after another and seen them drop from sight into the crannies of the lumber-pile, when the old Cat came running along the wall from the dock, carrying a small Wharf Rat. He had been ready to shoot her, too, but the sight of that Rat changed his plans: a rat-catching Cat was worthy to live. It happened to be they very first one she had ever caught, but it saved her life. She threaded the lumber-maze to the cracker-box and was probably puzzled to find that there were no Kittens to come at her call, and the Rabbit would not partake of the Rat. Pussy curled up to nurse the Rabbit, but she called from time to time to summon the Kittens. Guided by that call, the negro crawled quietly to the place, and peering down into the cracker-box, saw, to his intense surprise, that it contained the old Cat, a live Rabbit, and a dead Rat.

The mother Cat laid back her ears and snarled. The negro withdrew, but a minute later a board was dropped on the opening of the cracker-box, and the den with its tenants, dead and alive, was lifted into the bird-cellar.

"Say, boss, look a-hyar—hyar's where de little Rabbit got to wot we lost. Yo'sho t'ought Ah stoled him for de tater-bake."

Kitty and Bunny were carefully put in a large wire cage and exhibited as a happy family till a few days later, when the Rabbit took sick and died.

Pussy had never been happy in the cage. She had enough to eat and drink, but she craved her freedom—would likely have gotten 'death or liberty' now, but that during the four days' captivity she had so cleaned and slicked her fur that her unusual coloring was seen, and Jap decided to keep her.

LIFE II

Jap Malee was as disreputable a little Cockney bantam as ever sold cheap Canary-birds in a cellar. He was extremely poor, and the negro lived with him because the 'Henglish-man' was willing to share bed and board, and otherwise admit a perfect equality that few Americans conceded. Jap was perfectly honest according to his lights, but he had n't any lights; and it was well known that his chief revenue was derived from storing and restoring stolen Dogs and Cats. The half-dozen Canaries were mere blinds. Yet Jap believed in himself. "Hi tell you, Sammy, me boy, you'll see me with 'orses of my own yet," he would say, when some trifling success inflated his dirty little chest. He was not without ambition, in a weak, flabby, once-in-a-while way, and he sometimes wished to be known as a fancier. Indeed, he had once gone the wild length of offering a Cat for exhibition at the Knickerbocker High Society Cat and Pet Show, with three not over-clear objects: first, to gratify his ambition; second, to secure the exhibitor's free pass; and, third, "well, you kneow, one 'as to kneow the valuable Cats, you kneow, when one goes a-catting." But this was a society show, the exhibitor had to be introduced, and his miserable alleged half-Persian was scornfully rejected. The 'Lost and Found' columns of the papers were the only ones of interest to Jap, but he had noticed and saved a clipping about 'breeding for fur.' This was stuck on the wall of his den, and under its influence he set about what seemed a cruel experiment with the Slum Cat. First, he soaked her dirty fur with stuff to kill the two or three kinds of creepers she wore; and, when it had done its work, he washed her thoroughly in soap and warm water, in spite of her teeth, claws, and yowls. Kitty was savagely indignant, but a warm and happy glow spread over her as she dried off in a cage near the stove, and her fur began to fluff out with wonderful softness and whiteness. Jap and his assistant were much pleased with the result, and Kitty ought to have been. But this was preparatory: now for the experiment. "Nothing is so good for growing fur as plenty of oily food and continued exposure to cold weather," said the clipping. Winter was at hand, and Jap Malee put Kitty's cage out in the yard, protected only from the rain and the direct wind, and fed her with all the oil-cake and fish-heads she could eat. In a week a change began to show. She was rapidly getting fat and sleek—she had nothing to do but get fat and dress her fur. Her cage was kept clean, and nature responded to the chill weather and the oily food by making Kitty's coat thicker and glossier every day, so that by midwinter she was an unusually beautiful Cat in the fullest and finest of fur, with markings that were at least a rarity. Jap was much pleased with the result of the experiment, and as a very little success had a wonderful effect on him, he began to dream of the paths of glory. Why not send the Slum Cat to the show now coming on? The failure of the year before made him more careful as to details. "'T won't do, ye kneow, Sammy, to henter 'er as a tramp Cat, ye kneow," he observed to his help; "but it kin be arranged to suit the Knickerbockers. Nothink like a good noime, ye kneow. Ye see now it had orter be 'Royal' somethink or other—nothink goes with the Knickerbockers like 'Royal' anythink. Now 'Royal Dick,' or 'Royal Sam,' 'ow's that? But 'owld on; them's Tom names. Oi say, Sammy, wot's the noime of that island where ye wuz born?"

"Analostan Island, sah, was my native vicinity, sah."

"Oi say, now, that's good, ye kneow. 'Royal Analostan,' by Jove! The onliest pedigreed 'Royal Analostan' in the 'ole sheow, ye kneow. Ain't that foine?" and they mingled their cackles.

"But we'll 'ave to 'ave a pedigree, ye kneow." So a very long fake pedigree on the recognized lines was prepared. One dark afternoon Sam, in a borrowed silk hat, delivered the Cat and the pedigree at the show door. The darkey did the honors. He had been a Sixth Avenue barber, and he could put on more pomp and lofty hauteur in five minutes than Jap Malee could have displayed in a lifetime, and this, doubtless, was one reason for the respectful reception awarded the Royal Analostan at the Cat Show.

Jap was very proud to be an exhibitor; but he had all a Cockney's reverence for the upper class, and when on the opening day he went to the door, he was overpowered to see the array of carriages and silk hats. The gateman looked at him sharply, but passed him on his ticket, doubtless taking him for stable-boy to some exhibitor. The hall had velvet carpets before the long rows of cages. Jap, in his small cunning, was sneaking down the side rows, glancing at the Cats of all kinds, noting the blue ribbons and the reds, peering about but not daring to ask for his own exhibit, inly trembling to think what the gorgeous gathering of fashion would say if they discovered the trick he was playing on them. He had passed all around the outer aisles and seen many prize-winners, but no sign of Slum Kitty. The inner aisles were more crowded. He picked his way down them, but still no Kitty, and he decided that it was a mistake; the judges had rejected the Cat later. Never mind; he had his exhibitor's ticket, and now knew where several valuable Persians and Angoras were to be found.

In the middle of the centre aisle were the high-class Cats. A great

throng was there. The passage was roped, and two policemen were in place to keep the crowd moving. Jap wriggled in among them; he was too short to see over, and though the richly gowned folks shrunk from his shabby old clothes, he could not get near; but he gathered from the remarks that the gem of the show was there.

"Oh, is n't she a beauty!" said one tall woman.

"What distinction!" was the reply.

"One cannot mistake the air that comes only from ages of the most refined surroundings."

"How I should like to own that superb creature!"

"Such dignity—such repose!"

"She has an authentic pedigree nearly back to the Pharaohs, I hear"; and poor, dirty little Jap marvelled at his own cheek in sending his Slum Cat into such company.

"Excuse me, madame." The director of the show now appeared, edging his way through the crowd. "The artist of the 'Sporting Element' is here, under orders to sketch the 'pearl of the show' for immediate use. May I ask you to stand a little aside? That's it; thank you."

Oh, Mr. Director, cannot you persuade him to sell the beautiful creature?"

"Hm, I don't know," was the reply. "I understand he is a man of ample means and not at all approachable; but I'll try, I'll try, madame. He was quite unwilling to exhibit his treasure at all, so I understand from his butler. Here, you, keep out of the way," growled the director, as the shabby little man eagerly pushed between the artist and the blue-blooded Cat. But the disreputable one wanted to know where valuable Cats were to be found. He came near enough to get a glimpse of the cage, and there read a placard which announced that "The blue ribbon and *gold medal* of the Knickerbocker High Society Cat and Pet Show" had been awarded to the "thoroughbred, pedigreed Royal Analostan, imported and exhibited by J. Malee, Esq., the well-known fancier. (Not for sale.)" Jap caught his breath and stared again. Yes, surely; there, high in a gilded cage, on velvet cushions, with four policemen for guards, her fur bright black and pale gray, her bluish eyes slightly closed, was his Slum Kitty, looking the picture of a Cat bored to death with a lot of fuss that she likes as little as she understands it.

* * *

Jap Malee lingered around that cage, taking in the remarks, for hours— drinking a draught of glory such as he had never known in life before and rarely glimpsed in his dreams. But he saw that it would be wise for him to remain unknown; his "butler" must do all the business.

It was Slum Kitty who made that show a success. Each day her value went up in her owner's eyes. He did not know what prices had been given for Cats, and thought that he was touching a record pitch when his "butler" gave the director authority to sell the Analostan for one hundred dollars.

This is how it came about that the Slum Cat found herself transferred from the show to a Fifth Avenue mansion. She evinced a most unaccountable wildness at first. Her objection to petting, however, was explained on the ground of her aristocratic dislike of familiarity. Her retreat from the Lap-dog onto the centre of the dinner-table was understood to express a deep-rooted though mistaken idea of

There, high on velvet cushions, was his Slum Kitty

avoiding a defiling touch. Her assaults on a pet Canary were condoned for the reason that in her native Orient she had been used to despotic example. The patrician way in which she would get the cover off a milk-can was especially applauded. Her dislike of her silk-lined basket, and her frequent dashes against the plate-glass windows, were easily understood: the basket was too plain, and plate-glass was not used in her royal home. Her spotting of the carpet evidenced her Eastern modes of thought. The failure of her several attempts to catch Sparrows in the high-walled back yard was new proof of the royal impotency of her bringing up; while her frequent wallowings in the garbage-can were understood to be the manifestation of a little pardonable high-born eccentricity. She was fed and pampered, shown and praised; but she was not happy. Kitty was homesick! She clawed at that blue ribbon round her neck till she got it off; she jumped against the plate-glass because that seemed the road to outside; she avoided people and Dogs because they had always proved hostile and cruel; and she would sit and gaze on the roofs and back yards at the other side of the window, wishing she could be among them for a change.

But she was strictly watched, was never allowed outside—so that all the happy garbage-can moments occurred while these receptacles of joy were indoors. One night in March, however, as they were set out a-row for the early scavenger, the Royal Analostan saw her chance, slipped out of the door, and was lost to view.

Of course there was a grand stir; but Pussy neither knew nor cared anything about that—her one thought was to go home. It may have been chance that took her back in the direction of Gramercy Grange Hill, but she did arrive there after sundry small adventures. And now what? She was not at home, and she had cut off her living. She was beginning to be hungry, and yet she had a peculiar sense of happiness. She cowered in a front garden for some time. A raw east wind had been rising, and now it came to her with a particularly friendly message; man would have called it an unpleasant smell of the docks, but to Pussy it was welcome tidings from home. She trotted down the long street due east, threading the rails of front gardens, stopping like a statue for

an instant, or crossing the street in search of the darkest side, and came at length to the docks and to the water. But the place was strange. She could go north or south. Something turned her southward; and, dodging among docks and Dogs, carts and Cats, crooked arms of the bay and straight board fences, she got in, in an hour or two, among familiar scenes and smells; and, before the sun came up, she had crawled back weary and foot-sore through the same old hole in the same old fence and over a wall to her junk-yard back of the bird-cellar—yes, back into the very cracker-box where she was born.

Oh, if the Fifth Avenue family could only have seen her in her native Orient!

After a long rest she came quietly down from the cracker-box toward the steps leading to the cellar, engaged in her old-time pursuit of seeking for eatables. The door-opened, and there stood the negro. He shouted to the bird-man inside:

"Say, boss, come hyar. Ef dere ain't dat dar Royal Analostan am comed back!"

Jap came in time to see the Cat jumping the wall. They called loudly and in the most seductive, wheedling tones: "Pussy, Pussy, poor Pussy! Come, Pussy!" But Pussy was not prepossessed in their favor, and disappeared to forage in her old-time haunts.

The Royal Analostan had been a windfall for Jap—had been the means of adding many comforts to the cellar and several prisoners to the cages. It was now of the utmost importance to recapture her majesty. Stale meat-offal and other infallible lures were put out till Pussy, urged by the reëstablished hunger-pinch, crept up to a large fish-head in a box-trap; the negro, in watching, pulled the string that dropped the lid, and, a minute later, the Analostan was once more among the prisoners in the cellar. Meanwhile Jap had been watching the 'Lost and Found' column. There it was, "$25 reward," etc. That night Mr. Malee's butler called at the Fifth Avenue mansion with the missing cat. "Mr. Malee's compliments, sah. De Royal Analostan had recurred in her recent priorprietor's vicinity and residence, sah. Mr. Malee had pleasure in recuperating the Royal Analostan, sah." Of course Mr. Malee could not be rewarded, but the butler was open to any offer, and plainly showed that he expected the promised reward and something more.

Kitty was guarded very carefully after that; but so far from being disgusted with the old life of starving, and glad of her ease, she became wilder and more dissatisfied.

* * *

The spring was doing its New York best. The dirty little English Sparrows were tumbling over each other in their gutter brawls, Cats yowled all night in the areas, and the Fifth Avenue family were thinking of their country residence. They packed up, closed house, and moved off to their summer home, some fifty miles away, and Pussy, in a basket, went with them.

"Just what she needed: a change of air and scene to wean her away from her former owners and make her happy."

The basket was lifted into a Rumble-shaker. New sounds and passing smells were entered and left. A turn in the course was made. Then a roaring of many feet, more swinging of the basket; a short pause, another change of direction, then some clicks, some bangs, a long shrill whistle, and door-bells of a very big front door; a rumbling, a whizzing, an unpleasant smell, a hideous smell, a growing horrible, hateful choking smell, a deadly, griping, poisonous stench, with roaring that drowned poor Kitty's yowls, and just as it neared the point where endurance ceased, there was relief. She hear clicks and clacks. There was light; there was air. Then a man's voice called, "All out for 125th Street," though of course to Kitty it was a mere human bellow. The roaring almost ceased—did cease. Later the rackety-bang was renewed with plenty of sounds and shakes, though not the poisonous gas; a long, hollow, booming roar with a pleasant dock smell was quickly passed, and then there was a succession of jolts, roars, jars, stops, clicks, clacks, smells, jumps, shakes, more smells, more shakes,—big shakes, little shakes,—gases, smokes, screeches, door-bells, tremblings, roars, thunders, and some new smells, raps, taps, heavings, rumblings, and more smells, but all without any of the feel that the direction is changed. When at last it stopped, the sun came twinkling through the basket-lid. The Royal Cat was lifted into a Rumble-shaker of the old familiar style, and, swerving aside from their past course, very soon the noises of its wheels were grittings and rattlings; a new and horrible sound was added—the barking of Dogs, big and little and dreadfully close. The basket was lifted, and Slum Kitty had reached her country home.

Every one was officiously kind. They wanted to please the Royal Cat, but somehow none of them did, except, possibly, the big, fat cook that Kitty discovered on wandering into the kitchen. This unctuous person smelt more like a slum than anything she had met for months, and the Royal Analostan was proportionately attracted. The cook, when she learned that fears were entertained about the Cat staying, said: "Shure, she' d 'tind to thot; wanst a Cat licks her futs, shure she's at home." So she deftly caught the unapproachable royalty in her apron

and committed the horrible sacrilege of greasing the soles of her feet with pot-grease. Of course Kitty resented it—she resented everything in the place; but on being set down she began to dress her paws and found evident satisfaction in that grease. She licked all four feet for an hour, and the cook triumphantly announced that now "shure she'd be apt to shtay." And stay she did, but she showed a most surprising and disgusting preference for the kitchen, the cook, and the garbage-pail.

The family, though distressed by these distinguished peculiarities, were glad to see the Royal Analostan more contented and approachable. They gave her more liberty after a week or two. They guarded her from every menace. The Dogs were taught to respect her. No man or boy about the place would have dreamed of throwing a stone at the famous pedigreed Cat. She had all the food she wanted, but still she was not happy. She was hankering for many things, she scarcely knew what. She had everything—yes, but she wanted something else. Plenty to eat and drink—yes, but milk does not taste the same when you can go and drink all you want from a saucer; it has to be stolen out of a tin pail when you are belly-pinched with hunger and thirst, or it does not have the tang—it isn't milk.

Yes, there *was* a junk-yard back of the house and beside it and around it too, a big one, but it was everywhere poisoned and polluted with roses. The very Horses and Dogs had the wrong smells; the whole country round was a repellent desert of lifeless, disgusting gardens and hay-fields, without a single tenement or smoke-stack in sight. How she did hate it all! There was only one sweet-smelling shrub in the whole horrible place, and that was in a neglected corner. She did enjoy nipping that and rolling in the leaves; it was a bright spot in the grounds; but the only one, for she had not found a rotten fish-head nor seen a genuine garbage-can since she came, and altogether it was the most unlovely, unattractive, unsmellable spot she had ever known. She would surely have gone that first night had she had the liberty. The liberty was weeks in coming, and, meanwhile, her affinity with the cook had developed as a bond to keep her; but one day after a summer of discontent a succession of things happened to stir anew the slum instinct of the royal prisoner.

A great bundle of stuff from the docks had reached the country mansion. What it contained was of little moment, but it was rich with a score of the most piquant and winsome of dock and slum smells. The chords of memory surely dwell in the nose, and Pussy's past was conjured up with dangerous force. Next day the cook 'left' through some trouble over this very bundle. It was the cutting of cables, and that evening the youngest boy of the house, a horrid little American with no proper appreciation of royalty, was tying a tin to the blue-blooded one's tail, doubtless in furtherance of some altruistic project, when Pussy resented the liberty with a paw that wore five big fish-hooks for the occasion. The howl of downtrodden America roused America's mother. The deft and womanly blow that she aimed with her book was miraculously avoided, and Pussy took flight, up-stairs, of course. A hunted Rat runs down-stairs, a hunted Dog goes on the level, a hunted Cat runs up. She hid in the garret, baffled discovery, and waited till night came. Then, gliding down-stairs, she tried each screen-door in turn, till she found one unlatched, and escaped into the black August night. Pitch-black to man's eyes, it was simply gray to her, and she glided through the disgusting shrubbery and flower-beds, took a final nip at that one little bush that had been an attractive spot in the garden, and boldly took her back track of the spring.

How could she take a back track that she never saw? There is in all animals some sense of direction. It is very low in man and very high in Horses, but Cats have a large gift, and this mysterious guide took her westward, not clearly and definitely, but with a general impulse that was made definite simply because the road was easy to travel. In an hour she had covered two miles and reached the Hudson River. Her nose had told her many times that the course was true. Smell after smell came back, just as a man after walking a mile in a strange street may not recall a single feature, but will remember, on seeing it again, "Why, yes, I saw that before." So Kitty's main guide was the sense of direction, but it was her nose that kept reassuring her, "Yes, now you are right—we passed this place last spring."

At the river was the railroad. She could not go on the water; she must go north or south. This was a case where her sense of direction was clear; it said, "Go south," and Kitty trotted down the foot-path between the iron rails and the fence.

LIFE III

Cats can go very fast up a tree or over a wall, but when it comes to the long steady trot that reels off mile after mile, hour after hour, it is not the cat-hop, but the dog-trot, that counts. Although the travelling was good and the path direct, an hour had gone before two more miles were put between her and the Hades of roses. She was tired and a little foot-sore. She was thinking of rest when a Dog came running to the fence near by, and broke out into such a horrible barking close to her ear that Pussy leaped in terror. She ran as hard as she could down the path, at the same time watching to see if the Dog should succeed in passing the fence. No, not yet! but he ran close by it, growling horribly, while Pussy skipped along on the safe side. The barking of the Dog grew into a low rumble—a louder rumble and roaring—a terrifying thunder. A light shone. Kitty glanced back to see, not the Dog, but a huge Black Thing with a blazing red eye coming on, yowling and spitting like a yard full of Cats. She put forth all her powers to run, made such time as she had never made before, but dared not leap the fence. She was running like a Dog, was flying, but all in vain; the monstrous pursuer overtook her, but missed her in the darkness, and hurried past to be lost in the night, while Kitty crouched gasping for breath, half a mile nearer home since that Dog began to bark.

This was her first encounter with the strange monster, strange to her eyes only; her nose seemed to know him and told her this was another landmark on the home trail. But Pussy lost much of her fear of his kind. She learned that they were very stupid and could not find her if she slipped quietly under a fence and lay still. Before morning she had encountered several of them, but escaped unharmed from all.

About sunrise she reached a nice little slum on her home trail, and was lucky enough to find several unsterilized eatables in an ash-heap. She spent the day around a stable where were two Dogs and a number of small boys, that between them came near ending her career. It was so very like home; but she had no idea of staying there. She was driven by the old craving, and next evening set out as before. She had seen the one-eyed Thunder-rollers all day going by, and was getting used to them, so travelled steadily all that night. The next day was spent in a barn where she caught a Mouse, and the next night was like the last, except that a Dog she encountered drove her backward on her trail for a long way. Several times she was misled by angling roads, and wandered far astray, but in time she wandered back again to her general southward course. The days were passed in skulking under barns and hiding from Dogs and small boys, and the nights in limping along the track, for she was getting foot-sore; but on she went, mile after mile, southward, ever southward—Dogs, boys, Roarers, hunger— Dogs, boys, Roarers, hunger—yet on and onward still she went, and her nose from time to time cheered her by confidently reporting, "There surely is a smell we passed last spring."

* * *

So a week went by, and Pussy, dirty, ribbonless, foot-sore, and weary, arrived at the Harlem Bridge. Though it was enveloped in delicious smells, she did not like the look of that bridge. For half the night she wandered up and down the shore without discovering any other means of going south, excepting some other bridges, or anything of interest except that here the men were as dangerous as the boys. Somehow she had to come back to it; not only its smells were familiar, but from time to time, when a One-eye ran over it, there was that peculiar rumbling roar that was a sensation in the springtime trip. The calm of the late night was abroad when she leaped to the timber stringer and glided out over the water. She had got less that a third of the way across when a thundering One-eye came roaring at her from the opposite end. She was much frightened, but knowing their stupidity and blindness, she dropped to a low side beam and there crouched in hiding. Of course the stupid Monster missed her and passed on, and all would have been well, but it turned back, or another just like it came suddenly spitting behind her. Pussy leaped to the long track and made for the home shore. She might have got there had not a third of the Red-eyed Terrors come screeching at her from that side. She was running her hardest, but was caught between two foes. There was nothing for it but a desperate leap from the timbers into—she didn't know what. Down, down, down—plop, splash, plunge into the deep water, not cold, for it was August, but oh, so horrible! She spluttered and coughed when she came to the top, glanced around to see if the Monsters were swimming after her, and struck out for shore. She had never learned to swim, and yet she swam, for the simple reason that a Cat's position and actions in swimming are the same as her position and actions in walking. She had fallen into a place she did not like; naturally she tried to *walk* out, and the result was that she swam ashore. Which shore? The home-love never fails: the south side was the only shore for her, the one nearest home. She scrambled out all dripping wet, up the muddy bank and through coal-piles and dust-heaps, looking as black, dirty, and unroyal as it was possible for a Cat to look.

Once the shock was over, the Royal-pedigreed Slummer began to feel better for the plunge. A genial glow without from the bath, a genial sense of triumph within, for had she not outwitted three of the big Terrors?

Her nose, her memory, and her instinct of direction inclined her to get on the track again; but the place was infested with those Thunder-rollers, and prudence led her to turn aside and follow the river-bank with its musky home-reminders; and thus she was spared the unspeakable horrors of the tunnel.

She was over three days learning the manifold dangers and complexities of the East River docks. Once she got by mistake on a ferry-boat and was carried over to Long Island; but she took an early boat back. At length on the third night she reached familiar ground, the place she had passed the night of her first escape. From that her course was sure and rapid. She knew just where she was going and how to get there. She knew even the more prominent features in the Dog-scape now. She went faster, felt happier. In a little while surely she would be curled up in her native Orient—the old junk-yard. Another turn, and the block was in sight.

But—what! It was gone! Kitty couldn't believe her eyes; but she must, for the sun was not yet up. There where once had stood or leaned or slouched or straggled the houses of the block, was a great broken wilderness of stone, lumber, and holes in the ground.

Kitty walked all around it. She knew by the bearings and by the local color of the pavement that she was in her home, that there had lived the bird-man, and there was the old junk-yard; but all were gone, completely gone, taking their familiar odors with them, and Pussy turned sick at heart in the utter hopelessness of the case. Her place-love was her master-mood. She had given up all to come to a home that no longer existed, and for once her sturdy little heart was cast down. She wandered over the silent heaps of rubbish and found neither consolation nor eatables. The ruin had taken in several of the blocks and reached back from the water. It was not a fire; Kitty had seen one of those things. This looked more like the work of a flock of the Red-eyed Monsters. Pussy knew nothing of the great bridge that was to rise from this very spot.

When the sun came up she sought for cover. An adjoining block still stood with little change, and the Royal Analostan retired to that. She knew some of its trails; but once there, was unpleasantly surprised to find the place swarming with Cats that, like herself, were driven from their old grounds, and when the garbage-cans came out there were several Slummers at each. It meant a famine in the land, and Pussy, after standing it a few days, was reduced to seeking her other home on Fifth Avenue. She got there to find it shut up and deserted. She waited about for a day; had an unpleasant experience with a big man in a blue coat, and next night returned to the crowded slum.

September and October wore away. Many of the Cats died of starvation or were too weak to escape their natural enemies. But Kitty, young and strong, still lived.

Great changes had come over the ruined blocks. Though silent on the night when she first saw them, they were crowded with noisy workmen all day. A tall building, well advanced on her arrival, was completed at the end of October, and Slum Kitty, driven by hunger, went sneaking up to a pail that a negro had set outside. The pail, unfortunately, was not for garbage; it was a new thing in that region: a scrubbing-pail. A sad disappointment, but it had a sense of comfort— there were traces of a familiar touch on the handle. While she was studying it, the negro elevator-boy came out again. In spite of his blue clothes, his odorous person confirmed the good impression of the handle. Kitty had retreated across the street. He gazed at her.

"Sho ef dat don't look like de Royal Analostan! Hyar, Pussy, Pussy, Pu-s-s-s-s-y! Co-o-o-o-m-e, Pu-u-s-s-sy, hyar! I 'spec's she's sho hungry."

Hungry! She hadn't had a real meal for months. The negro went into the building and reappeared with a portion of his own lunch.

"Hyar, Pussy, Puss, Puss, Puss!" It seemed very good, but Pussy had her doubts of the man. At length he laid the meat on the pavement, and went back to the door. Slum Kitty came forward very warily; sniffed at the meat, seized it, and fled like a little Tigress to eat her prize in peace.

LIFE IV

This was the beginning of a new era. Pussy came to the door of the building now whenever pinched by hunger, and the good feeling for the negro grew. She had never understood that man before. He had always seemed hostile. Now he was her friend, the only one she had.

One week she had a streak of luck. Seven good meals on seven successive days; and right on the top of the last meal she found a juicy dead Rat, the genuine thing, a perfect windfall. She had never killed a full-grown Rat in all her lives, but seized the prize and ran off to hide it for future use. She was crossing the street in front of the new building when an old enemy appeared,—the Wharf Dog,—and Kitty retreated, naturally enough, to the door where she had a friend. Just as she neared it, he opened the door for a well-dressed man to come out, and both saw the Cat with her prize.

"Hello! Look at that for a Cat!"

"Yes, sah," answered the negro. "Dat's ma Cat, sah; she's a terror on Rats, sah! hez 'em about cleaned up, sah; dat's why she's so thin."

"Well, don't let her starve," said the man with the air of the landlord. "Can't you feed her?"

"De liver meat-man comes reg'lar, sah; quatah dollar a week, sah," said the negro, fully realizing that he was entitled to the extra fifteen cents for "the idea."

"That's all right. I'll stand it."

* * *

"M-e-a-t! M-e-a-t!" is heard the magnetic, cat-conjuring cry of the old liver-man, as his barrow is pushed up the glorified Scrimper's Alley, and Cats came crowding, as of yore, to receive their due.

There are Cats black, white, yellow, and gray to be remembered, and, above all, there are owners to be remembered. As the barrow rounds the corner near the new building it makes a newly scheduled stop.

"Hyar, you, get out o' the road, you common trash," cries the liver-man, and he waves his wand to make way for the little gray Cat with blue eyes and white nose. She receives an unusually large portion, for Sam is wisely dividing the returns evenly; and Slum Kitty retreats with her 'daily' into shelter of the great building, to which she is regularly attached. She has entered into her fourth life with prospects of happiness never before dreamed of. Everything was against her at first; now everything seems to be coming her way. It is very doubtful that her mind was broadened by travel, but she knew what she wanted and she got it. She has achieved her long-time great ambition by catching, not *a* Sparrow, but two of them, while they were clinched in mortal combat in the gutter.

There is no reason to suppose that she ever caught another Rat; but the negro secures a dead one when he can, for purposes of exhibition, lest her pension be imperilled. The dead one is left in the hall till the proprietor comes; then it is apologetically swept away. "Well, drat dat Cat, sah: dat Royal Analostan blood, sah, is terrors on Rats."

She has had several broods since. The negro thinks the Yellow Tom is the father of some of them, and no doubt the negro is right.

He has sold her a number of times with a perfectly clear conscience, knowing quite well that it is only a question of a few days before the Royal Analostan comes back again. Doubtless he is saving the money for some honorable ambition. She has learned to tolerate the elevator, and even to ride up and down on it. The negro stoutly maintains that once, when she heard the meat-man, while she was on the top floor, she managed to press the button that called the elevator to take her down.

She is sleek and beautiful again. She is not only one of the four hundred that form the inner circle about the liver-barrow, but she is recognized as the star pensioner among them. The liver-man is positively respectful. Not even the cream-and-chicken fed Cat of the pawn-broker's wife has such a position as the Royal Analostan. But in spite of her prosperity, her social position, her royal name and fake pedigree, the greatest pleasure of her life is to slip out and go a-slumming in the gloaming, for now, as in her previous lives, she is at heart, and likely to be, nothing but a dirty little Slum Cat.

ARNAUX

The Chronicle of a Homing Pigeon

W e passed through the side door of a big stable on West Nine-teenth Street. The mild smell of the well-kept stalls was lost in the sweet odor of hay, as we mounted a ladder and entered the long garret. The south end was walled off, and the familiar "Coo-oo, cooooo-oo, ruk-at-a-coo," varied with the "whirr, whirr, whirr" of wings, informed us that we were at the pigeon-loft.

This was the home of a famous lot of birds, and to-day there was to be a race among fifty of the youngsters. The owner of the loft had asked me, as an unprejudiced outsider, to be judge in the contest.

It was a training race of the young birds. They had been taken out for short distances to return to the loft. Now for the first time they were to be flown without the old ones. The point of start, Elizabeth, N.J., was a long journey for their first unaided attempt. "But then," the trainer remarked, "that's how we weed out the fools; only the best birds make it, and that's all we want back."

There was another side to the flight. It was to be a race among those that did return. Each of the men about the loft as well as several neighboring fanciers were interested in one or other of the Homers. They made up a purse for the winner, and on me was to devolve the important duty of deciding which should take the stakes. Not the first bird *back*, but the first bird *into the loft*, was to win, for one that returns to his neighborhood merely, without immediately reporting at home, is of little use as a letter-carrier.

The Homing Pigeon used to be called the Carrier because it carried messages, but here I found that name restricted to the show bird, the creature with absurdly developed wattles; the one that carries the messages is now called the Homer, or Homing Pigeon—the bird that always comes home. These Pigeons are not of any special color, nor have they any of the fancy adornments of the kind that figure in Bird shows. They are not bred for style, but for speed and for their mental gifts. They must be true to their home, able to return to it without fail. The sense of direction is now believed to be located in the bony labyrinth of the ear. There is no creature with finer sense of locality and direction than a good Homer, and the only visible proofs of it are the great bulge on each side of the head over the ears, and the superb wings that complete his equipment to obey the noble impulse of home-love. Now the mental and physical equipments of the last lot of young birds were to be put to test.

Although there were plenty of witnesses, I thought it best to close all but one of the pigeon-doors and stand ready to shut that behind the first arrival.

I shall never forget the sensations of that day. I had been warned: "They start at 12; they should be here at 12.30; but look out, they come like a whirlwind. You hardly see them till they're in."

We were ranged along the inside of the loft, each with an eye to a crack or a partly closed pigeon-door, anxiously scanning the south-western horizon, when one shouted: "Look out—here they come!" Like a white cloud they burst into view, low skimming over the city roofs, around a great chimney pile, and in two seconds after first being seen they were back. The flash of white, the rush of pinions, were all so sudden, so short, that, though preparing, I was unprepared. I was at the only open door. A whistling arrow of blue shot in, lashed my face with its pinions, and passed. I had hardly time to drop the little door, as a yell burst from the men, "Arnaux! Arnaux! I told you he would. Oh, he's a darling; only three months old and a winner—he's a little darling!" and Arnaux's owner danced, more for joy in his bird than in the purse he had won.

The men sat or kneeled and watched him in positive reverence as he gulped a quantity of water, then turned to the food-trough.

"Look at that eye, those wings, and did you ever see such a breast? Oh, but he's the real grit!" so his owner prattled to the silent ones whose birds had been defeated.

That was the first of Arnaux's exploits. Best of fifty birds from a good loft, his future was bright with promise.

He was invested with the silver anklet of the Sacred Order of the High Homer. It bore his number, 2590 C, a number which to-day means much to all men in the world of the Homing Pigeon.

In that trial flight from Elizabeth only forty birds had returned. It is usually so. Some were weak and got left behind, some were foolish and strayed. By this simple process of flight selection the pigeon-owners keep improving their stock. Of the ten, five were seen no more, but five returned later that day, not all at once, but straggling in; the last of the loiterers was a big, lubberly Blue Pigeon. The man in the loft at the time called: "Here comes that old sap-headed Blue that Jakey was betting on. I didn't suppose he would come back, and I didn't care, neither, for it's my belief he has a streak of Pouter."

The Big Blue, also called "Corner-box" from the nest where he was hatched, had shown remarkable vigor from the first. Though all were about the same age, he had grown faster, was bigger, and incidentally handsomer, though the fanciers cared little for that. He seemed fully aware of his importance, and early showed a disposition to bully his smaller cousins. His owner prophesied great things of him, but Billy, the stable-man, had grave doubts over the length of his neck, the bigness of his crop, his carriage, and his over-size. "A bird can't make time pushing a bag of wind ahead of him. Them long legs is dead weight, an' a neck like that ain't got no gimp in it," Billy would grunt disparagingly as he cleaned out the loft of a morning.

* * *

The training of the birds went on after this at regular times. The distance from home, of the start, was "jumped" twenty-five or thirty miles farther each day, and its direction changed till the Homers knew the country for one hundred and fifty miles around New York. The original fifty birds dwindled to twenty, for the rigid process weeds out not only the weak and ill-equipped, but those also who may have temporary ailments or accidents, or who may make the mistake of over-eating at the start. There were many fine birds in that flight, broad-breasted, bright-eyed, long-winged creatures, formed for swiftest flight, for high unconscious emprise, for these were destined to be messengers in the service of man in times of serious need. Their colors were mostly white, blue, or brown. They wore no uniform, but each and all of the chosen remnant had the brilliant eye and the bulging ears of the finest Homer blood; and, best and choicest of all, nearly always first among them was little Arnaux. He had not much to distinguish him when at rest, for now all of the band had the silver anklet, but in the air it was that Arnaux showed his make, and when the opening of the hamper gave the order "Start," it was Arnaux that first got under way, soared to the height deemed needful to exclude all local influence, divined the road to home, and took it, pausing not for food, drink, or company.

Notwithstanding Billy's evil forecasts, the Big Blue of the Corner-box was one of the chosen twenty. Often he was late in returning; he never was first, and sometimes when he came back hours behind the rest, it was plain that he was neither hungry nor thirsty, sure signs that he was a loiterer by the way. Still he had come back; and now he wore on his ankle, like the rest, the sacred badge and a number from the roll of possible fame. Billy despised him, set him in poor contrast with Arnaux, but his owner would reply: "Give him a chance; 'soon ripe, soon rotten,' an' I always notice the best bird is the slowest to show up at first."

Before a year little Arnaux had made a record. The hardest of all work is over the sea, for there is no chance of aid from landmarks; and the hardest of all times at sea is in fog, for then even the sun is blotted out and there is nothing whatever for guidance. With memory, sight, and hearing unavailable, the Homer has one thing left, and herein is his great strength, the inborn sense of direction. There is only one thing that can destroy this, and that is *fear*, hence the necessity of a stout little heart between those noble wings.

Arnaux, with two of his order, in course of training, had been shipped on an ocean steamer bound for Europe. They were to be released out of sight of land, but a heavy fog set in and forbade the start. The steamer took them onward, the intention being to send them back with the next vessel. When ten hours out the engine broke down, the fog settled dense over the sea, and the vessel was adrift and helpless as a log. She could only whistle for assistance, and so far as results were concerned, the captain might as well have wigwagged. Then the Pigeons were thought of. Starback, 2592 C, was first selected. A message for help was written on waterproof paper, rolled up, and lashed to his tail-feathers on the under side. He was thrown into the air and disappeared. Half an hour later, a second, the Big Blue Corner-box, 2600 C, was freighted with a letter. He flew up, but almost immediately returned and alighted on the rigging. He was a picture of pigeon fear; nothing could induce him to leave the ship. He was so terrorized that he was easily caught and ignominiously thrust back into the coop.

Now the third was brought out, a small, chunky bird. The shipmen did not know him, but they noted down from his anklet his name and number, Arnaux, 2590 C. It meant nothing to them. But the officer who held him noted that his heart did not beat so wildly as that of the last bird. The message was taken from the Big Blue. It ran:

10 A.M., Tuesday.

We broke our shaft two hundred and ten miles out from New York; we are drifting helplessly in the fog. Send out a tug as soon as possible. We are whistling one long, followed at once by one short, every sixty seconds.
(Signed)   THE CAPTAIN.

This was rolled up, wrapped in waterproof film, addressed to the Steamship Company, and lashed to the under side of Arnaux's middle tail-feather.

When thrown into the air, he circled round the ship, then round again higher, then again higher in a wider circle, and he was lost to view; and still higher till quite out of sight and feeling of the ship. Shut out from the use of all his senses now but one, he gave himself up to that. Strong in him it was, and untrammelled of that murderous despot *Fear*. True as a needle to the Pole went Arnaux now, no hesitation, no

He circled out of sight above the ship

doubts; within one minute of leaving the coop he was speeding straight as a ray of light for the loft where he was born, the only place on earth where he could be made content.

That afternoon Billy was on duty when the whistle of fast wings was heard; a blue Flyer flashed into the loft and made for the water-trough. He was gulping down mouthful after mouthful, when Billy gasped: "Why, Arnaux, it's you, you beauty." Then, with the quick habit of the pigeon-man, he pulled out his watch and marked the time, 2.40 P.M. A glance showed the tie string on the tail. He shut the door and dropped the catching-net quickly over Arnaux's head. A moment later he had the roll in his hand; in two minutes he was speeding to the office of the Company, for there was a fat tip in view. There he learned that Arnaux had made the two hundred and ten miles in fog, over sea, in four hours and forty minutes, and within one hour the needful help had set out for the unfortunate steamer.

Two hundred and ten miles in fog over sea in four hours and forty minutes! This was a noble record. It was duly inscribed in the rolls of the Homing Club. Arnaux was held while the secretary, with rubber stamp and indelible ink, printed on a snowy primary of his right wing the record of the feat, with the date and reference number.

Starback, the second bird, never was heard of again. No doubt he perished at sea.

Blue Corner-box came back on the tug.

* * *

That was Arnaux's first public record; but others came fast, and several curious scenes were enacted in that old pigeon-loft with Arnaux as the central figure. One day a carriage drove up to the stable; a white-haired gentleman got out, climbed the dusty stairs, and sat all morning in the loft with Billy. Peering from his gold-rimmed glasses, first at a lot of papers, next across the roofs of the city, waiting, watching, for what? News from a little place not forty miles away—news of greatest weight to him, tidings that would make or break him, tidings that must reach him before it could be telegraphed: a telegram meant at least an hour's delay at each end. What was faster than that for forty miles? In those days there was but one thing—a high-class Homer. Money would count for nothing if he could win. The best, the very best at any price he must have, and Arnaux, with seven indelible records on his pinions, was the chosen messenger. An hour went by, another, and a third was begun, when with whistle of wings, the blue meteor flashed into the loft. Billy slammed the door and caught him. Deftly he snipped the threads and handed the roll to the banker. The old man turned deathly pale, fumbled it open, then his color came back. "Thank God!" he gasped, and then went speeding to his Board meeting, master of the situation. Little Arnaux had saved him.

The banker wanted to buy the Homer, feeling in a vague way that he ought to honor and cherish him; but Billy was very clear about it. "What's the good? You can't buy a Homer's heart. You could keep him a prisoner, that's all; but nothing on earth could make him forsake the old loft where he was hatched." So Arnaux stayed at 211 West Nineteenth Street. But the banker did not forget.

There is in our country a class of miscreants who think a flying Pigeon is fair game, because it is probably far from home, or they shoot him because it is hard to fix the crime. Many a noble Homer, speeding with a life or death message, has been shot down by one of these wretches and remorselessly made into a pot-pie. Arnaux's brother Arnolf, with three fine records on his wings, was thus murdered in the act of bearing a hasty summons for the doctor. As he fell dying at the gunner's feet, his superb wings spread out displayed his list of victories. The silver badge on his leg was there, and the gunner was smitten with remorse. He had the message sent on; he returned the dead bird to the Homing Club, saying that he "found it." The owner came to see him; the gunner broke down under cross-examination, and was forced to admit that he himself had shot the Homer, but did so in behalf of a poor sick neighbor who craved a pigeon-pie.

There were tears in the wrath of the pigeon-man. "My bird, my beautiful Arnolf, twenty times has he brought vital messages, three times has he made records, twice has he saved human lives, and you'd shoot him for a pot-pie. I could punish you under the law, but I have no heart for such a poor revenge. I only ask you this, if ever again you have a sick neighbor who wants a pigeon-pie, come, we'll freely supply him with pie-breed squabs; but if you have a trace of manhood about you, you will never, never again shoot, or allow others to shoot, our noble and priceless messengers."

This took place while the banker was in touch with the loft, while his heart was warn for the Pigeons. He was a man of influence, and the Pigeon Protection legislation at Albany was the immediate fruit of Arnaux's exploit.

* * *

Billy had never liked the Corner-box Blue (2600 C); notwithstanding the fact that he still continued in the ranks of the Silver Badge, Billy believed he was poor stuff. The steamer incident seemed to prove him a coward; he certainly was a bully.

One morning when Billy went in there was a row, two Pigeons, a large and a small, alternately clinching and sparring all over the floor, feathers flying, dust and commotion everywhere. As soon as they were separated Billy found that the little one was Arnaux and the big one was the Corner-box Blue. Arnaux had made a good fight, but was overmatched, for the Big Blue was half as heavy again.

Soon it was very clear what they had fought over—a pretty little lady Pigeon of the bluest Homing blood. The Big Blue cock had kept up a state of bad feeling by his bullying, but it was the Little Lady that had made them close in mortal combat. Billy had no authority to wring the

Big Blue's neck, but he interfered as far as he could in behalf of his favorite Arnaux.

Pigeon marriages are arranged somewhat like those of mankind. Propinquity is the first thing: force the pair together for a time and let nature take its course. So Billy locked Arnaux and the Little Lady up together in a separate apartment for two weeks, and to make doubly sure he locked Big Blue up with an Available Lady in another apartment for two weeks.

Things turned out just as was expected. The Little Lady surrendered to Arnaux and the Available Lady to the Big Blue. Two nests were begun and everything shaped for a "lived happily ever after." But the Big Blue was very big and handsome. He could blow out his crop and strut in the sun and make rainbows all round his neck in a way that might turn the heart of the staidest Homerine.

Arnaux, though sturdily built, was small and except for his brilliant eyes, not especially good-looking. Moreover, he was often away on important business, and the Big Blue had nothing to do but stay around the loft and display his unlettered wings.

It is the custom of moralists to point to the lower animals, and especially to the Pigeon, for examples of love and constancy, and properly so, but, alas! there are exceptions. Vice is not by any means limited to the human race.

Arnaux's wife had been deeply impressed with the Big Blue, at the outset, and at length while her spouse was absent the dreadful thing took place.

Arnaux returned from Boston one day to find that the Big Blue, while he retained his own Available Lady in the corner-box, had also annexed the box and wife that belonged to himself, and a desperate battle followed. The only spectators were the two wives, but they maintained an indifferent aloofness. Arnaux fought with his famous wings, but they were none the better weapons because they now bore twenty records. His beak and feet were small, as became his blood, and his stout little heart could not make up for his lack of weight. The battle went against him. His wife sat unconcernedly in the nest, as though it were not her affair, and Arnaux might have been killed but for the timely arrival of Billy. He was angry enough to wring the Blue bird's neck, but the bully escaped from the loft in time. Billy took tender care of Arnaux for a few days. At the end of a week he was well again, and in ten days he was once more on the road. Meanwhile he had evidently forgiven his faithless wife, for, without any apparent feeling, he took up his nesting as before. That month he made two new records. He brought a message ten miles in eight minutes, and he came from Boston in four hours. Every moment of the way he had been impelled by the master-passion of homelove. But it was a poor home-coming if his wife figured at all in his thoughts, for he found her again flirting with the Big Blue cock. Tired as he was, the duel was renewed, and again would have been to a finish but for Billy's interference. He separated the fighters, then shut the Blue cock up in a coop, determined to get rid of him in some way. Meanwhile the "Any Age Sweepstakes" handicap from Chicago to New York was on, a race of nine hundred miles. Arnaux had been entered six months before. His forfeit-money was up, and notwithstanding his domestic complications, his friends felt that he must not fail to appear.

The birds were sent by train to Chicago, to be liberated at intervals there according to their handicap, and last of the start was Arnaux. They lost no time, and outside of Chicago several of these prime Flyers joined by common impulse into a racing flock that went through air on the same invisible track. A Homer may make a straight line when following his general sense of direction, but when following a familiar back track he sticks to the well-remembered landmarks. Most of the birds had been trained by way of Columbus and Buffalo. Arnaux knew the Columbus route, but also he knew that by Detroit, and after leaving Lake Michigan, he took the straight line for Detroit. Thus he caught up on his handicap and had the advantage of many miles. Detroit, Buffalo, Rochester, with their familiar towers and chimneys, faded behind him, and Syracuse was near at hand. It was now late afternoon; six hundred miles in twelve hours he had flown and was undoubtedly leading the race; but the usual thirst of the Flyer had attacked him. Skimming over the city roofs, he saw a loft of Pigeons, and descending from his high course in two or three great circles, he followed the ingoing Birds to the loft and drank greedily at the water-trough, as he had often done before, and as every pigeon-lover hospitably expects the messengers to do. The owner of the loft was there and noted the strange Bird. He stepped quietly to where he could inspect him. One of his own Pigeons made momentary opposition to the stranger, and Arnaux, sparring sidewise with an open wing in Pigeon style, displayed the long array of printed records. The man was a fancier. His interest was aroused; he pulled the string that shut the flying door, and in a few minutes Arnaux was his prisoner.

The robber spread the much-inscribed wings, read record after

record, and glancing at the silver badge—it should have been gold—he read his name—Arnaux; then exclaimed: "Arnaux! Arnaux! Oh, I've heard of you, you little beauty, and it's glad I am to trap you." He snipped the message from his tail, unrolled it, and read: "Arnaux left Chicago this morning at 4 a.m., scratched in the Any Age Sweepstakes for New York."

"Six hundred miles in twelve hours! By the powers, that's a record-breaker." And the pigeon-stealer gently, almost reverently, put the fluttering Bird safely into a padded cage. "Well," he added, "I know it's no use trying to make you stay, but I can breed from you and have some of your strain."

So Arnaux was shut up in a large and comfortable loft with several other prisoners. The man, though a thief, was a lover of Homers; he gave his captive everything that could insure his comfort and safety. For three months he left him in that loft. At first Arnaux did nothing all day but walk up and down the wire screen, looking high and low for means of escape; but in the fourth month he seemed to have abandoned the attempt, and the watchful jailer began the second part of his scheme. He introduced a coy young lady Pigeon. But it did not seem to answer; Arnaux was not even civil to her. After a time the jailer removed the female, and Arnaux was left in solitary confinement for a month. Now a different female was brought in, but with no better luck; and thus it went on—for a year different charmers were introduced. Arnaux either violently repelled them or was scornfully indifferent, and at times the old longing to get away, came back with twofold power, so that he darted up and down the wire front or dashed with all his force against it.

When the storied feathers of his wings began their annual moult, his jailer saved them as precious things, and as each new feather came he reproduced on it the record of its owner's fame.

Two years went slowly by, and the jailer had put Arnaux in a new loft and brought in another lady Pigeon. By chance she closely resembled the faithless one at home. Arnaux actually heeded the newcomer. Once the jailer thought he saw his famous prisoner paying some slight attention to the charmer, and, yes, he surely saw her preparing a nest. Then assuming that they had reached a full under-standing, the jailer, for the first time, opened the outlet, and Arnaux was free. Did he hang around in doubt? Did he hesitate? No, not for one moment. As soon as the drop of the door left open the way, he shot through, he spread those wonderful blazoned wings, and, with no second thought for the latest Circe, sprang from the hated prison loft—away and away.

* * *

We have no means of looking into the Pigeon's mind; we may go wrong in conjuring up for it deep thoughts of love and welcome home; but we are safe in this, we cannot too strongly paint, we cannot too highly praise and glorify that wonderful God-implanted, mankind-fostered home-love that glows unquenchably in this noble bird. Call it what you like, a mere instinct deliberately constructed by man for his selfish ends, explain it away if you will, dissect it, misname it, and it still is there, in overwhelming, imperishable master-power, as long as the brave little heart and wings can beat.

Home, home, sweet home! Never had mankind a stronger love of home than Arnaux. The trials and sorrows of the old pigeon-loft were forgotten in that all-dominating force of his nature. Not years of prison bars, not later loves, nor fear of death, could down its power; and Arnaux, had the gift of song been his, must surely have sung as sings a hero in his highest joy, when sprang he from the 'lighting board, up-circling free, soaring, drawn by the only impulse that those glorious wings would honor,—up, up, in widening, heightening circles of ashy blue in the blue, flashing those many lettered wings of white, till they seemed like jets of fire—up and on, driven by that home-love, faithful to his only home and to his faithless mate; closing his eyes, they say; closing his ears, they tell; shutting his mind,—we all believe,—to nearer things, to two years of his life, to one half of his prime, but soaring in the blue, retiring, as a saint might do, into his inner self, giving himself up to that inmost guide. He was the captain of the ship, but the pilot, the chart and compass, all, were that deep-implanted instinct. One thousand feet above the trees the inscrutable whisper came, and Arnaux in arrowy swiftness now was pointing for the south-southeast. The little flashes of white fire on each side were lost in the low sky, and the reverent robber of Syracuse saw Arnaux nevermore.

The fast express was steaming down the valley. It was far ahead, but Arnaux overtook and passed it, as the flying wild Duck passes the swimming Muskrat. High in the valleys he went, low over the hills of Chenango, where the pines were combing the breezes.

Out from his oak-tree eyrie a Hawk came wheeling and sailing, silent, for he had marked the Flyer, and meant him for his prey. Arnaux turned neither right nor left, nor raised nor lowered his flight, nor lost a wing-beat. The Hawk was in waiting in the gap ahead, and Arnaux passed him, even as a Deer in his prime may pass by a Bear in his pathway. Home! home! was the only burning thought, the blinding impulse.

Beat, beat, beat, those flashing pinions went with speed unslacked on the now familiar road. In an hour the Catskills were at hand. In two hours he was passing over them. Old friendly places, swiftly coming now, lent ·more force to his wings. Home! home! was the silent song that his heart was singing. Like the traveller dying of thirst, that sees the palm-trees far ahead, his brilliant eyes took in the distant smoke of Manhattan.

Out from the crest of the Catskills there launched a Falcon. Swiftest of the race of rapine, proud of his strength, proud of his wings, he rejoiced in a worthy prey. Many and many a Pigeon had been borne to his nest, and riding the wind he came, swooping, reserving his strength, awaiting the proper time. Oh, how well he knew the very moment! Down, down like a flashing javelin; no wild Duck, no Hawk could elude him, for this was a Falcon. Turn back now, O Homer, and save yourself; go round the dangerous hills. Did he turn? Not a whit! for this was Arnaux. Home! home! home! was his only thought. To meet the danger, he merely added to his speed; and the Peregrine stooped; stooped at what?—a flashing of color, a twinkling of whiteness—and went back empty. While Arnaux cleft the air of the valley as a stone from a sling, to be lost—a white-winged bird—a spot with flashing halo—and, quickly, a speck in the offing. On down the dear valley of Hudson, the well-known highway; for two years he had not seen it! Now he dropped low as the noon breeze came north and ruffled the river below him. Home! home! home! and the towers of a city are coming in view! Home! home! past the great spider-bridge of Poughkeepsie, skimming, skirting the river-banks. Low now by the bank as the wind arose. Low, alas! too low! What fiend was it tempted a gunner in June to lurk on that hill by the margin? what devil directed his gaze to the twinkling of white that came from the blue to the northward? Oh, Arnaux, Arnaux, skimming low, forget not the gunner of old! Too low, too low you are clearing that hill. Too low—*too late!* Flash—bang! and the death-hail has reached him; reached, maimed, but not downed him. Out of the flashing pinions broken feathers printed with records went fluttering earthward. The "naught" of his sea record was gone. Not two hundred and ten, but twenty-one miles it now read. Oh, shameful pillage! A dark stain appeared on his bosom, but Arnaux kept on. Home, home, homeward bound. The danger was past in an instant. Home, homeward he steered straight as before, but the wonderful speed was diminished; not a mile a minute now; and the wind made undue sounds in his tattered pinions. The stain in his breast told of broken force; but on, straight on, he flew. Home, home was in sight, and the pain in his breast was forgotten. The tall towers of the

city were in clear view of his far-seeing eye as he skimmed by the high cliffs of Jersey. On, on—the pinion might flag, the eye might darken, but the home-love was stronger and stronger.

Under the tall Palisades, to be screened from the wind, he passed, over the sparkling water, over the trees, under the Peregrines' eyrie, under the pirates' castle where the great grim Peregrines sat; peering like black-masked highwaymen they marked the on-coming Pigeon. Arnaux knew them of old. Many a message was lying undelivered in that nest, many a record-bearing plume had fluttered away from its fastness. But Arnaux had faced them before, and now he came as before—on, onward, swift, but not as he had been; the deadly gun had sapped his force, had lowered his speed. On, on; and the Peregrines, biding their time, went forth like two bow-bolts; strong and lightning-swift they went against one weak and wearied.

The pirates in ambush

Why tell of the race that followed? Why paint the despair of a brave little heart in sight of the home he had craved in vain? In a minute all was over. The Peregrines screeched in their triumph. Screeching and sailing, they swung to their eyrie, and the prey in their claws was the body, the last of the bright little Arnaux. There on the rocks the beaks and claws of the bandits were red with the life of the hero. Torn asunder were those matchless wings, and their records were scattered unnoticed. In sun and in storm they lay till the killers themselves were killed and their strong-hold rifled. And none knew the fate of the peerless Bird till deep in the dust and rubbish of that pirate-nest the avenger found, among others of its kind, a silver ring, the sacred badge of the High Homer, and read upon it the pregnant inscription:

"ARNAUX, 2590 C."

BADLANDS BILLY

The Wolf that Won

THE HOWL BY NIGHT

Do you know the three calls of the hunting Wolf:—the long-drawn deep howl, the muster, that tells of game discovered but too strong for the finder to manage alone; and the higher ululation that ringing and swelling is the cry of the pack on a hot scent; and the sharp bark coupled with a short howl that, seeming least of all, is yet a gong of doom, for this is the cry *"Close in"*—this is the finish?

We were riding the Badland Buttes, King and I, with a pack of various hunting Dogs stringing behind or trotting alongside. The sun had gone from the sky, and a blood-streak marked the spot where he died, away over Sentinel Butte. The hills were dim, the valleys dark, when from the nearest gloom there rolled a long-drawn cry that all men recognize instinctively—melodious, yet with a tone in it that sends a shudder up the spine, though now it has lost all menace for mankind. We listened for a moment. It was the Wolf-hunter who broke silence: "That's Badlands Billy; ain't it a voice? He's out for his beef to-night."

ANCIENT DAYS

In pristine days the Buffalo herds were followed by bands of Wolves that preyed on the sick, the weak, and the wounded. When the Buffalo were exterminated the Wolves were hard put for support, but the Cattle came and solved the question for them by taking the Buffaloes' place. This caused the wolf-war. The ranchmen offered a bounty for each Wolf killed, and every cowboy out of work, was supplied with traps and poison for wolf-killing. The very expert made this their sole business and became known as wolvers. King Ryder was one of these. He was a quiet, gentle-spoken fellow, with a keen eye and an insight into animal life that gave him especial power over Broncos and Dogs, as well as Wolves and Bears, though in the last two cases it was power merely to surmise where they were and how best to get at them. He

299

had been a wolver for years, and greatly surprised me by saying that "never in all his experience had he known a Gray-wolf to attack a human being."

We had many camp-fire talks while the other men were sleeping, and then it was I learned the little that he knew about Badlands Billy. "Six times have I seen him and the seventh will be Sunday, you bet. He takes his long rest then." And thus on the very ground where it all fell out, to the noise of the night wind and the yapping of the Coyote, interrupted sometimes by the deep-drawn howl of the hero himself, I heard chapters of this history which, with others gleaned in many fields, gave me the story of the Big Dark Wolf of Sentinel Butte.

IN THE CAÑON

Away back in the spring of '92 a wolver was "wolving" on the east side of the Sentinel Mountain that so long was a principal landmark of the old Plainsmen. Pelts were not good in May, but the bounties were high, five dollars a head, and double for She-wolves. As he went down to the creek one morning he saw a Wolf coming to drink on the other side. He had an easy shot, and on killing it found it was a nursing She-wolf. Evidently her family were somewhere near, so he spent two or three days searching in all the likely places, but found no clue to the den.

Two weeks afterward, as the wolver rode down an adjoining cañon, he saw a Wolf come out of a hole. The ever-ready rifle flew up, and another ten-dollar scalp was added to his string. Now he dug into the den and found the litter, a most surprising one indeed, for it consisted not of the usual five or six Wolf-pups, but of eleven, and these, strange to say, were of two sizes, five of them larger and older than the other six. Here were two distinct families with one mother, and as he added their scalps to his string of trophies the truth dawned on the hunter. One lot was surely the family of the She-wolf he had killed two weeks before. The case was clear: the little ones awaiting the mother that was never to come, had whined piteously and more loudly as their hunger-pangs increased; the other mother passing had heard the Cubs; her heart was tender now, her own little ones had so recently come, and she cared for the orphans, carried them to her own den, and was providing for the double family when the rifleman had cut the gentle chapter short.

Many a wolver has dug into a wolf-den to find nothing. The old Wolves or possibly the Cubs themselves often dig little side pockets and off galleries, and when an enemy is breaking in they hide in these. The loose earth conceals the small pocket and thus the Cubs escape. When the wolver retired with his scalps he did not know that the biggest of all the Cubs, was still in the den, and even had he waited about for two hours, he might have been no wiser. Three hours later the sun went down and there was a slight scratching afar in the hole; first two little gray paws, then a small black nose appeared in a soft sand-pile to one side of the den. At length the Cub came forth from his hiding. He had been frightened by the attack on the den; now he was perplexed by its condition.

It was thrice as large as it had been and open at the top now. Lying near were things that smelled like his brothers and sisters, but they were repellent to him. He was filled with fear as he sniffed at them, and sneaked aside into a thicket of grass, as a Night-hawk boomed over his head. He crouched all night in that thicket. He did not dare to go near the den, and knew not where else he could go. The next morning when two Vultures came swooping down on the bodies, the Wolf-cub ran off in the thicket, and seeking its deepest cover, was led down a ravine to a wide valley. Suddenly there arose from the grass a big She-wolf, like his mother, yet different, a stranger, and instinctively the stray Cub sank to the earth, as the old Wolf bounded on him. No doubt the Cub had been taken for some lawful prey, but a whiff set that right. She stood over him for an instant. He grovelled at her feet. The impulse to kill him or at least give him a shake died away. He had the smell of a young Cub. Her own were about his age, her heart was touched, and when he found courage enough to put his nose up and smell her nose, she made no angry demonstration except a short half-hearted growl. Now, however, he had smelled something that he sorely needed. He had not fed since the day before, and when the old Wolf turned to leave him, he tumbled after her on clumsy puppy legs. Had the Mother-wolf been far from home he must soon have been left behind, but the nearest hollow was the chosen place, and the Cub arrived at the den's mouth soon after the Mother-wolf.

A stranger is an enemy, and the old one rushing forth to the defense, met the Cub again, and again was restrained by something that rose in her responsive to the smell. The Cub had thrown himself on his back in utter submission, but that did not prevent his nose reporting to him the good thing almost within reach. The She-wolf went into the den and curled herself about her brood; the Cub persisted in following. She snarled as he approached her own little ones, but disarming wrath each time by submission and his very cubhood, he was presently among her brood, helping himself to what he wanted so greatly, and thus he adopted himself into her family. In a few days he was so much one of them that the mother forgot about his being a stranger. Yet he was different from them in several ways—older by two weeks, stronger, and marked on the neck and shoulders with what afterward grew to be a dark mane.

Little Duskymane could not have been happier in his choice of a foster-mother, for the Yellow Wolf was not only a good hunter with a fund of cunning, but she was a Wolf of modern ideas as well. The old tricks of tolling a Prairie Dog, relaying for Antelope, houghing a Bronco or flanking a Steer she had learned partly from instinct and partly from the example of her more experienced relatives, when they joined to form the winter bands. But, just as necessary nowadays, she had learned that all men carry guns, that guns are irresistible, that the only way to avoid them is by keeping out of sight while the sun is up, and yet that at night they are harmless. She had a fair comprehension of

Billy finds a foster-mother

traps, indeed she had been in one once, and though she left a toe behind in pulling free, it was a toe most advantageously disposed of; thenceforth, though not comprehending the nature of the trap, she was thoroughly imbued with the horror of it, with the idea indeed that iron is dangerous, and at any price it should be avoided.

On one occasion, when she and five others were planning to raid a Sheep yard, she held back at the last minute because some new-strung wires appeared. The others rushed in to find the Sheep beyond their reach, themselves in a death-trap.

Thus she had learned the newer dangers, and while it is unlikely that she had any clear mental conception of them she had acquired a wholesome distrust of all things strange, and a horror of one or two in particular that proved her lasting safeguard. Each year she raised her brood successfully and the number of Yellow Wolves increased in the country. Guns, traps, men and the new animals they brought had been learned, but there was yet another lesson before her—a terrible one indeed.

About the time Duskymane's brothers were a month old his foster-mother returned in a strange condition. She was frothing at the mouth, her legs trembled, and she fell in a convulsion near the doorway of the den, but recovering, she came in. Her jaws quivered, her teeth rattled a little as she tried to lick the little ones; she seized her own front leg and bit it so as not to bite them, but at length she grew quieter and calmer. The Cubs had retreated in fear to a far pocket, but now they returned and crowded about her to seek their usual food. The mother recovered, but was very ill for two or three days, and those days with the poison in her system worked disaster for the brood. They were terribly sick; only the strongest could survive, and when the trial of strength was over, the den contained only the old one and the Black-maned Cub, the one she had adopted. Thus little Duskymane became her sole charge; all her strength was devoted to feeding him, and he thrived apace.

Wolves are quick to learn certain things. The reactions of smell are the greatest that a Wolf can feel, and thenceforth both Cub and foster-mother experienced a quick, unreasoning sense of fear and hate the moment the smell of strychnine reached them.

THE RUDIMENTS OF WOLF TRAINING

With the sustenance of seven at his service the little Wolf had every reason to grow, and when in the autumn he began to follow his mother on her hunting trips he was as tall as she was. Now a change of region was forced on them, for numbers of little Wolves were growing up. Sentinel Butte, the rocky fastness of the plains, was claimed by many that were big and strong; the weaker must move out, and with them Yellow Wolf and the Dusky Cub.

Wolves have no language in the sense that man has; their vocabulary is probably limited to a dozen howls, barks, and grunts expressing the simplest emotions; but they have several other modes of

conveying ideas, and one very special method of spreading information—the Wolf-telephone. Scattered over their range are a number of
recognized "centrals." Sometimes these are stones, sometimes the
angle of cross-trails, sometimes a Buffalo-skull—indeed, any conspicuous object near a main trail is used. A Wolf calling here, as a Dog
does at a telegraph post, or a Muskrat at a certain mudpie point, leaves
his body-scent and learns what other visitors have been there recently
to do the same. He learns also whence they came and where they went,
as well as something about their condition, whether hunted, hungry,
gorged, or sick. By this system of registration a Wolf knows where his
friends, as well as his foes, are to be found. And Duskymane, following
after the Yellow Wolf, was taught the places and uses of the many
signal-stations without any conscious attempt at teaching on the part of
his foster-mother. Example backed by his native instincts was indeed
the chief teacher, but on one occasion at least there was something very
like the effort of a human parent to guard her child in danger.

The Dark Cub had learned the rudiments of Wolf life: that the way
to fight Dogs is to run, and to fight as you run, never grapple, but snap,
snap, snap, and make for the rough country where Horses cannot bring
their riders.

He learned not to bother about the Coyotes that follow for the
pickings when you hunt; you cannot catch them and they do you no
harm.

He knew he must not waste time dashing after Birds that alight on
the ground; and that he must keep away from the little black and white
Animal with the bushy tail. It is not very good to eat, and it is very,
very bad to smell.

Poison! Oh, he never forgot that smell from the day when the den
was cleared of all his foster-brothers.

He now knew that the first move in attacking Sheep was to scatter
them; a lone Sheep is a foolish and easy prey; that the way to round up
a band of Cattle was to frighten a Calf.

He learned that he must always attack a Steer behind, a Sheep in
front, and a Horse in the middle, that is, on the flank, and never, never
attack a man at all, never even face him. But an important lesson was
added to these, one in which the mother consciously taught him of a
secret foe.

THE LESSON ON TRAPS

A Calf had died in branding-time and now, two weeks later, was in its
best state for perfect taste, not too fresh, not over-ripe—that is, in a
Wolf's opinion—and the wind carried this information afar. The Yellow
Wolf and Duskymane were out for supper, though not yet knowing
where, when the tidings of veal arrived, and they trotted up the wind.
The Calf was in an open place, and plain to be seen in the moonlight. A
Dog would have trotted right up to the carcass, an old-time Wolf might
have done so, but constant war had developed constant vigilance in the

Yellow Wolf, and trusting nothing and no one but her nose, she slacked her speed to a walk. On coming in easy view she stopped, and for long swung her nose, submitting the wind to the closest possible chemical analysis. She tried it with her finest tests, blew all the membranes clean again and tried it once more; and this was the report of the trusty nostrils, yes, the unanimous report. First, rich and racy smell of Calf, seventy per cent.; smells of grass, bugs, wood, flowers, trees, sand, and other uninteresting negations, fifteen per cent.; smell of her Cub and herself, positive but ignorable, ten per cent.; smell of human tracks, two per cent.; smell of smoke, one per cent.; of sweaty leather smell, one per cent.; of human body-scent (not discernible in some samples), one-half per cent.; smell of iron, a trace.

The old Wolf crouched a little but sniffed hard with swinging nose; the young Wolf imitatively did the same. She backed off to a greater distance; the Cub stood. She gave a low whine; he followed unwillingly. She circled around the tempting carcass; a new smell was recorded—Coyote trail-scent, soon followed by Coyote body-scent. Yes, there they were sneaking along a near ridge, and now as she passed to one side the samples changed, the wind had lost nearly every trace of Calf; miscellaneous, commonplace, and uninteresting smells were there instead. The human track-scent was as before, the trace of leather was gone, but fully one-half per cent. of iron-odor, and body-smell of man raised to nearly two per cent.

Fully alarmed, she conveyed her fear to the Cub, by her rigid pose, her air intent, and her slightly bristling mane.

She continued her round. At one time on a high place the human body-scent was doubly strong, then as she dropped it faded. Then the wind brought the full calf-odor with several track-scents of Coyotes and sundry Birds. Her suspicions were lulling as in a smalling circle she neared the tempting feast from the windward side. She had even advanced straight toward it for a few steps when the sweaty leather sang loud and strong again, and smoke and iron mingled like two strands of a parti-colored yarn. Centring all her attention on this, she advanced within two leaps of the Calf. There on the ground was a scrap of leather telling also of a human touch, close at hand the Calf, and now the iron and smoke on the full vast smell of Calf were like a snake trail across the trail of a whole Beef herd. It was so slight that the Cub, with the appetite and impatience of youth, pressed up against his mother's shoulder to go past and eat without delay. She seized him by the neck and flung him back. A stone struck by his feet rolled forward and stopped with a peculiar clink. The danger smell was greatly increased at this, and the Yellow Wolf backed slowly from the feast, the Cub unwillingly following.

As he looked wistfully he saw the Coyotes drawing nearer, mindful chiefly to avoid the Wolves. He watched their really cautious advance; it seemed like heedless rushing compared with his mother's approach. The Calf smell rolled forth in exquisite and overpowering excellence now, for they were tearing the meat, when a sharp clank was heard and a yelp from a Coyote. At the same time the quiet night was

shocked with a roar and a flash of fire. Heavy shots spattered Calf and Coyotes, and yelping like beaten Dogs they scattered, excepting one that was killed and a second struggling in the trap set here by the ever-active wolvers. The air was charged with the hateful smells redoubled now, and horrid smells additional. The Yellow Wolf glided down a hollow and led her Cub away in flight, but, as they went, they saw a man rush from the bank near where the mother's nose had warned her of the human scent. They saw him kill the caught Coyote and set the traps for more.

Their narrow escape from trap and gun

THE BEGUILING OF THE YELLOW WOLF

The life game is a hard game, for we may win ten thousand times, and if we fail but once our gain is gone. How many hundred times had the Yellow Wolf scorned the traps; how many Cubs she had trained to do the same! Of all the dangers to her life she best knew traps.

October had come; the Cub was now much taller than the mother. The wolver had seen them once—a Yellow Wolf followed by another, whose long, awkward legs, big, soft feet, thin neck, and skimpy tail proclaimed him this year's Cub. The record of the dust and sand said that the old one had lost a right front toe, and that the young one was of giant size.

It was the wolver that thought to turn the carcass of the Calf to profit, but he was disappointed in getting Coyotes instead of Wolves. It was the beginning of the trapping season, for this month fur is prime. A young trapper often fastens the bait on the trap; an experienced one does not. A good trapper will even put the bait at one place and the trap ten or twenty feet away, but at a spot that the Wolf is likely to cross in circling. A favorite plan is to hide three or four traps around an open place, and scatter some scraps of meat in the middle. The traps are buried out of sight after being smoked to hide the taint of hands and iron. Sometimes no bait is used except a little piece of cotton or a tuft of feathers that may catch the Wolf's eye or pique its curiosity and tempt it to circle on the fateful, treacherous ground. A good trapper varies his methods continually so that the Wolves cannot learn his ways. Their only safeguards are perpetual vigilance and distrust of all smells that are known to be of man.

The wolver, with a load of the strongest steel traps, had begun his autumn work on the 'Cottonwood.'

An old Buffalo trail crossing the river followed a little draw that climbed the hills to the level upland. All animals use these trails, Wolves and Foxes as well as Cattle and Deer: they are the main thoroughfares. A cottonwood stump not far from where it plunged to the gravelly stream was marked with Wolf signs that told the wolver of its use. Here was an excellent place for traps, not on the trail, for Cattle were here in numbers, but twenty yards away on a level, sandy spot he set four traps in a twelve-foot square. Near each he scattered two or three scraps of meat; three or four white feathers on a spear of grass in the middle completed the setting. No human eye, few animal noses, could have detected the hidden danger of that sandy ground, when the sun and wind and the sand itself had dissipated the man-track taint.

The Yellow Wolf had seen and passed, and taught her giant son to pass, such traps a thousand times before.

The Cattle came to water in the heat of the day. They strung down the Buffalo path as once the Buffalo did. The little Vesper-birds flitted before them, the Cowbirds rode on them, and the Prairie-dogs chattered at them, just as they once did at the Buffalo.

— Down from the gray-green mesa with its green-gray rocks, they marched with imposing solemnity, importance, and directness of purpose. Some frolicsome Calves, playing alongside the trail, grew sober and walked behind their mothers as the river flat was reached. The old Cow that headed the processsion sniffed suspiciously as she passed the "trap set," but it was far away, otherwise she would have pawed and bellowed over the scraps of bloody beef till every trap was sprung and harmless.

But she led to the river. After all had drunk their fill they lay down on the nearest bank till late afternoon. Then their unheard dinner-gong aroused them, and started them on the backward march to where the richest pastures grew.

One or two small birds had picked at the scraps of meat, some blue-bottle flies buzzed about, but the sinking sun saw the sandy mask untouched.

A brown Marsh Hawk came skimming over the river flat as the sun began his color play. Blackbirds dashed into thickets, and easily avoided his clumsy pounce. It was too early for the Mice, but, as he skimmed the ground, his keen eye caught the flutter of feathers by the trap and turned his flight. The feathers in their uninteresting emptiness were exposed before he was near, but now he saw the scraps of meat. Guileless of cunning, he alighted and was devouring a second lump when—*clank*—the dust was flirted high and the Marsh Hawk was held by his toes, struggling vainly in the jaws of a powerful wolf-trap. He was not much hurt. His ample wings winnowed from time to time, in efforts to be free, but he was helpless, even as a Sparrow might be in a rat-trap, and when the sun had played his fierce chromatic scale, his swan-song sung, and died as he dies only in the blazing west, and the shades had fallen on the melodramatic scene of the Mouse in the elephant-trap, there was a deep, rich sound on the high flat butte, answered by another, neither very long, neither repeated, and both instinctive rather than necessary. One was the muster-call of an ordinary Wolf, the other the answer of a very big male, not a pair in this case, but mother and son—Yellow Wolf and Duskymane. They came trotting together down the Buffalo trail. They paused at the telephone box on the hill and again at the old cottonwood root, and were making for the river when the Hawk in the trap fluttered his wings. The old Wolf turned toward him,—a wounded bird on the ground surely, and she rushed forward. Sun and sand soon burn all trail-scents; there was nothing to warn her. She sprang on the flopping bird and a chop of her jaws ended his troubles, but a horrid sound—the gritting of her teeth on steel—told her of peril. She dropped the Hawk and sprang backward from the dangerous ground, but landed in the second trap. High on her foot its death-grip closed, and leaping with all her strength, to escape, she set her fore foot in another of the lurking grips of steel. Never had a trap been so baited before. Never was she so unsuspicious. Never was catch more sure. Fear and fury filled the old Wolf's heart; she tugged and strained, she chewed the chains, she snarled and foamed. One trap with its buried log, she might have dragged; with two, she was helpless. Struggle as she might, it only worked those relentless jaws more deeply into her feet. She snapped wildly at the air; she tore the dead Hawk into shreds; she roared the short, barking roar of a crazy Wolf. She bit at the traps, at her cub, at herself. She tore her legs that were held; she gnawed in frenzy at her flank, she chopped off her tail in her madness; she splintered all her teeth on the steel, and filled her bleeding, foaming jaws with clay and sand.

She struggled till she fell, and writed about or lay like dead, till strong enough to rise and grind the chains again with her teeth.

And so the night passed by.

And Duskymane? Where was he? The feeling of the time when his foster-mother had come home poisoned, now returned; but he was even more afraid of her. She seemed filled with fighting hate. He held away and whined a little; he slunk off and came back when she lay still, only to retreat again, as she sprang forward, raging at him, and then renewed her efforts at the traps. He did not understand it, but he knew this much, she was in terrible trouble, and the cause seemed to be the same as that which had scared them the night they had ventured near the Calf.

Duskymane hung about all night, fearing to go near, not knowing what to do, and helpless as his mother.

At dawn the next day a sheepherder seeking lost Sheep discovered her from a neighboring hill. A signal mirror called the wolver from his camp. Duskymane saw the new danger. He was a mere Cub, though so tall; he could not face the man, and fled at his approach.

The wolver rode up to the sorry, tattered, bleeding She-wolf in the trap. He raised his rifle and soon the struggling stopped.

The wolver read the trail and the signs about, and remembering those he had read before, he divined that this was the Wolf with the great Cub—the She-wolf of Sentinel Butte.

Duskymane heard the "crack" as he scurried off into cover. He could scarcely know what it meant, but he never saw his kind old foster-mother again. Thenceforth he must face the world alone.

THE YOUNG WOLF WINS A PLACE AND FAME

Instinct is no doubt a Wolf's first and best guide, but gifted parents are a great start in life. The dusky-maned cub had had a mother of rare excellence and he reaped the advantage of all her cleverness. He had inherited an exquisite nose and had absolute confidence in its admonitions. Mankind has difficulty in recognizing the power of nostrils. A Gray-wolf can glance over the morning wind as a man does

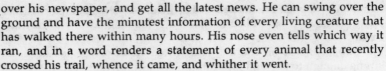

over his newspaper, and get all the latest news. He can swing over the ground and have the minutest information of every living creature that has walked there within many hours. His nose even tells which way it ran, and in a word renders a statement of every animal that recently crossed his trail, whence it came, and whither it went.

That power had Duskymane in the highest degree; his broad, moist nose was evidence of it to all who are judges of such things. Added to this, his frame was of unusual power and endurance, and last, he had early learned a deep distrust of everything strange, and, call it what we will, shyness, wariness or suspicion, it was worth more to him than all his cleverness. It was this as much as his physical powers that made a success of his life. Might is right in wolf-land, and Duskymane and his mother had been driven out of Sentinel Butte. But it was a very delectable land and he kept drifting back to his native mountain. One or two big Wolves there resented his coming. They drove him off several times, yet each time he returned he was better able to face them; and before he was eighteen months old he had defeated all rivals and established himself again on his native ground; where he lived like a robber baron, levying tribute on the rich lands about him and finding safety in the rocky fastness.

Wolver Ryder often hunted in that country, and before long, he came across a five-and-one-half-inch track, the foot-print of a giant Wolf. Roughly reckoned, twenty to twenty-five pounds of weight or six inches of stature is a fair allowance for each inch of a Wolf's foot; this Wolf therefore stood thirty-three inches at the shoulder and weighed about one hundred and forty pounds, by far the largest wolf he had ever met. King had lived in Goat country, and now in Goat language he exclaimed: "You bet, ain't that an old Billy?" Thus by trivial chance it was that Duskymane was known to his foe, as 'Badlands Billy.'

Ryder was familiar with the muster-call of the Wolves, the long, smooth cry, but Billy's had a singular feature, a slurring that was always distinctive. Ryder had heard this before, in the Cottonwood Cañon, and when at length he got a sight of the big Wolf with the black mane, it struck him that this was also the Cub of the old Yellow fury that he had trapped.

O - w - w - w

These were among the things he told me as we sat by the fire at night. I knew of the early days when any one could trap or poison Wolves, of the passing of those days, with the passing of the simple Wolves; of the new race of Wolves with new cunning that were defying the methods of the ranchmen, and increasing steadily in numbers. Now the wolver told me of the various ventures that Penroof had made with different kinds of Hounds: of Foxhounds too thin-skinned to fight; of Greyhounds that were useless when the animal was out of sight; of Danes too heavy for the rough country, and, last, of the composite pack with some of all kinds, including at times a Bull-terrier to lead them in the final fight.

He told of hunts after Coyotes, which usually were successful because the Coyotes sought the plains, and were easily caught by the Greyhounds. He told of killing some small Gray-wolves with this very pack, usually at the cost of the one that led them; but above all he dwelt on the wonderful prowess of "that thar cussed old Black Wolf of Sentinel Butte," and related the many attempts to run him down or corner him—an unbroken array of failures. For the big Wolf, with exasperating persistence, continued to live on the finest stock of the Penroof brand, and each year was teaching more Wolves how to do the same with perfect impunity.

I listened even as gold-hunters listen to stories of treasure trove, for these were the things of my world. These things indeed were uppermost in all our minds, for the Penroof pack was lying around our camp-fire now. We were out after Badlands Billy.

THE VOICE IN THE NIGHT
AND THE BIG TRACK IN THE MORNING

One night late in September after the last streak of light was gone from the west and the Coyotes had begun their yapping chorus, a deep, booming sound was heard. King took out his pipe, turned his head and said: "That's him—that's old Billy. He's been watching us all day from some high place, and now when the guns are useless he's here to have a little fun with us."

Two or three Dogs arose, with bristling manes, for they clearly recognized that this was no Coyote. They rushed out into the night, but did not go far; their brawling sounds were suddenly varied by loud yelps, and they came running back to the shelter of the fire. One was so badly cut in the shoulder that he was useless for the rest of the hunt. Another was hurt in the flank—it seemed the less serious wound, and yet next morning the hunters buried that second Dog.

The men were furious. They vowed speedy vengeance, and at dawn were off on the trail. The Coyotes yelped their dawning song, but they melted into the hills when the light was strong. The hunters

searched about for the big Wolf's track, hoping that the Hounds would be able to take it up and find him, but they either could not or would not.

They found a Coyote, however, and within a few hundred yards they killed him. It was a victory, I suppose, for Coyotes kill Calves and Sheep, but somehow I felt the common thought of all: "Mighty brave Dogs for a little Coyote, but they could not face the big Wolf last night."

Young Penroof, as though in answer to one of the unput questions, said:

"Say, boys, I believe old Billy had a hull bunch of Wolves with him last night."

"Didn't see but one track," said King gruffly.

In this way the whole of October slipped by; all day hard riding after doubtful trails, following the Dogs, who either could not keep the big trail or feared to do so, and again and again we had news of damage done by the Wolf; sometimes a cowboy would report it to us; and sometimes we found the carcasses ourselves. A few of these we poisoned, though it is considered a very dangerous thing to do while running Dogs. The end of the month found us a weather-beaten, dispirited lot of men, with a worn-out lot of Horses, and a footsore pack, reduced in numbers from ten to seven. So far we had killed only one Gray-wolf and three Coyotes; Badlands Billy had killed at least a dozen Cows and Dogs at fifty dollars a head. Some of the boys decided to give it up and go home, so King took advantage of their going, to send a letter, asking for reënforcements including all the spare Dogs at the ranch.

During the two days' wait we rested our Horses, shot some game, and prepared for a harder hunt. Late on the second day the new Dogs arrived—eight beauties—and raised the working pack to fifteen.

The weather now turned much cooler, and in the morning, to the joy of the wolvers, the ground was white with snow. This surely meant success. With cool weather for the Dogs and Horses to run; with the big Wolf not far away, for he had been heard the night before; and with tracking snow, so that once found he could not baffle us,—escape for him was impossible.

We were up at dawn, but before we could get away, three men came riding into camp. They were the Penroof boys back again. The change of weather had changed their minds; they knew that with snow we might have luck.

"Remember now," said King, as all were mounting, "we don't want any but Badlands Billy this trip. Get him an' we kin bust up the hull combination. It is a five-and-a-half-inch track."

And each measured off on his quirt handle, or on his glove, the exact five and a half inches that was to be used in testing the tracks he might find.

Not more than an hour elapsed before we got a signal from the rider who had gone west-ward. One shot: that means "attention," a pause while counting ten, then two shots: that means "*come on.*"

King gathered the Dogs and rode direct to the distant figure on the hill. All hearts beat high with hope, and we were not disappointed. Some small Wolf tracks had been found, but here at last was the big track, nearly six inches long. Young Penroof wanted to yell and set out at full gallop. It was like hunting a Lion; it was like finding happiness long deferred. The hunter knows nothing more inspiring than the clean-cut line of fresh tracks that is leading to a wonderful animal, he has long been hunting in vain. How King's eye gleamed as he gloated over the sign!

RUN DOWN AT LAST

It was the roughest of all rough riding. It was a far longer hunt than we had expected, and was full of little incidents, for that endless line of marks was a minute history of all that the big Wolf had done the night before. Here he had circled at the telephone box and looked for news; there he had paused to examine an old skull; here he had shied off and swung cautiously up wind to examine something that proved to be an old tin can; there at length he had mounted a low hill and sat down, probably giving the muster-howl, for two Wolves had come to him from different directions, and they then had descended to the river flat where the Cattle would seek shelter during the storm. Here all three had visited a Buffalo skull; there they trotted in line; and yonder they separated, going three different ways, to meet—yes—here—oh, what a sight, a fine Cow ripped open, left dead and *uneaten*. Not to their taste, it seems, for see! within a mile is another killed by them. Not six hours ago, they had feasted. Here their trails scatter again, but not far, and the snow tells plainly how each had lain down to sleep. The Hounds' manes bristled as they sniffed those places. King had held the Dogs well in hand, but now they were greatly excited. We came to a hill whereon the Wolves had turned and faced our way, then fled at full speed,—so said the trail,—and now it was clear that they had watched us from that hill, and were not far away.

The pack kept well together, because the Greyhounds, seeing no quarry, were merely puttering about among the other Dogs, or running back with the Horses. We went as fast as we could, for the Wolves were speeding. Up mesas and down coulees we rode, sticking closely to the Dogs, though it was the roughest country that could be picked. One gully after another, an hour and another hour, and still the threefold track went bounding on; another hour and no change, but interminable climbing, sliding, struggling, through brush and over boulders, guided by the far-away yelping of the Dogs.

Now the chase led downward to the low valley of the river, where there was scarcely any snow. Jumping and scrambling down hills, recklessly leaping dangerous gullies and slippery rocks, we felt that we could not hold out much longer; when on the lowest, dryest level the pack split, some went up, some went down, and others straight on. Oh, how King did swear! He knew at once what it meant. The Wolves had scattered, and so had divided the pack. Three Dogs after a Wolf would have no chance, four could not kill him, two would certainly be killed. And yet this was the first encouraging sign we had seen, for it meant that the Wolves were hard pressed. We spurred ahead to stop the Dogs, to pick for them the only trail. But that was not so easy. Without snow here and with countless Dog tracks, we were foiled. All we could do was to let the Dogs choose, but keep them to a single choice. Away we went as before, hoping, yet fearing that we were not on the right track. The Dogs ran well, very fast indeed. This was a bad sign, King said, but we could not get sight of the track because the Dogs overran it before we came.

After a two-mile run the chase led upward again in snow country; the Wolf was sighted, but to our disgust, we were on the track of the smallest one.

"I thought so," growled young Penroof. "Dogs was altogether too keen for a serious proposition. Kind o' surprised it ain't turned out a Jack-rabbit."

Within another mile he had turned to bay in a willow thicket. We heard him howl the long-drawn howl for help, and before we could reach the place King saw the Dogs recoil and scatter. A minute later there sped from the far side of the thicket a small Gray-wolf and a Black One of very much greater size.

"By golly, if he didn't yell for help, and Billy come back to help him; that's great!" exclaimed the wolver. And my heart went out to the brave old Wolf that refused to escape by abandoning his friend.

The next hour was a hard repetition of the gully riding, but it was on the highlands where there was snow, and when again the pack was split, we strained every power and succeeded in keeping them on the big "five-fifty track," that already was wearing for me the glamour of romance.

Evidently the Dogs preferred either of the others, but we got them going at last. Another half hour's hard work and far ahead, as I rose to a broad flat plain, I had my first glimpse of the Big Black Wolf of Sentinel Butte.

"Hurrah! Badlands Billy! Hurrah! Badlands Billy!" I shouted in salute, and the others took up the cry.

We were on his track at last, thanks to himself. The Dogs joined in with a louder baying, the Greyhounds yelped and made straight for him, and the Horses sniffed and sprang more gamely as they caught the thrill. The only silent one was the black-maned Wolf, and as I marked his size and power, and above all his long and massive jaws, I knew why the Dogs preferred some other trail.

With head and tail low he was bounding over the snow. His

tongue was lolling long; plainly he was hard pressed. The wolvers' hands flew to their revolvers, though he was three hundred yards ahead; they were out for blood, not sport. But an instant later he had sunk from view in the nearest sheltered cañon.

Now which way would he go, up or down the cañon? Up was toward his mountain, down was better cover. King and I thought "up," so pressed westward along the ridge. But the others rode eastward, watching for a chance to shoot.

Soon we had ridden out of hearing. We were wrong—the Wolf had gone down, but we heard no shooting. The cañon was crossable here; we reached the other side and then turned back at a gallop, scanning the snow for a trail, the hills for a moving form, or the wind for a sound of life.

"Squeak, squeak," went our saddle leathers, "puff—puff" our Horses, and their feet 'ka-ka-lump, ka-ka-lump."

WHEN BILLY WENT BACK TO HIS MOUNTAIN

We were back opposite to where the Wolf had plunged, but saw no sign. We rode at an easy gallop, on eastward, a mile, and still on, when King gasped out, "Look at that!" A dark spot was moving on the snow ahead. We put on speed. Another dark spot appeared, and another, but they were not going fast. In five minutes we were near them, to find— three of our own Greyhounds. They had lost sight of the game, and with that their interest waned. Now they were seeking us. We saw nothing there of the chase or of the other hunters. But hastening to the next ridge we stumbled on the trail we sought and followed as hard as though in view. Another cañon came in our path, and as we rode and looked for a place to cross, a wild din of Hounds came from its brushy depth. The clamor grew and passed up the middle.

We raced along the rim, hoping to see the game. The Dogs appeared near the farther side, not in a pack, but a long, straggling line. In five minutes more they rose to the edge, and ahead of them was the great Black Wolf. He was loping as before, head and tail low. Power was plain in every limb, and double power in his jaws and neck, but I thought his bounds were shorter now, and that they had lost their spring. The Dogs slowly reached the upper level, and sighting him they

broke into a feeble cry; they, too, were nearly spent. The Greyhounds
saw the chase, and leaving us they scrambled down the cañon and up
the other side at impetuous speed that would surely break them down,
while we rode, vainly seeking means of crossing.

How the wolver raved to see the pack lead off in the climax of the
chase, and himself held up behind. But he rode and wrathed and still
rode, up to where the cañon dwindled—rough land and a hard ride. As
we neared the great flat mountain, the feeble cry of the pack was heard
again from the south, then toward the high Butte's side, and just a trifle
louder now. We reined in on a hillock and scanned the snow. A moving
speck appeared, then others, not bunched, but in a straggling train, and
at times there was a far faint cry. They were headed towards us, coming
on, yes! coming, but so slowly, for not one was really running now.
There was the grim old Cow-killer limping over the ground, and far
behind a Greyhound, and another, and farther still, the other Dogs in
order of their speed, slowly, gamely, dragging themselves on that
pursuit. Many hours of hardest toil had done their work. The Wolf had
vainly sought to fling them off. Now was his hour of doom, for he was
spent; they still had some reserve. Straight to us for a time they came,
skirting the base of the mountain, crawling.

We could not cross to join them, so held our breath and gazed with
ravenous eyes. They were nearer now, the wind brought feeble notes
from the Hounds. The big Wolf turned to the steep ascent, up a well-
known trail, it seemed, for he made no slip. My heart went with him,
for he had come back to rescue his friend, and a momentary thrill of
pity came over us both, as we saw him glance around and drag himself
up the sloping way, to die on his mountain. There was no escape for
him, beset by fifteen Dogs with men to back them. He was not walking,
but tottering upward; the Dogs behind in line, were now doing a little
better, were nearing him. We could hear them gasping; we scarcely
heard them bay—they had no breath for that; upward the grim
procession went, circling a spur of the Butte and along a ledge that
climbed and narrowed, then dropped for a few yards to a shelf that
reared above the cañon. The foremost Dogs were closing, fearless of a
foe so nearly spent.

Here in the narrowest place, where one wrong step meant death,
the great Wolf turned and faced them. With fore-feet braced, with head
low and tail a little raised, his dusky mane a-bristling, his glittering
tusks laid bare, but uttering no sound that we could hear, he faced the
crew. His legs were weak with toil, but his neck, his jaws, and his heart
were strong, and—now all you who love the Dogs had better close the
book—on—up and down—fifteen to one, they came, the swiftest first,
and how it was done, the eye could scarcely see, but even as a stream of
water pours on a rock to be splashed in broken jets aside, that stream of
Dogs came pouring down the path, in single file perforce, and
Duskymane received them as they came. A feeble spring, a counter-
lunge, a gash, and "Fango's down," has lost his foothold and is gone.
Dander and Coalie close and try to clinch; a rush, a heave, and they are
fallen from that narrow path. Blue-spot then, backed by mighty Oscar

The Great Wolf turned and faced them

and fearless Tige—but the Wolf is next the rock and the flash of combat clears to show him there alone, the big Dogs gone; the rest close in, the hind-most force the foremost on—down—to their death. Slash, chop and heave, from the swiftest to the biggest, to the last, down—down— he sent them whirling from the ledge to the gaping gulch below, where rocks and snags of trunks were sharp to do their work.

In fifty seconds it was done. The rock had splashed the stream aside—the Penroof pack was all wiped out; and Badlands Billy stood there, alone again on his mountain.

A moment he waited to look for more to come. There were no more, the pack was dead; but waiting he got his breath, then raising his voice for the first time in that fatal scene, he feebly gave a long yell of triumph, and scaling the next low bank, was screened from view in a cañon of Sentinel Butte.

We stared like men of stone. The guns in our hands were forgotten. It was all so quick, so final. We made no move till the Wolf was gone. It was not far to the place: we went on foot to see if any had escaped. Not one was left alive. We could do nothing—we could say nothing.

THE HOWL AT SUNSET

A week later we were riding the upper trail back of the Chimney Pot, King and I. "The old man is pretty sick of it," he said. "He'd sell out if he could. He don't know what's the next move."

The sun went down beyond Sentinel Butte. It was dusk as we reached the turn that led to Dumont's place, and a deep-toned rolling howl came from the river flat below, followed by a number of higher-pitched howls in answering chorus. We could see nothing, but we listened hard. The song was repeated, the hunting-cry of the Wolves. It faded, the night was stirred by another, the sharp bark and the short howl, the signal "close in"; a bellow came up, very short, for it was cut short.

And King as he touched his Horse said grimly: "That's him, he is out with the pack, an' thar goes another Beef."

THE BOY AND THE LYNX

He was barely fifteen, a lover of sport and uncommonly keen, even for a beginner. Flocks of Wild Pigeons had been coming all day across the blue Lake of Caygeonull, and perching in lines on the dead limbs of the great rampikes that stood as monuments of fire, around the little clearing in the forest, they afforded tempting marks; but he followed them for hours in vain. They seemed to know the exact range of the old-fashioned shotgun and rose on noisy wings each time before he was near enough to fire. At length a small flock scattered among the low green trees that grew about the spring, near the log shanty, and taking advantage of the cover, Thorburn went in gently. He caught sight of a single Pigeon close to him, took a long aim and fired. A sharp crack resounded at almost the same time and the bird fell dead. Thorburn rushed to seize the prize just as a tall young man stepped into view and picked it up.

"Hello, Corney! you got my bird!"

"Your burrud! Sure yours flew away thayre. I saw them settle hayer and thought I'd make sure of wan with the rifle."

A careful examination showed that a rifle-ball as well as a charge of shot had struck the Pigeon. The gunners had fired on the same bird. Both enjoyed the joke, though it had its serious side, for food as well as ammunition was scarce in that backwoods home.

Corney, a superb specimen of a six-foot Irish-Canadian in early manhood, now led away to the log shanty where the very scarcity of luxuries and the roughness of their lives were sources of merriment. For the Colts, though born and bred in the backwoods of Canada, had lost nothing of the spirit that makes the Irish blood a world-wide synonym of heartiness and wit.

Corney was the eldest son of a large family. The old folks lived at Petersay, twenty-five miles to the southward. He had taken up a "claim" to carve his own home out of the woods at Fenebonk, and his grown sisters, Margat, staid and reliable, and Loo, bright and witty, were keeping house for him. Thorburn Alder was visiting them. He had just recovered from a severe illness and had been sent to rough it in the

319

woods in hope of winning some of the vigor of his hosts. Their home was of unhewn logs, unfloored, and roofed with sods, which bore a luxuriant crop of grass and weeds. The primitive woods around were broken in two places: one where the roughest of roads led southward to Petersay; the other where the sparkling lake rolled on a pebbly shore and gave a glimpse of their nearest neighbor's house—four miles across the water.

Their daily round had little change. Corney was up at daybreak to light the fire, call his sisters, and feed the horses while they prepared breakfast. At six the meal was over and Corney went to his work. At noon, which Margat knew by the shadow of a certain rampike falling on the spring, a clear notification to draw fresh water for the table, Loo would hang a white rag on a pole, and Corney, seeing the signal, would return from summer fallow or hayfield, grimy, swarthy, and ruddy, a picture of manly vigor and honest toil. Thor might be away all day, but at night, when they again assembled at the table, he would come from lake or distant ridge and eat a supper like the dinner and breakfast, for meals as well as days were exact repeats: pork, bread, potatoes, and tea, with occasionally eggs supplied by a dozen hens around the little log stable, with, rarely, a variation of wild meat, for Thor was not a hunter and Corney had little time for anything but the farm.

THE LYNX

A huge four-foot basswood had gone the way of all trees. Death had been generous—had sent the three warnings: it was the biggest of its kind, its children were grown up, it was hollow. The wintry blast that sent it down had broken it across and revealed a great hole where should have been its heart. A long wooden cavern in the middle of a sunny opening, it now lay, and presented an ideal home for a Lynx when she sought a sheltered nesting-place for her coming brood.

Old was she and gaunt, for this was a year of hard times for the Lynxes. A Rabbit plague the autumn before had swept away their main support; a winter of deep snow and sudden crusts had killed off nearly all the Partridges; a long wet spring had destroyed the few growing coveys and had kept the ponds and streams so full that Fish and Frogs were safe from their armed paws, and this mother Lynx fared no better than her kind.

The little ones—half starved before they came—were a double drain, for they took the time she might have spent in hunting.

The Northern Hare is the favorite food of the Lynx, and in some years she could have killed fifty in one day, but never one did she see this season. The plague had done its work too well.

One day she caught a Red-squirrel which had run into a hollow log that proved a trap. Another day a fetid Blacksnake was her only food. A day was missed, and the little ones whined piteously for their natural food and failing drink. One day she saw a large black animal of unpleasant but familiar smell. Swiftly and silently she sprang to make attack. She struck it once on the nose, but the Porcupine doubled his head under, his tail flew up, and the mother Lynx was speared in a dozen places with the little stinging javelins. She drew them all with her teeth, for she had "learned Porcupine" years before, and only the hard push of want would have made her strike one now.

A Frog was all she caught that day. On the next, as she ranged the farthest woods in a long, hard hunt, she heard a singular calling voice. It was new to her. She approached it cautiously, up wind, got many new odors and some more strange sounds in coming. The loud, clear, rolling call was repeated as the mother Lynx came to an opening in the forest. In the middle of it were two enormous muskrat or beaver-houses, far bigger than the biggest she ever before had seen. They were made partly of logs and situated, not in a pond, but on a dry knoll. Walking about them were a number of Partridges, that is, birds like Partridges, only larger and of various colors, red, yellow, and white.

One day she found a Porcupine

She quivered with the excitement that in a man would have been called buck-fever. Food—food—abundance of food, and the old huntress sank to earth. Her breast was on the ground, her elbows above her back, as she made stalk, her shrewdest, subtlest stalk; one of those Partrides must go untried, no error in this hunt; if it took hours—all day—she must approach with certainty to win before the quarry took to flight.

Only a few bounds it was from wood shelter to the great rat-house, but she was an hour in crawling that small space. From stump to brush, from log to bunch of grass she sneaked, a flattened form, and the Partridges saw her not. They fed about, the biggest uttering the ringing call that first had fallen on her ear. Once they seemed to sense their peril, but a long await dispelled the fear. Now they were almost in reach, and she trembled with all the eagerness of the hunting heart and the hungry maw. Her eye centred on a white one not quite the nearest, but the color seemed to hold her gaze.

There was an open space around the rat-house; outside that were tall weeds, and stumps were scattered everywhere. The white bird wandered behind these weeds, the red one of the loud voice flew to the top of the rat-mound and sang as before. The mother Lynx sank lower yet. It seemed an alarm note; but no, the white one still was there; she could see its feathers gleaming through the weeds. An open space now lay about. The huntress, flattened like an empty skin, trailed slow and silent on the ground behind a log no thicker than her neck; if she could reach that tuft of brush she could get unseen to the weeds and then would be near enough to spring. She could smell them now—the rich and potent smell of life, of flesh and blood, that set her limbs a-tingle and her eyes a-glow.

The Partridges still scratched and fed; another flew to the high top, but the white one remained. Five more slow-gliding, silent steps, and the Lynx was behind the weeds, the white bird shining through; she gauged the distance, tried the footing, swung her hind legs to clear some fallen brush, then *leaped* direct with all her force, and the white one never knew the death it died, for the fateful gray shadow dropped, the swift and deadly did their work, and before the other birds could realize the foe or fly, the Lynx was gone, with the white bird squirming in her jaws.

Uttering an unnecessary growl of inborn ferocity and joy she bounded into the forest, and bee-like sped for home. The last quiver had gone from the warm body of the victim when she heard the sound of heavy feet ahead. She leaped on a log. The wings of her prey were muffling her eyes, so she laid the bird down and held it safely with one paw. The sound drew nearer, the bushes bent, and a Boy stepped into view. The old Lynx knew and hated his kind. She had watched them at night, had followed them, had been hunted and hurt by them. For a moment they stood face to face. The huntress growled a warning that was also a challenge and a defiance, picked up the bird and bounded from the log into the sheltering bushes. It was a mile or two to the den, but she stayed not to eat till the sunlit opening and the big basswood came to view; then a low "prr—prr" called forth the little ones to revel with their mother in a plenteous meal of the choicest food.

THE HOME OF THE LYNX

At first Thor, being town-bred, was timid about venturing into the woods beyond the sound of Corney's axe; but day by day he went farther, guiding himself, not by unreliable moss on trees, but by sun, compass, and landscape features. His purpose was to learn about the wild animals rather than to kill them; but the naturalist is close kin to the sportsman, and the gun was his constant companion. In the clearing, the only animal of any size was a fat Woodchuck; it had a hole under a stump some hundred yards from the shanty. On sunny mornings it used to lie basking on the stump, but eternal vigilance is the price of every good thing in the woods. The Woodchuck was always alert and Thor tried in vain to shoot or even to trap him.

"Hyar," said Corney one morning, "time we had some fresh meat." He took down his rifle, an old-fashioned brass-mounted small-bore, and loading with care that showed the true rifleman, he steadied the weapon against the door-jamb and fired. The Woodchuck fell backward and lay still. Thor raced to the place and returned in triumph with the animal, shouting: "Plumb through the head—one hundred and twenty yards."

Corney controlled the gratified smile that wrestled with the corners of his mouth, but his bright eyes shone a trifle brighter for the moment.

It was no mere killing for killing's sake, for the Woodchuck was spreading a belt of destruction in the crop around his den. Its flesh supplied the family with more than one good meal and Corney showed Thor how to use the skin. First the pelt was wrapped in hardwood ashes for twenty-four hours. This brought the hair off. Then the skin was soaked for three days in soft soap and worked by hand, as it dried, till it came out a white strong leather.

Thor's wanderings extended farther in search of the things which always came as surprises however much he was looking for them. Many days were blanks and others would be crowded with incidents, for unexpectedness is above all the peculiar feature of hunting, and its lasting charm. One day he had gone far beyond the ridge in a new direction and passed through an open glade where lay the broken trunk of a huge basswood. The size impressed it on his memory. He swung past the glade to make for the lake, a mile to the west, and twenty minutes later he started back as his eye rested on a huge black animal in the crotch of a hemlock, some thirty feet from the ground. A Bear! At last, this was the test of nerve he had half expected all summer; had been wondering how that mystery "himself" would act under this very trial. He stood still; his right hand dived into his pocket and, bringing out three or four buckshot, which he carried for emergency, he dropped them on top of the birdshot already in the gun, then rammed a wad to hold them down.

The Bear had not moved and the boy could not see its head, but now he studied it carefully. It was not such a large one—no, it was a small one, yes, very small—a cub. A cub! That meant a mother Bear at hand, and Thor looked about with some fear, but seeing no signs of any except the little one, he levelled the gun and fired.

Then to his surprise down crashed the animal quite dead; it was not a Bear, but a large Porcupine. As it lay there he examined it with wonder and regret, for he had no wish to kill such a harmless creature. On its grotesque face he found two or three long scratches which proved that he had not been its only enemy. As he turned away he noticed some blood on his trousers, then saw that his left hand was bleeding. He had wounded himself quite severely on the quills of the animal without knowing it. He was sorry to leave the specimen there, and Loo, when she learned of it, said it was a shame not to skin it when she "needed a fur-lined cape for the winter."

On another day Thor had gone without a gun, as he meant only to gather some curious plants he had seen. They were close to the clearing; he knew the place by a fallen elm. As he came to it he heard a peculiar sound. Then on the log his eye caught two moving things. He lifted a bough and got a clear view. They were the head and tail of an enormous Lynx. It had seen him and was glaring and grumbling; and under its foot on the log was a white bird that a second glance showed to be one of their own precious hens. How fierce and cruel the brute looked! How Thor hated it! and fairly gnashed his teeth with disgust that now, when his greatest chance was come, he for once was without his gun. He was in not a little fear, too, and stood wondering what to do. The Lynx growled louder; its stumpy tail twitched viciously for a minute, then it picked up its victim, and leaping from the log was lost to view.

As it was a very rainy summer, the ground was soft everywhere, and the young hunter was led to follow tracks that would have defied an expert in dryer times. One day he came on piglike footprints in the woods. He followed them with little difficulty, for they were new, and a heavy rain two hours before had washed out all other trails. After about half a mile they led him to an open ravine, and as he reached its brow he saw across it a flash of white; then his keen young eyes made out the forms of a Deer and a spotted Fawn gazing at him curiously. Though on their trail he was not a little startled. He gazed at them open-mouthed. The mother turned and raised the danger flag, her white tail, and bounded lightly away, to be followed by the youngster, clearing low trunks with an effortless leap, or bending down with catlike suppleness when they came to a log upraised so that they might pass below.

He never again got a chance to shoot at them, though more than once he saw the same two tracks, or believed they were the same, as for some cause never yet explained, Deer were scarcer in that unbroken forest than they were in later years when clearings spread around.

He never again saw *them*; but he saw the mother once—he thought it was the same—she was searching the woods with her nose, trying the ground for trails; she was nervous and anxious, evidently seeking. Thor remembered a trick that Corney had told him. He gently stooped, took up a broad blade of grass, laid it between the edges of his thumbs, then blowing through this simple squeaker he made a short, shrill bleat, a fair imitation of a Fawn's cry for the mother, and the Deer, though a long way off, came bounding toward him. He snatched his gun, meaning to kill her, but the movement caught her eye. She stopped. Her mane bristled a little; she sniffed and looked inquiringly at him. Her big soft eyes touched his heart, held back his hand; she took a cautious step nearer, got a full whiff of her mortal enemy, bounded behind a big tree and away before his merciful impulse was gone. "Poor thing," said Thor, "I believe she has lost her little one."

Yet once more the Boy met a Lynx in the woods. Half an hour after seeing the lonely Deer he crossed the long ridge that lay some miles north of the shanty. He had passed the glade where the great basswood lay when a creature like a big bob-tailed Kitten appeared and looked innocently at him. His gun went up, as usual, but the Kitten merely cocked its head on one side and fearlessly surveyed him. Then a second one that he had not noticed before began to play with the first, pawing at its tail and inviting its brother to tussle.

Thor's first thought to shoot was stayed as he watched their gambols, but the remembrance of his feud with their race came back. He had almost raised the gun when a fierce rumble close at hand gave him a start, and there, not ten feet from him, stood the old one, looking big and fierce as a Tigress. It was surely folly to shoot at the young ones now. The boy nervously dropped some buckshot on the charge while the snarling growl rose and fell, but before he was ready to shoot at her the old one had picked up something that was by her feet; the boy got a glimpse of rich brown with white spots—the limp form of a newly killed Fawn. Then she passed out of sight. The Kittens followed, and he saw her no more until the time when, life against life, they were weighed in the balance together.

THE TERROR OF THE WOODS

Six weeks had passed in daily routine when one day the young giant seemed unusually quiet as he went about. His handsome face was very sober and he sang not at all that morning.

He and Thor slept on a hay-bunk in one corner of the main room, and that night the Boy awakened more than once to hear his companion groaning and tossing in his sleep.

Corney arose as usual in the morning and fed the horses, but lay down again while the sisters got breakfast. He roused himself by an effort and went back to work, but came home early. He was trembling from head to foot. It was hot summer weather, but he could not be kept warm. After several hours a reaction set in and Corney was in a high fever. The family knew well now that he had the dreaded chills and fever of the backwoods. Margat went out and gathered a lapful of

There stood the old one, . . . as fierce as a Tigress

pipsissewa to make tea, of which Corney was encouraged to drink copiously.

But in spite of all their herbs and nursing the young man got worse. At the end of ten days he was greatly reduced in flesh and incapable of work, so on one of the "well days" that are usual in the course of the disease he said:

"Say, gurruls, I can't stand it no longer. Guess I better go home. I'm well enough to drive to-day, for a while anyway; if I'm took down I'll lay in the wagon, and the horses will fetch me home. Mother'll have me all right in a week or so. If you run out of grub before I come back take the canoe to Ellerton's."

So the girls harnessed the horses; the wagon was partly filled with hay, and Corney, weak and white-faced, drove away on the long rough road, and left them feeling much as though they were on a desert island and their only boat had been taken from them.

Half a week had scarcely gone before all three of them, Margat, Loo, and Thor, were taken down with a yet more virulent form of chills and fever.

Corney had had every other a "well day," but with these three there were no "well days" and the house became an abode of misery.

Seven days passed, and now Margat could not leave her bed and Loo was barely able to walk around the house. She was a brave girl with a fund of drollery which did much toward keeping up all their spirits, but her merriest jokes fell ghastly from her wan, pinched face. Thor, though weak and ill, was the strongest and did for the others, cooking and serving each day a simple meal, for they could eat very little, fortunately, perhaps, as there was very little, and Corney could not return for another week.

Soon Thor was the only one able to rise, and one morning when he dragged himself to cut the little usual slice of their treasured bacon he found, to his horror, that the whole piece was gone. It had been stolen, doubtless by some wild animal, from the little box on the shady side of the house, where it was kept safe from flies. Now they were down to flour and tea. He was in despair, when his eye lighted on the Chickens about the stable; but what's the use? In his feeble state he might as well try to catch a Deer or a Hawk. Suddenly he remembered his gun and very soon was preparing a fat Hen for the pot. He boiled it whole as the easiest way to cook it, and the broth was the first really tempting food they had had for some time.

They kept alive for three wretched days on that Chicken, and when it was finished Thor again took down his gun—it seemed a much heavier gun now. He crawled to the barn, but he was so weak and shaky that he missed several times before he brought down a fowl. Corney had taken the rifle away with him and three charges of gun ammunition were all that now remained.

Thor was surprised to see how few Hens there were now, only three or four. There used to be over a dozen. Three days later he made another raid. He saw but one Hen and he used up his last ammunition to get that.

His daily routine now was a monotony of horror. In the morning, which was his "well time," he prepared a little food for the household and got ready for the night of raging fever by putting a bucket of water on a block at the head of each bunk. About one o'clock, with fearful regularity, the chills would come on, with trembling from head to foot and chattering teeth, and cold, cold, within and without. Nothing seemed to give any warmth—fire seemed to have lost its power. There was nothing to do but to lie and shake and suffer all the slow torture of freezing to death and shaking to pieces. For six hours it would keep up, and to the torture, nausea lent its horrid aid throughout; then about seven or eight o'clock in the evening a change would come; a burning fever set in; no ice could have seemed cool to him then; water—water— was all he craved, and drank and drank until three or four in the morning, when the fever would abate, and a sleep of total exhaustion followed.

"If you run out of food take the canoe to Ellerton's," was the brother's last word. Who was to take the canoe?

There was but half a Chicken now between them and starvation, and no sign of Corney.

For three interminable weeks the deadly program dragged along. It went on the same yet worse, as the sufferers grew weaker—a few days more and the Boy also would be unable to leave his couch. Then what?

Despair was on the house and the silent cry of each was, "Oh, God! will Corney never come?"

THE HOME OF THE BOY

On the day of that last Chicken, Thor was all morning carrying water enough for the coming three fevers. The chill attacked him sooner than it was due and his fever was worse than ever before.

He drank deeply and often from the bucket at his head. He had filled it, and it was nearly emptied when about two in the morning the fever left him and he fell asleep.

In the gray dawn he was awakened by a curious sound not far away—a splashing of water. He turned his head to see two glaring eyes within a foot of his face—a great Beast lapping the water in the bucket by his bed.

Thor gazed in horror for a moment, then closed his eyes, sure that he was dreaming, certain that this was a nightmare of India with a Tiger by his couch; but the lapping continued. He looked up; yes, it still was there. He tried to find his voice but uttered only a gurgle. The great furry head quivered, a sniff came from below the shining eyeballs, and the creature, whatever it was, dropped to its front feet and went across the hut under the table. Thor was fully awake now; he rose slowly on his elbow and feebly shouted "Sssh-hi," at which the shining eyes reappeared under the table and the gray form came forth. Calmly it walked across the ground and glided under the lowest log at a place where an old potato-pit left an opening and disappeared.

What was it? The sick boy hardly knew—some savage Beast of prey, undoubtedly. He was totally unnerved. He shook with fear and a sense of helplessness, and the night passed in fitful sleep and sudden starts awake to search the gloom again for those fearful eyes and the great gray gliding form. In the morning he did not know whether it were not all a delirium, yet he made a feeble effort to close the old cellar hole with some firewood.

The three had little appetite, but even that they restrained since now they were down to part of a Chicken, and Corney, evidently he supposed they had been to Ellerton's and got all the food they needed.

Again that night, when the fever left him weak and dozing, Thor was awakened by a noise in the room, a sound of crunching bones. He looked around to see dimly outlined against the little window, the form of a large animal on the table. Thor shouted; he tried to hurl his boot at the intruder. It leaped lightly to the ground and passed out of the hole, again wide open.

It was no dream this time, he knew, and the women knew it, too; not only had they heard the creature, but the Chicken, the last of their food, was wholly gone.

Poor Thor barely left his couch that day. It needed all the querulous complaints of the sick women to drive him forth. Down by the spring he found a few berries and divided them with the others. He made his usual preparations for the chills and the thirst, but he added this—by the side of his couch he put an old fish spear—the only weapon he could find, now the gun was useless—a pine-root candle and some matches. He knew the Beast was coming back again—was coming hungry. It would find no food; what more natural, he thought, than take the living prey lying there so helpless? And a vision came of the limp brown form of the little Fawn, borne off in those same cruel jaws.

Once again he barricaded the hole with firewood, and the night

passed as usual, but without any fierce visitor. Their food that day was flour and water, and to cook it Thor was forced to use some of his barricade. Loo attempted some feeble joke, guessed she was light enough to fly now and tried to rise, but she got no farther than the edge of the bunk. The same preparations were made, and the night wore on, but early in the morning, Thor was again awakened rudely by the sound of lapping water by his bed, and there, as before, were the glowing eyeballs, the great head, the gray form relieved by the dim light from the dawning window.

Thor put all his strength into what was meant for a bold shout, but it was merely a feeble screech. He rose slowly and called out: "Loo, Margat! The Lynx—here's the Lynx again!"

"May God help ye, for we can't," was the answer.

"Sssh-hi!" Thor tried again to drive the Beast away. It leaped on to the table by the window and stood up growling under the useless gun. Thor thought it was going to leap through the glass as it faced the window a moment; but it turned and glared toward the Boy, for he could see both eyes shining. He rose slowly to the side of his bunk and he prayed for help, for he felt it was kill or be killed. He struck a match and lighted his pine-root candle, held that in his left hand and in his right took the old fish-spear, meaning to fight, but he was so weak he had to use the fish-spear as a crutch. The great Beast stood on the table still, but was crouching a little as though for a spring. Its eyes glowed red in the torchlight. Its short tail was switching from side to side and its growling took a higher pitch. Thor's knees were smiting together, but he levelled the spear and made a feeble lunge toward the brute. It sprang at the same moment, not at him, as he first thought—the torch and the boy's bold front had had effect—it went over his head to drop on the ground beyond and at once to slink under the bunk.

He made a feeble lunge at the brute

This was only a temporary repulse. Thor set the torch on a ledge of the logs, then took the spear in both hands. He was fighting for his life, and he knew it. He heard the voices of the women feebly praying. He saw only the glowing eyes under the bed and heard the growling in higher pitch as the Beast was nearing action. He steadied himself by a great effort and plunged the spear with all the force he could give it.

It struck something softer than the logs: a hideous snarl came forth. The boy threw all his weight on the weapon; the Beast was struggling to get at him; he felt its teeth and claws grating on the handle, and in spite of himself it was coming on; its powerful arms and claws were reaching for him now; he could not hold out long. He put on all his force, just a little more it was than before; the Beast lurched, there was a growling, a crack, and sudden yielding; the rotten old spear-head had broken off, the Beast sprang out—at him—past him— never touched him, but across through the hole and away, to be seen no more.

Thor fell on the bed and lost all consciousness.

He lay there he knew not how long, but was awakened in broad daylight by a loud, cheery voice:

"Hello! Hello!—are ye all dead? Loo! Thor! Margat!"

He had no strength to answer, but there was a trampling of horses outside, a heavy step, the door was forced open, and in strode Corney, handsome and hearty as ever. But what a flash of horror and pain came over his face on entering the silent shanty!

"Dead?" he gasped. "Who's dead—where are you? Thor?" Then, "Who is it? Loo? Margat?"

"Corney—Corney," came feebly from the bunk. "They're in there. They're awful sick. We have nothing to eat."

"Oh, what a fool I be!" said Corney again and again. "I made sure ye'd go to Ellerton's and get all ye wanted."

"We had no chance, Corney; we were all three brought down at once, right after you left. Then the Lynx came and cleared up the Hens, and all in the house, too."

"Well, ye got even with her," and Corney pointed to the trail of blood across the mud floor and out under the logs.

Good food, nursing, and medicine restored them all.

A month or two later, when the women wanted a new leaching-barrel, Thor said: "I know where there is a hollow basswood as big as a hogshead."

He and Corney went to the place, and when they cut off what they needed, they found in the far end of it the dried-up bodies of two little Lynxes with that of the mother, and in the side of the old one was the head of a fish-spear broken from the handle.

LITTLE WARHORSE

The History of a Jack-rabbit

The Little Warhorse knew practically all the Dogs in town. First, there was a very large brown Dog that had pursued him many times, a Dog that he always got rid of by slipping through a hole in a board fence. Second, there was a small active Dog that could follow through that hole, and him he baffled by leaping a twenty-foot irrigation ditch that had steep sides and a swift current. The Dog could not make this leap. It was "sure medicine" for that foe, and the boys still call the place "Old Jacky's Jump." But there was a Greyhound that could leap better than the Jack, and when he could not follow through a fence, he jumped over it. He tried the Warhorse's mettle more than once, and Jacky only saved himself by his quick dodging, till they got to an Osage hedge, and here the Greyhound had to give it up. Besides these, there was in town a rabble of big and little Dogs that were troublesome, but easily left behind in the open.

In the country there was a Dog at each farm-house, but only one that the Warhorse really feared; that was a long-legged, fierce, black Dog, a brute so swift and pertinacious that he had several times forced the Warhorse almost to the last extremity.

For the town Cats he cared little; only once or twice had he been threatened by them. A huge Tom-cat flushed with many victories came crawling up to where he fed one moonlight night. Jack Warhorse saw the black creature with the glowing eyes, and a moment before the final

rush, he faced it, raised up on his haunches,—his hind legs,—at full length on his toes,—with his broad ears towering up yet six inches higher; then letting out a loud *churrr-churrr*, his best attempt at a roar, he sprang five feet forward and landed on the Cat's head, driving in his sharp hind nails, and the old Tom fled in terror from the weird two-legged giant. This trick he had tried several times with success, but twice it turned out a sad failure: once, when the Cat proved to be a mother whose Kittens were near; then Jack Warhorse had to flee for his life; and the other time was when he made the mistake of landing hard on a Skunk.

But the Greyhound was the dangerous enemy, and in him the Warhorse might have found his fate, but for a curious adventure with a happy ending for Jack.

He fed by night; there were fewer enemies about then, and it was easier to hide; but one day at dawn in winter he had lingered long at an alfalfa stack and was crossing the open snow toward his favorite form, when, as ill-luck would have it, he met the Greyhound prowling outside the town. With open snow and growing daylight there was no chance to hide, nothing but a run in the open with soft snow that hindered the Jack more than it did the Hound.

Off they went—superb runners in fine fettle. How they skimmed across the snow, raising it in little *puff—puff—puffs*, each time their nimble feet went down. This way and that, swerving and dodging, went the chase. Everything favored the Dog,—his empty stomach, the cold weather, the soft snow,—while the Rabbit was handicapped by his heavy meal of alfalfa. But his feet went *puff—puff* so fast that a dozen of the little snowjets were in view at once. The chase continued in the open; no friendly hedge was near, and every attempt to reach a fence was cleverly stopped by the Hound. Jack's ears were losing their bold up-cock, a sure sign of failing heart or wind, when all at once these flags went stiffly up, as under sudden renewal of strength. The Warhorse put forth all his power, not to reach the hedge to the north, but over the open prairie eastward. The Greyhound followed, and within fifty yards the Jack dodged to foil his fierce pursuer; but on the next tack he was on his eastern course again, and so tacking and dodging, he kept the line direct for the next farm-house, where was a very high board fence with a hen-hole, and where also there dwelt his other hated enemy, the big black Dog. An outer hedge delayed the Greyhound for a moment and gave Jack time to dash through the hen-hole into the yard, where he hid to one side. The Greyhound rushed around to the low gate, leaped over that among the Hens, and as they fled cackling and fluttering, some Lambs bleated loudly. Their natural guardian, the big black Dog, ran to the rescue, and Warhorse slipped out again by the hole at which he had entered. Horrible sounds of Dog hate and fury were heard behind him in the hen-yard, and soon the shouts of men were added. How it ended he did not know or seek to learn, but it was remarkable that he never afterward was troubled by the swift Greyhound that formerly lived in Newchusen.

* * *

Hard times and easy times had long followed in turn and been taken as matters of course; but recent years in the State of Kaskado had brought to the Jack-rabbits a succession of remarkable ups and downs. In the old days they had their endless fight with Birds and Beasts of Prey, with cold and heat, with pestilence and with flies whose sting bred a loathsome disease, and yet had held their own. But the settling of the country by farmers made many changes.

Dogs and guns arriving in numbers reduced the ranks of Coyotes, Foxes, Wolves, Badgers, and Hawks that preyed on the Jack, so that in a few years the Rabbits were multiplied in great swarms; but now Pestilence broke out and swept them away. Only the strongest—the double-seasoned—remained. For a while a Jack-rabbit was a rarity; but during this time another change came in. The Osage-orange hedges planted everywhere afforded a new refuge, and now the safety of a Jack-rabbit was less often his speed than his wits, and the wise ones, when pursued by a Dog or Coyote, would rush to the nearest hedge through a small hole and escape while the enemy sought for a larger one by which to follow. The Coyotes rose to this and developed the trick of the relay chase. In this one Coyote takes one field, another the next, and if the Rabbit attempts the "hedge-ruse" they work from each side and usually win their prey. The Rabbit remedy for this, is keen eyes to see the second Coyote, avoidance of that field, then good legs to distance the first enemy.

Thus the Jack-rabbits, after being successively numerous, scarce, in myriads, and rare, were now again on the increase, and those which survived, selected by a hundred hard trials, were enabled to flourish where their ancestors could not have outlived a single season.

Their favorite grounds were, not the broad open stretches of the big ranches, but the complicated, much-fenced fields of the farms, where these were so small and close as to be like a big straggling village.

One of these vegetable villages had sprung up around the railway station of Newchusen. The country a mile away was well supplied with Jack-rabbits of the new and selected stock. Among them was a little lady Rabbit called "Bright-eyes," from her leading characteristic as she sat gray in the gray brush. She was a good runner, but was especially successful with the fence-play that baffled the Coyotes. She made her nest out in an open pasture, an untouched tract of the ancient prairie. Here her brood were born and raised. One like herself was bright-eyed, in coat of silver-gray, and partly gifted with her ready wits, but in the other, there appeared a rare combination of his mother's gifts with the best that was in the best strain of the new Jack-rabbits of the plains.

This was the one whose adventures we have been following, the one that later on the turf won the name of Little Warhorse and that afterward achieved a world-wide fame.

Ancient tricks of his kind he revived and put to new uses, and ancient enemies he learned to fight with new-found tricks.

When a mere baby he discovered a plan that was worthy of the wisest Rabbit in Kaskado. He was pursued by a horrible little Yellow Dog, and he had tried in vain to get rid of him by dodging among the fields and farms. This is good play against a Coyote, because the farmers and the Dogs will often help the Jack, without knowing it, by attacking the Coyote. But now the plan did not work at all, for the little Dog managed to keep after him through one fence after another, and Jack Warhorse, not yet full-grown, much less seasoned, was beginning to feel the strain. His ears were no longer up straight, but angling back and at times drooping to a level, as he darted through a very little hole in an Osage hedge, only to find that his nimble enemy had done the same without loss of time. In the middle of the field was a small herd of cattle and with them a calf.

There is in wild animals a curious impulse to trust any stranger when in desperate straits. The foe behind they know means death. There is just a chance, and the only one left, that the stranger may prove friendly; and it was this last desperate chance that drew Jack Warhorse to the Cows.

It is quite sure that the Cows would have stood by in stolid indifference so far as the Rabbit was concerned, but they have a deep-rooted hatred of a Dog, and when they saw the Yellow Cur coming bounding toward them, their tails and noses went up; they sniffed angrily, then closed up ranks, and led by the Cow that owned the Calf, they charged at the Dog, while Jack took refuge under a low thorn-bush. The Dog swerved aside to attack the Calf, at least the old Cow thought he did, and she followed him so fiercely that he barely escaped from that field with his life.

It was a good old plan—one that doubtless came from the days when Buffalo and Coyote played the parts of Cow and Dog. Jack never forgot it, and more than once it saved his life.

In colour as well as in power he was a rarity.

Animals are colored in one or other of two general plans: one that matches them with their surroundings and helps them to hide—this is called "protective"; the other that makes them very visible for several purposes—this is called "directive." Jack-rabbits are peculiar in being painted both ways. As they squat in their form in the gray brush or clods, they are soft gray on their ears, head, back, and sides; they match the ground and cannot be seen until close at hand—they are *protectively* colored. But the moment it is clear to the Jack that the approaching foe will find him, he jumps up and dashes away. He throws off all disguise now, the gray seems to disappear; he makes a lightning change, and his ears show snowy white with black tips, the legs are white, his tail is a black spot in a blaze of white. He is a black-and-white Rabbit now. His coloring is all *directive*. How is it done? Very simply. The front side of the ear is gray, the back, black and white. The black tail with its white halo, and the legs, are tucked below. He is sitting on them. The gray mantle is pulled down and enlarged as he sits, but when he jumps up it shrinks somewhat, all his black-and-white marks are now shown, and just as his colors formerly whispered, "I am a clod," they now shout aloud, "I am a Jack-rabbit."

Why should he do this? Why should a timid creature running for his life thus proclaim to all the world his name instead of trying to hide? There must be some good reason. It must pay, or the Rabbit would never have done it. The answer is, if the creature that scared him up was one of his own kind—i.e., this was a false alarm—then at once, by showing his national colors, the mistake is made right. On the other hand, if it be a Coyote, Fox, or Dog, they see at once, this is a Jack-rabbit, and know that it would be waste of time for them to pursue him. They say in effect, "This is a Jack-rabbit, and I cannot catch a Jack in open race." They give it up, and that, of course, saves the Jack a great deal of unnecessary running and worry. The black-and-white spots are the national uniform and flag of the Jacks. In poor specimens they are apt to be dull, but in the finest specimens they are not only larger, but brighter than usual, and the Little Warhorse, gray when he sat in his form, blazed like charcoal and snow, when he flung his defiance to the Fox and buff Coyote, and danced with little effort before them, first a black-and-white Jack, then a little white spot, and last a speck of thistledown, before the distance swallowed him.

Many of the farmers' Dogs had learned the lesson: "A grayish Rabbit you may catch, but a very black-and-white one is hopeless." They might, indeed, follow for a time, but that was merely for the fun of a chivvy, and his growing power often led Warhorse to seek the chase for the sake of a little excitement, and to take hazards that others less gifted were most careful to avoid.

Jack, like all other wild animals, had a certain range or country which was home to him, and outside of this he rarely strayed. It was about three miles across, extending easterly from the centre of the village. Scattered through this he had a number of "forms," or "beds" as they are locally called. These were mere hollows situated under a sheltering bush or bunch of grass, without lining excepting the

accidental grass and in-blown leaves. But comfort was not forgotten. Some of them were for hot weather; they faced the north, were scarcely sunk, were little more than shady places. Some for the cold weather were deep hollows with southern exposure, and others for the wet were well roofed with herbage and faced the west. In one or other of these he spent the day, and at night he went forth to feed with his kind, sporting and romping on the moonlight nights like a lot of puppy Dogs, but careful to be gone by sunrise, and safely tucked in a bed that was suited to the weather.

The safest ground for the Jacks was among the farms, where not only Osage hedges, but also the newly arrived barb-wire, made hurdles and hazards in the path of possible enemies. But the finest of the forage is nearer to the village among the truck-farms—the finest of forage and the fiercest of dangers. Some of the dangers of the plains were lacking, but the greater perils of men, guns, Dogs, and impassable fences are much increased. Yet those who knew Warhorse best were not at all surprised to find that he had made a form in the middle of a market-gardener's melon-patch. A score of dangers beset him here, but there was also a score of unusual delights and a score of holes in the fence for times when he had to fly, with at least twoscore of expedients to help him afterward.

* * *

Newchusen was a typical Western town. Everywhere in it, were to be seen strenuous efforts at uglification, crowned with unmeasured success. The streets were straight level lanes without curves or beauty-spots. The houses were cheap and mean structures of flimsy boards and tar paper, and not even honest in their ugliness, for each of them was pretending to be something better than itself. One had a false front to make it look like two stories, another was of imitation brick, a third pretended to be a marble temple.

But all agreed in being the ugliest things ever used as human dwellings, and in each could be read the owner's secret thought—to stand it for a year or so, then move out somewhere else. The only beauties of the place, and those unintentional, were the long lines of hand-planted shade-trees, uglified as far as possible with whitewashed trunks and croppy heads, but still lovable, growing, living things.

The only building in town with a touch of picturesqueness was the grain elevator. It was not posing as a Greek temple or a Swiss châlet, but simply a strong, rough, honest, grain elevator. At the end of each street was a vista of the prairie, with its farm-houses, windmill pumps, and long lines of Osage-orange hedges. Here at least was something of interest—the gray-green hedges, thick, sturdy, and high, were dotted with their golden mock-oranges, useless fruit, but more welcome here than rain in a desert; for these balls were things of beauty, and swung on their long tough boughs they formed with the soft green leaves a color-chord that pleased the weary eye.

Such a town is a place to get out of, as soon as possible, so thought the traveller who found himself laid over here for two days in late winter. He asked after the sights of the place. A white Muskrat stuffed in a case "down to the saloon"; old Baccy Bullin, who had been scalped by the Indians forty years ago; and a pipe once smoked by Kit Carson, proved unattractive, so he turned toward the prairie, still white with snow.

A mark among the numerous Dog tracks caught his eye: it was the track of a large Jack-rabbit. He asked a passer-by if there were any Rabbits in town.

"No, I reckon not. I never seen none," was the answer. A mill-hand gave the same reply, but a small boy with a bundle of newspapers said: "You bet there is; there's lots of them out there on the prairie, and they come in town a-plenty. Why, there's a big, big feller lives right round Si Kalb's melon-patch—oh, an awful big feller, and just as black and as white as checkers!" and thus he sent the stranger eastward on his walk.

The "big, big, awful big one" was the Little Warhorse himself. He did n't live in Kalb's melon-patch; he was there only at odd times. He was not there now; he was in his west-fronting form or bed, because a raw east wind was setting in. It was due east of Madison Avenue, and as the stranger plodded that way the Rabbit watched him. As long as the man kept the road the Jack was quiet, but the road turned shortly to the north, and the man by chance left it and came straight on. Then the Jack saw trouble ahead. The moment the man left the beaten track, he bounded from his form, and wheeling, he sailed across the prairie due east.

A Jack-rabbit running from its enemy ordinarily covers eight or nine feet at a bound, and once in five or six bounds, it makes an observation hop, leaping not along, but high in the air, so as to get above all herbage and bushes and take in the situation. A silly young Jack will make an observation hop as often as one in four, and so waste a great deal of time. A clever Jack will make one hop in eight or nine, do for observation. But Jack Warhorse as he sped, got all the information he needed, in one hop out of a dozen, while ten to fourteen feet were covered by each of his flying bounds. Yet another personal peculiarity showed in the trail he left. When a Cottontail or a Woodhare runs, his tail is curled up tight on his back, and does not touch the snow. When a Jack runs, his tail hangs downward or backward, with the tip curved or straight, according to the individual; in some, it points straight down, and so, often leaves a little stroke behind the foot-marks. The Warhorse's tail of shining black, was of unusual length, and at every bound, it left in the snow, a long stroke, so long that that alone was almost enough to tell which Rabbit had made the track.

Now some Rabbits seeing only a man without any Dog would have felt little fear, but Warhorse, remembering some former stinging experiences with a far-killer, fled when the foe was seventy-five yards away, and skimming low, he ran southeast to a fence that ran easterly. Behind this he went like a low-flying Hawk, till a mile away he reached another of his beds; and here, after an observation taken as he stood on his heels, he settled again to rest.

The warhorse doing a spy-hop

But not for long. In twenty minutes his great megaphone ears, so close to the ground, caught a regular sound—crunch, crunch, crunch—the tramp of a human foot, and he started up to see the man with the shining stick in his hand, now drawing near.

Warhorse bounded out and away for the fence. Never once did he rise to a "spy-hop" till the wire and rails were between him and his foe, an unnecessary precaution as it chanced, for the man was watching the trail and saw nothing of the Rabbit.

Jack skimmed along, keeping low and looking out for other enemies. He knew now that the man was on his track, and the old instinct born of ancestral trouble with Weasels was doubtless what prompted him to do the double trail. He ran in a long, straight course to a distant fence, followed its far side for fifty yards, then doubling back he retraced his trail and ran off in a new direction till he reached another of his dens or forms. He had been out all night and was very ready to rest, now that the sun was ablaze on the snow; but he had hardly got the place a little warmed when the "tramp, tramp, tramp" announced the enemy, and he hurried away.

After a half-a-mile run he stopped on a slight rise and marked the man still following, so he made a series of wonderful quirks in his trail, a succession of blind zigzags that would have puzzled most trailers; then running a hundred yards past a favorite form, he returned to it from the other side, and settled to rest, sure that now the enemy would be finally thrown off the scent.

It was slower than before, but still it came—"tramp, tramp, tramp."

Jack awoke, but sat still. The man tramped by on the trail one hundred yards in front of him, and as he went on, Jack sprang out unseen, realizing that this was an unusual occasion needing a special effort. They had gone in a vast circle around the home range of the Warhorse and now were less than a mile from the farm-house of the black Dog. There was that wonderful board fence with the happily planned hen-hole. It was a place of good memory—here more than once he had won, here especially he had baffled the Greyhound.

These doubtless were the motive thoughts rather than any plan of playing one enemy against another, and Warhorse bounded openly across the snow to the fence of the big black Dog.

The hen-hole was shut, and Warhorse, not a little puzzled, sneaked around to find another, without success, until, around the front, here was the gate wide open, and inside lying on some boards was the big Dog, fast asleep. The Hens were sitting hunched up in the warmest corner of the yard. The house Cat was gingerly picking her way from barn to kitchen, as Warhorse halted in the gateway.

The black form of his pursuer was crawling down the far white prairie slope. Jack hopped quietly into the yard. A long-legged Rooster, that ought to have minded his own business, uttered a loud cackle as he saw the Rabbit hopping near. The Dog lying in the sun raised his head and stood up, and Jack's peril was dire. He squatted low and turned himself into a gray clod. He did it cleverly, but still might have been lost but for the Cat. Unwittingly, unwillingly, she saved him. The black Dog had taken three steps toward the Warhorse, though he did not know the Rabbit was there, and was now blocking the only way of escape from the yard, when the Cat came round the corner of the house, and leaping to a window-ledge brought a flower-pot rolling down. By that single awkward act she disturbed the armed neutrality existing between herself and the Dog. She fled to the barn, and of course a flying foe is all that is needed to send a Dog on the war-path. They passed within thirty feet of the crouching Rabbit. As soon as they were well gone, Jack turned, and without even a "Thank you, Pussy," he fled to the open and away on the hard-beaten road.

The Cat had been rescued by the lady of the house; the Dog was once more sprawling on the boards when the man on Jack's trail arrived. He carried, not a gun, but a stout stick, sometimes called "dog-medicine," and that was all that prevented the Dog attacking the enemy of his prey.

This seemed to be the end of the trail. The trick, whether planned or not, was a success, and the Rabbit got rid of his troublesome follower.

Next day the stranger made another search for the Jack and found, not himself, but his track. He knew it by its tail-mark, its long leaps and few spy-hops, but with it and running by it was the track of a smaller Rabbit. Here is where they met, here they chased each other in play, for no signs of battle were there to be seen; here they fed or sat together in the sun, there they ambled side by side, and here again they sported in the snow, always together. There was only one conclusion: this was the mating season. This was a pair of Jack-rabbits—the Little Warhorse and his mate.

* * *

Next summer was a wonderful year for the Jack-rabbits. A foolish law had set a bounty on Hawks and Owls and had caused a general massacre of these feathered policemen. Consequently the Rabbits had multiplied in such numbers that they now were threatening to devastate the country.

The farmers, who were the sufferers from the bounty law, as well as the makers of it, decided on a great Rabbit drive. All the county was invited to come, on a given morning, to the main road north of the county, with the intention of sweeping the whole region up-wind and at length driving the Rabbits into a huge corral of close wire netting. Dogs were barred as unmanageable, and guns as dangerous in a crowd; but every man and boy carried a couple of long sticks and a bag full of stones. Women came on horseback and in buggies; many carried rattles or horns and tins to make a noise. A number of the buggies trailed a string of old cans or tied laths to scrape on the wheel-spokes, and thus add no little to the deafening clatter of the drive. As Rabbits have marvellously sensitive hearing, a noise that is distracting to mankind, is likely to prove bewildering to them.

The weather was right, and at eight in the morning the word to advance was given. The line was about five miles long at first, and there was a man or a boy every thirty or forty yards. The buggies and riders kept perforce almost entirely to the roads; but the beaters were supposed, as a point of honor, to face everything, and keep the front unbroken. The advance was roughly in three sides of a square. Each man made as much noise as he could, and threshed every bush in his path. A number of Rabbits hopped out. Some made for the lines, to be at once assailed by a shower of stones that laid many of them low. One or two did get through and escaped, but the majority were swept before the drive. At first the number seen was small, but before three miles were covered the Rabbits were running ahead in every direction. After five miles—and that took about three hours—the word for the wings to close in was given. The space between the men was shortened up till they were less than ten feet apart, and the whole drive converged on the corral with its two long guide wings or fences; the end lines joined these wings, and the surround was complete. The drivers marched rapidly now; scores of the Rabbits were killed as they ran too near the beaters. Their bodies strewed the ground, but the swarms seemed to increase; and in the final move, before the victims were cooped up in the corral, the two-acre space surrounded was a whirling throng of skurrying, jumping, bounding Rabbits. Round and round they circled and leaped, looking for a chance to escape; but the inexorable crowd grew thicker as the ring grew steadily smaller, and the whole swarm was forced along the chute into the tight corral, some to squat stupidly in the middle, some to race round the outer wall, some to seek hiding in corners or under each other.

And the Little Warhorse—where was he in all this? The drive had swept him along, and he had been one of the first to enter the corral. But a curious plan of selection had been established. The pen was to be a death-trap for the Rabbits, except the best, the soundest. And many were there that were unsound; those that think of all wild animals as pure and perfect things, would have been shocked to see how many halt, maimed, and diseased there were in that pen of four thousand or five thousand Jack-rabbits.

It was a Roman victory—the rabble of prisoners was to be butchered. The choicest were to be reserved for the arena. The arena? Yes, that is the Coursing Park.

In that corral trap, prepared beforehand for the Rabbits, were a number of small boxes along the wall, a whole series of them, five hundred at least, each large enough to hold one Jack.

In the last rush of driving, the swiftest Jacks got first to the pen. Some were swift and silly; when once inside they rushed wildly round and round. Some were swift and wise; they quickly sought the hiding afforded by the little boxes; all of these were now full. Thus five hundred of the swiftest and wisest had been selected, in, not by any means an infallible way, but the simplest and readiest. These five hundred were destined to be coursed by Greyhounds. The surging mass of over four thousand were ruthlessly given to slaughter.

Five hundred little boxes with five hundred bright-eyed Jack-rabbits were put on the train that day, and among them was Little Jack Warhorse.

* * *

Rabbits take their troubles lightly, and it is not to be supposed that any great terror was felt by the boxed Jacks, once the uproar of the massacre was over; and when they reached the Coursing Park near the great city and were turned out one by one, very gently,—yes, gently; the Roman guards were careful of their prisoners, being responsible for them,—the Jacks found little to complain of, a big inclosure with plenty of good food, and no enemies to annoy them.

The very next morning their training began. A score of hatchways were opened into a much larger field—the Park. After a number of Jacks had wandered out through these doors a rabble of boys appeared and drove them back, pursuing them noisily until all were again in the smaller field, called the Haven. A few days of this taught the Jack-rabbits that when pursued their safety was to get back by one of the hatches into the Haven.

Now the second lesson began. The whole band were driven out of a side door into a long lane which led around three sides of the Park to another inclosure at the far end. This was the Starting Pen. Its door into the arena—that is, the Park—was opened, the Rabbits driven forth, and then a mob of boys and Dogs in hiding, burst forth and pursued them across the open. The whole army went bobbing and bounding away, some of the younger ones soaring in a spy-hop, as a matter of habit; but low skimming ahead of them all was a gorgeous black-and-white one; clean-limbed and bright-eyed, he had attracted attention in the pen, but now in the field he led the band with easy lope that put him as far ahead of them all as they were ahead of the rabble of common Dogs.

"Luk at thot, would ye—but ain't he a Little Warhorse?" shouted a villainous-looking Irish stable-boy, and thus he was named. When halfway across the course the Jacks remembered the Haven, and all swept toward it and in like a snow-cloud over the drifts.

This was the second lesson—to lead straight for the Haven as soon as driven from the Pen. In a week all had learned it, and were ready for the great opening meet of the Coursing Club.

The Little Warhorse was now well known to the grooms and hangers-on; his colors usually marked him clearly, and his leadership was in a measure recognized by the long-eared herd that fled with him. He figured more or less with the Dogs in the talk and betting of the men.

"Wonder if old Dignam is going to enter Minkie this year?"

"Faix, an' if he does I bet the Little Warrhorrse will take the gimp out av her an' her runnin' mate."

"I'll bet three to one that my old Jen will pick the Warhorse up before he passes the grand stand," growled a dog-man.

"An' it's meself will take thot bet in dollars," said Mickey, "an', moore than thot, Oi'll put up a hull month's stuff thot there ain't a dog in the mate thot kin turrn the Warrhorrse oncet on the hull coorse."

So they wrangled and wagered, but each day, as they put the Rabbits through their paces, there were more of those who believed that they had found a wonderful runner in the Warhorse, one that would give the best Greyhounds something that is rarely seen, a straight stern chase from Start to Grand Stand and Haven.

* * *

The first morning of the meet arrived bright and promising. The Grand Stand was filled with a city crowd. The usual types of a racecourse appeared in force. Here and there were to be seen the dog-grooms leading in leash single Greyhounds or couples, shrouded in blankets, but showing their sinewy legs, their snaky necks, their shapely heads with long reptilian jaws, and their quick, nervous yellow eyes—hybrids of natural force and human ingenuity, the most wonderful running-machines ever made of flesh and blood. Their keepers guarded them like jewels, tended them like babies, and were careful to keep them from picking up odd eatables, as well as prevent them smelling unusual objects or being approached by strangers. Large sums were wagered on these Dogs, and a cunningly placed tack, a piece of doctored meat, yes, an artfully compounded smell, has been known to turn a superb young runner into a lifeless laggard, and to the owner this might spell *ruin*. The Dogs entered in each class are paired off, as each contest is supposed to be a duel; the winners in the first series are then paired again. In each trial, a Jack is driven from the Starting-pen; close by in one leash are the rival Dogs, held by the slipper. As soon as the Hare is well away, the man has to get the Dogs evenly started and slip them together. On the field is the judge, scarlet-coated and well mounted. He follows the chase. The Hare, mindful of his training, speeds across the open, toward the Haven, in full view of the Grand Stand. The Dogs follow the Jack. As the first one comes near enough to be dangerous, the Hare balks him by dodging. Each time the Hare is turned, scores for the Dog that did it, and a final point is made by the kill.

Sometimes the kill takes place within one hundred yards of the start—that means a poor Jack; mostly it happens in front of the Grand Stand; but on rare occasions it chances that the Jack goes sailing across the open Park a good half-mile and, by dodging for time, runs to safety in the Haven. Four finishes are posible: a speedy kill; a speedy winning of the Haven; new Dogs to relieve the first runners, who would suffer heart-collapse in the terrific strain of their pace, if kept up many minutes in hot weather; and finally, for Rabbits that by continued dodging defy and jeopardize the Dogs, and yet do not win the Haven, there is kept a *loaded shotgun*.

There is just as much jockeying at a Kaskado coursing as at a Kaskado horse-race, just as many attempts at fraud, and it is just as necessary to have the judge and slipper beyond suspicion.

The day before the next meet a man of diamonds saw Irish Mickey—by chance. A cigar was all that visibly passed, but it had a green wrapper that was slipped off before lighting. Then a word: "If you wuz slipper to-morrow and it so came about that Dignam's Minkie gets done, wall,—it means another cigar."

"Faix, an' if I wuz slipper I could load the dice so Minkie would niver score a p'int, but her runnin' mate would have the same bad luck."

"That so?" The diamond man looked interested. "All right—fix it so; it means two cigars."

Slipper Slyman had always dealt on the square, had scorned many approaches—that was well known. Most believed in him, but there were some malcontents, and when a man with many gold seals approached the Steward and formulated charges, serious and well-backed, they must perforce suspend the slipper pending an inquiry, and thus Mickey Doo reigned in his stead.

Mickey was poor and not over-scrupulous. Here was a chance to make a year's pay in a minute, nothing wrong about it, no harm to the Dog or the Rabbit either.

One Jack-rabbit is much like another. Everybody knows that; it was simply a question of choosing your Jack.

The preliminaries were over. Fifty Jacks had been run and killed. Mickey had done his work satisfactorily; a fair slip had been given to every leash. He was still in command as slipper. Now came the final for the cup—the cup and the large stakes.

* * *

There were the slim and elegant Dogs awaiting their turn. Minkie and her rival were first. Everything had been fair so far, and who can say that what followed was unfair? Mickey could turn out which Jack he pleased.

"Number three!" he called to his partner.

Out leaped the Little Warhorse,—black and white his great ears, easy and low his five-foot bounds; gazing wildly at the unwonted crowd about the Park, he leaped high in one surprising spy-hop.

"Hrrrr!" shouted the slipper, and his partner rattled a stick on the fence. The Warhorse's bounds increased to eight or nine feet.

"Hrrrr!" and they were ten or twelve feet. At thirty yards the Hounds were slipped—an even slip; some thought it could have been done at twenty yards.

"Hrrrrrr! Hrrrrrr!" and the Warhorse was doing fourteen-foot leaps, not a spy-hop among them.

"Hrrrrr!" wonderful Dogs! how they sailed; but drifting ahead of them, like a white seabird or flying scud, was the Warhorse. Away past the Grand Stand. And the Dogs—were they closing the gap of start? Closing! It was lengthening! In less time than it takes to tell it, that black-and-white thistledown had drifted away through the Haven door,—the door so like that good old hen-hole,—and the Greyhounds pulled up amidst a roar of derisio and cheers for the Little Warhorse. How Mickey did laugh! How Dignam did swear! How the newspaper men did scribble—scribble—scribble!

Next day there was a paragraph in all the papers: "WONDERFUL FEAT OF A JACK-RABBIT. The Little Warhorse, as he has been styled, completely skunked two of the most famous Dogs on the turf," etc.

There was a fierce wrangle among the dogmen. This was a tie, since neither had scored, and Minkie and her rival were allowed to run again; but that half-mile had been too hot, and they had no show for the cup.

Mickey met "Diamonds" next day, *by chance*.

"Have a cigar, Mickey."

"Oi will thot, sor. Faix, thim's so foine, I'd loike two—thank ye, sor."

* * *

From that time the Little Warhorse became the pride of the Irish boy. Slipper Slyman had been honorably reinstated and Mickey reduced to the rank of Jack-starter, but that merely helped to turn his sympathies from the Dogs to the Rabbits, or rather to the Warhorse, for of all the five hundred that were brought in from the drive he alone had won renown. There were several that crossed the Park to run again another day, but he alone had crossed the course without getting even a turn. Twice a week the meets took place; forty or fifty Jacks were killed each time, and the five hundred in the pen had been nearly all eaten of the arena.

The Warhorse had run each day, and as often had made the Haven. Mickey became wildly enthusiastic about his favorite's powers. He begot a positive affection for the clean-limbed racer, and stoutly maintained against all that it was a positive honor to a Dog to be disgraced by such a Jack.

It is so seldom that a Rabbit crosses the track at all, that when Jack did it six times without having to dodge, the papers took note of it, and after each meet there appeared a notice: "The Little Warhorse crossed again today; old-timers say it shows how our Dogs are deteriorating."

After the sixth time the rabbit-keepers grew enthusiastic, and Mickey, commander-in-chief of the brigade, became intemperate in his admiration. "Be jabers, he has a right to be torned loose. He has won his freedom loike ivery Amerikin done," he added, by way of appeal to the patriotism of the Steward of the race, who was, of course, the real owner of the Jacks.

"All right, Mick; if he gets across thirteen times you can ship him back to his native land," was the reply.

Shure now, an' won't you make it tin, sor?"

"No, no; I need him to take the conceit out of some of the new Dogs that are coming."

"Thirteen toimes and he is free, sor; it's a bargain."

A new lot of Rabbits arrived about this time, and one of these was colored much like Little Warhorse. He had no such speed, but to prevent mistakes Mickey caught his favorite by driving him into one of the padded shipping boxes, and proceeded with the gate-keeper's punch to earmark him. The punch was sharp; a clear star was cut out of the thin flap, when Mickey exclaimed: "Faix, an' Oi'll punch for ivery toime ye cross the coorse." So he cut six stars in a row. "Thayer now, Warrhorrse, shure it's a free Rabbit ye'll be when ye have yer thirteen stars loike our flag of liberty hed when *we* got free."

Within a week the Warhorse had vanquished the new Greyhounds and had stars enough to go round the right ear and begin on the left. In a week more the thirteen runs were completed, six stars in the left ear and seven in the right, and the newspapers had new material.

"Whoop!" How Mickey hoorayed! "An' it's a free Jack ye are, Warrhorrse! Thirteen always wuz a lucky number. I never knowed it to fail."

* * *

"Yes, I know I did," said the Steward. "But I want to give him one more run. I have a bet on him against a new Dog here. It won't hurt him now; he can do it. Oh, well. Here now, Mickey, don't you get sassy. One run more this afternoon. The Dogs run two or three times a day; why not the Jack?"

"They're not shtakin' thayre loives, sor."

"Oh, you get out."

Many more Rabbits had been added to the pen,—big and small, peaceful and warlike,—and one big Buck of savage instincts, seeing Jack Warhorse's hurried dash into the Haven that morning, took advantage of the moment to attack him.

At another time Jack would have thumped his skull, as he once did the Cat's, and settled the affair in a minute; but now it took several minutes, during which he himself got roughly handled; so when the afternoon came he was suffering from one or two bruises and stiffening wounds; not serious, indeed, but enough to lower his speed.

The start was much like those of previous runs. The Warhorse steaming away low and lightly, his ears up and the breezes whistling through his thirteen stars.

Minkie with Fango, the new Dog, bounded in eager pursuit, but, to the surprise of the starters, the gap grew smaller. The Warhorse was losing ground, and right before the Grand Stand old Minkie turned him, and a cheer went up from the dog-men, for all knew the runners. Within fifty yards Fango scored a turn, and the race was right back to the start. There stood Slyman and Mickey. The Rabbit dodged, the Greyhounds plunged; Jack could not get away, and just as the final snap seemed near, the Warhorse leaped straight for Mickey, and in an instant was hidden in his arms, while the starter's feet flew out in energetic kicks to repel the furious Dogs. It is not likely that the Jack knew Mickey for a friend; he only yielded to the old instinct to fly from a certain enemy to a neutral or a possible friend, and, as luck would have it, he had wisely leaped and well. A cheer went up from the benches as Mickey hurried back with his favorite. But the dog-men protested "it wasn't a fair run—they wanted it finished." They appealed to the Steward. He had backed the Jack against Fango. He was sore now, and ordered a new race.

An hour's rest was the best Mickey could get for him. Then he went as before, with Fango and Minkie in pursuit. He seemed less stiff now—he ran more like himself; but a little past the Stand he was turned by Fango and again by Minkie, and back and across, and here and there, leaping frantically and barely eluding his foes. For several minutes it lasted. Mickey could see that Jack's ears were sinking. The new Dog leaped. Jack dodged almost under him to escape, and back only to meet the second Dog; and now both ears were flat on his back. But the Hounds were suffering too. Their tongues were lolling out; their jaws and heaving sides were splashed with foam. The Warhorse's ears went up again. His courage seemed to revive in their distress. He made a straight dash for the Haven; but the straight dash was just what the Hounds could do, and within a hundred yards he was turned again, to begin another desperate game of zigzag. Then the dog-men saw danger for their Dogs, and two new ones were slipped—two fresh Hounds;

surely they could end the race. *But they did not.* The first two were vanquished—gasping—out of it, but the next two were racing near. The Warhorse put forth all his strength. He left the first two far behind— was nearly to the Haven when the second two came up.

Nothing but dodging could save him now. His ears were sinking, his heart was pattering on his ribs, but his spirit was strong. He flung himself in wildest zigzags. The Hounds tumbled over each other. Again and again they thought they had him. One of them snapped off the end of his long black tail, yet he escaped; but he could not get to the Haven. The luck was against him. He was forced nearer to the Grand Stand. A thousand ladies were watching. The time limit was up. The second Dogs were suffering, when Mickey came running, yelling like a madman—words—imprecations—crazy sounds:

"Ye blackguard hoodlums! Ye dhirty, cowardly bastes!" and he rushed furiously at the Dogs, intent to do them bodily harm.

Officers came running and shouting, and Mickey, shrieking hatred and defiance, was dragged from the field, reviling Dogs and men with every horrid, insulting name he could think of or invent.

"Fair play! Whayer's yer fair play, ye liars, ye dhirty cheats, ye bloody cowards!" And they drove him from the arena. The last he saw of it was the four foaming Dogs feebly dodging after a weak and worn-out Jack-rabbit, and the judge on his Horse beckoning to the man with the gun.

The gate closed behind him, and Mickey heard a *bang—bang*, an unusual uproar mixed with yelps of Dogs, and he knew that Little Jack Warhorse had been served with finish No. 4.

All his life he had loved Dogs, but his sense of fair play was outraged. He could not get in, nor see in from where he was. He raced along the lane to the Haven, where he might get a good view, and arrived in time to see—Little Jack Warhorse with his half-masted ears limp into the Haven; and he realized at once that the man with the gun had missed, had hit the wrong runner, for there was the crowd at the Stand watching two men who were carrying a wounded Greyhound, while a veterinary surgeon was ministering to another that was panting on the ground.

Mickey looked about, seized a little shipping-box, put it at the angle of the Haven, carefully drove the tired thing into it, closed the lid, then, with the box under his arm, he scaled the fence unseen in the confusion and was gone.

The second dogs were suffering

'It didn't matter; he had lost his job anyway.' He tramped away from the city. He took the train at the nearest station and travelled some hours, and now he was in Rabbit country again. The sun had long gone down; the night with its stars was over the plain when among the farms, the Osage and alfalfa, Mickey Doo opened the box and gently put the Warhorse out.

Grinning as he did so, he said: "Shure an' it's ould Oireland thot's proud to set the thirteen stars at liberty wance moore."

For a moment the Little Warhorse gazed in doubt, then took three or four long leaps and a spy-hop to get his bearings. Now spreading his national colors and his honor-marked ears, he bounded into his hard-won freedom, strong as ever, and melted into the night of his native plain.

He has been seen many times in Kaskado, and there have been many Rabbit drives in that region, but he seems to know some means of baffling them now, for, in all the thousands that have been trapped and corralled, they have never since seen the star-spangled ears of Little Jack Warhorse.

SNAP

The Story of a Bull-terrier

It was dusk on Hallowe'en when first I saw him. Early in the morning I had received a telegram from my college chum Jack: "Lest we forget. Am sending you a remarkable pup. Be polite to him; it's safer." It would have been just like Jack to have sent an infernal machine or a Skunk rampant and called it a pup, so I awaited the hamper with curiosity. When it arrived I saw it was marked "Dangerous," and there came from within a high-pitched snarl at every slight provocation. On peering through the wire netting I saw it was not a baby Tiger but a small white Bull-terrier. He snapped at me and at any one or anything that seemed too abrupt or too near for proper respect, and his snarling growl was unpleasantly frequent. Dogs have two growls: one deep-rumbled, and chesty; that is polite warning—the retort courteous; the other mouthy and much higher in pitch: this is the last word before actual onslaught. The Terrier's growls were all of the latter kind. I was a dog-man and thought I knew all about Dogs, so, dismissing the porter, I got out my all-round jackknife-toothpick-nailhammer-hatchet-toolbox-fire-shovel, a specialty of our firm, and lifted the netting. Oh, yes, I knew all about Dogs. The little fury had been growling out a whole-souled growl for every tap of the tool, and when I turned the box on its side, he made a dash straight for my legs. Had not his foot gone through the wire netting and held him, I might have been hurt, for his heart was evidently in his work; but I stepped on the table out of reach and tried to reason with him. I have always believed in talking to animals. I maintain that they gather something of our intention at least, even if they do not understand our words; but the Dog evidently put me down for a hypocrite and scorned my approaches. At first he took his post under the table and kept up a circular watch for a leg trying to get down. I felt sure I could have controlled him with my eye, but I could not bring it to bear where I was, or rather where he was; thus I was left a prisoner. I am a very cool person, I flatter myself; in fact, I represent a hardware firm, and, in coolness, we are not excelled by any but perhaps the nosy gentlemen that sell wearing-apparel. I got out a cigar and smoked tailor-style on the table, while my little tyrant below kept watch for legs. I got out the telegram and read it: "Remarkable pup. Be polite to him; it's safer." I think it was my coolness rather than my politeness that did it, for in half an hour the growling ceased. In an hour he no longer jumped at a newspaper cautiously pushed over the edge to test his humor; possibly the irritation of the cage was wearing off, and by the time I had lit my third cigar, he waddled out to the fire and lay down; not ignoring me, however, I had no reason to complain of that kind of contempt. He kept one eye on me, and I kept both eyes, not on him, but on his stumpy tail. If that tail should swing sidewise once I should feel I was winning; but it did not swing. I got a book and put in time on that table till my legs were cramped and the fire burned low. About 10 p.m. it was chilly, and at half-past ten the fire was out. My Hallowe'en present got up, yawned and stretched, then walked under my bed, where he found a fur rug. By stepping lightly from the table to the dresser, and then on to the mantel-shelf, I also reached bed, and, very quietly undressing, got in without provoking any criticism from my master. I had not yet fallen asleep when I heard a sight scrambling and felt "thump-thump" on the bed, then over my feet and legs; Snap evidently had found it too cool down below, and proposed to have the best my house afforded.

He curled up on my feet in such a way that I was very uncomfortable and tried to readjust matters, but the slightest wriggle of my toe was enough to make him snap at it so fiercely that nothing but thick woollen bedclothes saved me from being maimed for life.

I was an hour moving my feet—a hair's-breadth at a time—till they were so that I could sleep in comfort; and I was awakened several times during the night by angry snarls from the Dog—I suppose because I dared to move a toe without his approval, though once I believe he did it simply because I was snoring.

In the morning I was ready to get up before Snap was. You see, I call him Snap—Gingersnap in full. Some Dogs are hard to name, and some do not seem to need it—they name themselves.

I was ready to rise at seven. Snap was not ready till eight, so we rose at eight. He had little to say to the man who made the fire. He allowed me to dress without doing it on the table. As I left the room to get breakfast, I remarked:

"Snap, my friend, some men would whip you into a different way, but I think I know a better plan. The doctors nowadays favor the 'no-breakfast cure.' I shall try that."

It seemed cruel, but I left him without food all day. It cost me something to repaint the door where he scratched it, but at night he was quite ready to accept a little food at my hands.

In a week we were very good friends. He would sleep on my bed now and allow me to move my feet without snapping at them, intent to do me serious bodily harm. The no-breakfast cure had worked wonders; in three months we were—well, simply man and Dog, and he amply justified the telegram he came with.

He seemed to be without fear. If a small Dog came near, he would take not the slightest notice; if a medium-sized Dog, he would stick his

Snap

stub of a tail rigidly up in the air, then walk around him, scratching contemptuously with his hind feet, and looking at the sky, the distance, the ground, anything but the Dog, and noting his presence only by frequent high-pitched growls. If the stranger did not move on at once, the battle began, and then the stranger usually moved on very rapidly. Snap sometimes got worsted, but no amount of sad experience could ever inspire him with a grain of caution. Once, while riding in a cab during the Dog Show, Snap caught sight of an elephantine St. Bernard taking an airing. Its size aroused such enthusiasm in the Pup's little breast that he leaped from the cab window to do battle, and broke his leg.

Evidently fear had been left out of his make-up and its place supplied with an extra amount of ginger, which was the reason of his full name. He differed from all other Dogs I have ever known. For example, if a boy threw a stone at him, he ran, not away, but toward the boy, and if the crime was repeated, Snap took the law into his own hands; thus he was at least respected by all. Only myself and the porter at the office seemed to realize his good points, and we only were admitted to the high honor of personal friendship, an honor which I appreciated more as months went on, and by midsummer not Carnegie, Vanderbilt, and Astor together could have raised money enough to buy a quarter of a share in my litte Dog Snap.

* * *

Though not a regular traveller, I was ordered out on the road in the autumn, and then Snap and the landlady were left together, with unfortunate developments. Contempt on his part—fear on hers; and hate on both.

I was placing a lot of barb-wire in the northern tier of States. My letters were forwarded once a week, and I got several complaints from the landlady about Snap.

Arrived at Mendoza, in North Dakota, I found a fine market for wire. Of course my dealings were with the big storekeepers, but I went about among the ranchmen to get their practical views on the different styles, and thus I met the Penroof Brother's Cow-outfit.

One cannot be long in Cow country now without hearing a great deal about the depredations of the ever wily and destructive Gray-wolf. The day has gone by when they can be poisoned wholesale, and they are a serious drain on the rancher's profits. The Penroof Brothers, like most live cattle-men, had given up all attempts at poisoning and trapping, and were trying various breeds of Dogs as Wolf-hunters, hoping to get a little sport out of the necessary work of destroying the pests.

Foxhounds had failed—they were too soft for fighting; Great Danes were too clumsy, and Greyhounds could not follow the game unless they could see it. Each breed had some fatal defect, but the cow-men hoped to succeed with a mixed pack, and the day when I was invited to join in a Mendoza Wolf-hunt, I was amused by the variety of Dogs that followed. There were several mongrels, but there were also a few highly bred Dogs—in particular, some Russian Wolfhounds that must have cost a lot of money.

Hilton Penroof, the oldest boy, "The Master of Hounds," was unusually proud of them, and expected them to do great things.

"Greyhounds are too thin-skinned to fight a Wolf, Danes are too slow, but you'll see the fur fly when the Russians take a hand."

Thus the Greyhounds were there as runners, the Danes as heavy backers, and the Russians to do the important fighting. There were also two or three Foxhounds, whose fine noses were relied on to follow the trail if the game got out of view.

It was a fine sight as we rode away among the Badland Buttes that October day. The air was bright and crisp, and though so late, there was neither snow nor frost. The Horses were fresh, and once or twice showed me how a Cow-pony tries to get rid of his rider.

The Dogs were keen for sport, and we did start one or two gray spots in the plain that Hilton said were Wolves or Coyotes. The Dogs trailed away at full cry, but at night, beyond the fact that one of the Greyhounds had a wound on his shoulder, there was nothing to show that any of them had been on a Wolf-hunt.

"It's my opinion yer fancy Russians is no good, Hilt," said Garvin, the younger brother. "I'll back that litte black Dane against the lot, mongrel an' all as he is."

"I don't understand it," growed Hilton. "There ain't a Coyote, let alone a Gray-wolf, kin run away from them Greyhounds; them Foxhounds kin folly a trail three days old, an' the Danes could lick a Grizzly."

"I reckon," said the father, "they kin run, an' they kin track, an' they kin lick a Grizzly, *maybe*, but the fac' is they don't want to tackle a Gray-wolf. The hull darn pack is scairt—an' I wish we had our money out o' them."

Thus the men grumbled and discussed as I drove away and left them.

There seemed only one solution of the failure. The Hounds were swift and strong, but a Gray-wolf seems to terrorize all Dogs. They have not the nerve to face him, and so, each time he gets away, and my thoughts flew back to the fearless little Dog that had shared my bed for the last year. How I wished he was out here, then these lubberly giants of Hounds would find a leader whose nerve would not fail at the moment of trial.

At Baroka, my next stop, I got a batch of mail including two letters from the landlady; the first to say that "that beast of a Dog was acting up scandalous in my room," and the other still more forcible, demanding his immediate removal.

"Why not have him expressed to Mendoza?" I thought. "It's only twenty hours; they'll be glad to have him. I can take him home with me when I go through."

* * *

My next meeting with Gingersnap was not as different from the first as one might have expected. He jumped on me, made much vigorous pretense to bite, and growled frequently, but it was a deep-chested growl and his stump waggled hard.

The Penroofs had had a number of Wolfhunts since I was with them, and were much disgusted at having no better success than before. The Dogs could find a Wolf nearly every time they went out, but they could not kill him, and the men were not near enough at the finish to learn why.

Old Penroof was satisfied that "thar wasn't one of the hull miserable gang that had the grit of a Jack-rabbit."

We were off at dawn the next day—the same procession of fine Horses and superb riders; the big blue Dogs, the yellow Dogs, the spotted Dogs, as before; but there was a new feature, a little white Dog that stayed close by me, and not only any Dogs, but Horses that came too near were apt to get a surprise from his teeth. I think he quarrelled with every man, Horse, and Dog in the country, with the exception of a Bull-terrier belonging to the Mendoza hotel man. She was the only one smaller than himself, and they seemed very good friends.

I shall never forget the view of the hunt I had that day. We were on one of those large, flat-headed buttes that give a kingdom to the eye, when Hilton, who had been scanning the vast country with glasses, exclaimed: "I see him. There he goes, toward Skull Creek. Guess it's a Coyote."

Now the first thing is to get the Greyhounds to see the prey—not an easy matter, as they cannot use the glasses, and the ground was covered with sage-brush higher than the Dogs' heads.

But Hilton called, "Hu, hu, Dander," and leaned aside from his saddle, holding out his foot at the same time. With one agile bound Dander leaped to the saddle and there stood balancing on the Horse while Hilton kept pointing. "There he is, Dander; sic him—see him down there." The Dog gazed earnestly where his master pointed, then seeming to see, he sprang to the ground with a slight yelp and sped away. The other Dogs followed after, in an ever-lengthening procession, and we rode as hard as we could behind them, but losing time, for the ground was cut with gullies, spotted with badger-holes, and covered with rocks and sage that made full speed too hazardous.

We all fell behind, and I was last, of course, being least accustomed to the saddle. We got several glimpses of the Dogs flying over the level plain or dropping from sight in gullies to reappear at the other side. Dander, the Greyhound, was the recognized leader, and as we mounted another ridge we got sight of the whole chase—a Coyote at full speed, the Dogs a quarter of a mile behind, but gaining. When next we saw them the Coyote was dead, and the Dogs sitting around panting, all but two of the Foxhounds and Gingersnap.

"Too late for the fracas," remarked Hilton, glancing at these last Foxhounds. Then he proudly petted Dander. "Didn't neet yer purp after all, ye see."

"Takes a heap of nerve for ten big Dogs to face one little Coyote," remarked the father, sarcastically. "Wait till we run onto a Gray."

Next day we were out again, for I made up my mind to see it to a finish.

From a high point we caught sight of a moving speck of gray. A moving white speck stands for Antelope, a red speck for Fox, a gray speck for either Gray-wolf or Coyote, and which of these is determined by its tail. If the glass shows the tail down, it is a Coyote; if up, it is the hated Gray-wolf.

Dander was shown the game as before and led the motley mixed procession—as he had before—Greyhounds, Wolfhounds, Foxhounds, Danes, Bull-terrier, horsemen. We got a momentary view of the pursuit; a Gray-wolf it surely was, loping away ahead of the Dogs. Somehow I thought the first Dogs were not running so fast now as they had after the Coyote. But no one knew the finish of the hunt. The Dogs came back to us one by one, and we saw no more of that Wolf.

Sarcastic remarks and recrimination were now freely indulged in by the hunters.

"Pah! scairt, plumb scairt," was the father's disgusted comment on the pack. "They could catch up easy enough, but when he turned on them, they lighted out for home—pah!"

"Where's that thar onsurpassable, fearless, scaired-o'-nort Tarrier?" asked Hilton, scornfully.

"I don't know," said I. "I am inclined to think he never saw the Wolf; but if he ever does, I'll bet he sails in for death or glory."

That night several Cows were killed close to the ranch, and we were spurred on to another hunt.

It opened much like the last. Late in the afternoon we sighted a gray fellow with tail up, not half a mile off. Hilton called Dander up on the saddle. I acted on the idea and called Snap to mine. His legs were so short that he had to leap several times before he made it, scrambling up at last with my foot as a half-way station. I pointed and "sic-ed" for a minute before he saw the game, and then he started out after the Greyhounds, already gone, with energy that was full of promise.

The chase this time led us, not to the rough brakes along the river, but toward the high open country, for reasons that appeared later. We were close together as we rose to the upland and sighted the chase half a mile off, just as Dander came up with the Wolf and snapped at his haunch. The Gray-wolf turned round to fight, and we had a fine view. The Dogs came up by twos and threes, barking at him in a ring, till last the little white one rushed up. He wasted no time barking, but rushed straight at the Wolf's throat and missed it, yet seemed to get him by the nose; then the ten big Dogs closed in, and in two minutes the Wolf was dead. We had ridden hard to be in at the finish, and though our view was distant, we saw at least that Snap had lived up to the telegram, as well as to my promises for him.

Now it was my turn to crow, and I did not lose the chance. Snap had shown them how, and at last the Mendoza pack had killed a Gray-wolf without help from the men.

There were two things to mar the victory somewhat: first, it was a young Wolf, a mere Cub, hence his foolish choice of country; second, Snap was wounded—the Wolf had given him a bad cut in the shoulder.

As we rode in proud procession home, I saw he limped a little. "Here," I cried, "come up, Snap." He tried once or twice to jump to the saddle, but could not. "Here, Hilton, lift him up to me."

"Thanks; I'll let you handle your own rattlesnakes," was the reply, for all knew now that it was not safe to meddle with his person. "Here, Snap, take hold," I said, and held my quirt to him. He seized it, and by that I lifted him to the front of my saddle and so carried him home. I cared for him as though he had been a baby. He had shown those Cattle-men how to fill the weak place in their pack; the Foxhounds may be good and the Greyhounds swift and the Russians and Danes

fighters, but they are no use at all without the crowning moral force of
grit, that none can supply so well as a Bull-terrier. On that day the
Cattle-men learned how to manage the Wolf question, as you will find
if ever you are at Mendoza; for every successful Wolf pack there has
with it a Bull-terrier, preferably of the Snap-Mendoza breed.

* * *

Next day was Hallowe'en, the anniversary of Snap's advent. The
weather was clear, bright, not too cold, and there was no snow on the
ground. The men usually celebrated the day with a hunt of some sort,
and now, of course, Wolves were the one object. To the disappointment
of all, Snap was in bad shape with his wound. He slept, as usual, at my
feet, and bloody stains now marked the place. He was not in condition
to fight, but we were bound to have a Wolf-hunt, so he was beguiled to
an outhouse and locked up, while we went off, I, at least, with a sense
of impending disaster. I *knew* we should fail without my Dog, but I did
not realize how bad a failure it was to be.

Afar among the buttes of Skull Creek we had roamed when a
white ball appeared bounding through the sage-brush, and in a minute
more Snap came, growling and stump-waggling, up to my Horse's side.
I could not send him back; he would take no such orders, not even from
me. His wound was looking bad, so I called him, held down the quirt,
and jumped him to my saddle.

"There," I thought, "I'll keep you safe till we get home." Yes, I
thought; but I reckoned not with Snap. The voice of Hilton, "Hu, hu,"
announced that he had sighted a Wolf. Dander and Riley, his rival, both
sprang to the point of observation, with the result that they collided
and fell together, sprawling, in the sage. But Snap, gazing hard, had
sighted the Wolf, not so very far off, and before I knew it, he leaped
from the saddle and bounded zigzag, high, low, in and under the sage,
straight for the enemy, leading the whole pack for a few minutes. Not
far, of course. The great Greyhounds sighted the moving speck, and the
usual procession strung out on the plain. It promised to be a fine hunt,
for the Wolf had less than half a mile start and all the Dogs were fully
interested.

"They've turned up Grizzly Gully," cried Garvin. "This way, and
we can head them off."

So we turned and rode hard around the north side of Hulmer's
Butte, while the chase seemed to go round the south.

We galloped to the top of Cedar Ridge and were about to ride
down, when Hilton shouted, "By George, here he is! We're right onto
him." He leaped from his Horse, dropped the bridle, and ran forward. I
did the same. A great Gray-wolf came lumbering across an open plain
toward us. His head was low, his tail out level, and fifty yards behind
him was Dander, sailing like a Hawk over the ground, going twice as
fast as the Wolf. In a minute the Hound was alongside and snapped,
but bounded back, as the Wolf turned on him. They were just below us

now and not fifty feet away. Garvin drew his revolver, but in a fateful moment Hilton interfered: "No; no; let's see it out." In a few seconds the next Greyhound arrived, then the rest in order of swiftness. Each came up full of fight and fury, determined to go right in and tear the Gray-wolf to pieces; but each in turn swerved aside, and leaped and barked around at a safe distance. After a minute or so the Russians appeared—fine big Dogs they were. Their distant intention no doubt was to dash right at the old Wolf; but his fearless front, his sinewy frame and death-dealing jaws, awed them long before they were near him, and they also joined the ring, while the desperado in the middle faced this way and that, ready for any or all.

Now the Danes came up, huge-limbed creatures, any one of them as heavy as the Wolf. I heard their heavy breathing tighten into a threatening sound as they plunged ahead, eager to tear the foe to pieces; but when they saw him there, grim, fearless, mighty of jaw, tireless of limb, ready to die if need be, but sure of this, he would not die alone—well, those great Danes—all three of them—were stricken, as the rest had been, with a sudden bashfulness: yes, they would go right in presently—not now, but as soon as they had got their breath; they were not afraid of a Wolf, oh, no. I could read their courage in their voices. They knew perfectly well that the first Dog to go in was going to get hurt, but never mind that—presently; they would bark a little more to get up enthusiasm.

And as the ten big Dogs were leaping round the silent Wolf at bay, there was a rustling in the sage at the far side of the place; then a snow-white rubber ball, it seemed, came bounding, but grew into a little Bull-terrier, and Snap, slowest of the pack, and last, came panting hard, so hard he seemed gasping. Over the level open he made, straight to the changing ring around the Cattle-killer whom none dared face. Did he hesitate? Not for an instant; through the ring of the yelping pack, straight for the old despot of the range, right for his throat, he sprang; and the Gray-wolf struck with his twenty scimitars. But the little one, if foiled at all, sprang again, and then what came I hardly knew. There was a whirling mass of Dogs. I thought I saw the little White One clinched on the Gray-wolf's nose. The pack was all around; we could not help them now. But they did not need us; they had a leader of dauntless mettle, and when in a little while the final scene was done,

The bounding ball of white

there on the ground lay the Gray-wolf, a giant of his kind, and clinched on his nose was the little white Dog.

We were standing around within fifteen feet, ready to help, but had no chance till we were not needed.

The Wolf was dead, and I hallooed to Snap, but he did not move. I bent over him. "Snap—Snap, it's all over; you've killed him." But the Dog was very still, and now I saw two deep wounds in his body. I tried to lift him. "Let go, old fellow; it's all over." He growled feebly, and at last let go of the Wolf. The rough cattle-men were kneeling around him now; old Penroof's voice was trembling as he muttered, "I wouldn't had him hurt for twenty steers." I lifted him in my arms, called to him and stroked his head. He snarled a little, a farewell as it proved, for he licked my hand as he did so, then never snarled again.

That was a sad ride home for me. There was the skin of a monstrous Wolf, but no other hint of triumph. We buried the fearless one on a butte back of the ranch-house. Penroof, as he stood by, was heard to grumble: "By jingo, that was grit—cl'ar grit! Ye can't raise Cattle without grit."

THE WINNIPEG WOLF

It was during the great blizzard of 1882 that I first met the Winnipeg Wolf. I had left St. Paul in the middle of March to cross the prairies to Winnipeg, expecting to be there in twenty-four hours, but the Storm King had planned it otherwise and sent a heavy-laden eastern blast. The snow came down in a furious, steady torrent, hour after hour. Never before had I seen such a storm. All the world was lost in snow—snow, snow, snow—whirling, biting, stinging, drifting snow—and the puffing, monstrous engine was compelled to stop at the command of those tiny, feathery crystals of spotless purity.

Many strong hands with shovels came to the delicately curled snowdrifts that barred our way, and in an hour the engine could pass—only to stick in another drift yet farther on. It was dreary work—day after day, night after night, sticking in the drifts, digging ourselves out, and still the snow went whirling and playing about us.

"Twenty-two hours to Emerson," said the official; but nearly two weeks of digging passed before we did reach Emerson, and the poplar country where the thickets stop all drifting of the snow. Thenceforth the train went swiftly, the poplar woods grew more thickly—we passed for miles through solid forests, then perhaps through an open space. As we neared St. Boniface, the eastern outskirts of Winnipeg, we dashed across a little glade fifty yards wide, and there in the middle was a group that stirred me to the very soul.

In plain view was a great rabble of Dogs, large and small, black, white, and yellow, wriggling and heaving this way and that way in a rude ring; to one side was a little yellow Dog stretched and quiet in the snow; on the outer part of the ring was a huge black Dog bounding about and barking, but keeping ever behind the moving mob. And in the midst, the centre and cause of it all, was a great, grim, Wolf.

Wolf? He looked like a Lion. There he stood, all alone—resolute—calm—with bristling mane, and legs braced firmly, glancing this way and that, to be ready for an attack in any direction. There was a curl on his lips—it looked like scorn, but I suppose it was really the fighting snarl of tooth display. Led by a wolfish-looking Dog that should have

He looked like a lion

been ashamed, the pack dashed in, for the twentieth time no doubt. But the great gray form leaped here and there, and chop, chop, chop went those fearful jaws, no other sound from the lonely warrior; but a death yelp from more than one of his foes, as those that were able again sprang back, and left him statuesque as before, untamed, unmaimed, and contemptuous of them all.

How I wished for the train to stick in a snowdrift now, as so often before, for all my heart went out to that Gray-wolf; I longed to go and help him. But the snow-deep glade flashed by, the poplar trunks shut out the view, and we went on to our journey's end.

This was all I saw, and it seemed little; but before many days had passed I knew surely that I had been favored with a view, in broad daylight, of a rare and wonderful creature, none less than the Winnipeg Wolf.

His was a strange history—a Wolf that preferred the city to the country, that passed by the Sheep to kill the Dogs, and that always hunted alone.

In telling the story of *le Garou*, as he was called by some, although I speak of these things as locally familiar, it is very sure that to many citizens of the town they were quite unknown. The smug shopkeeper on the main street had scarcely heard of him until the day after the final scene at the slaughter-house, when his great carcass was carried to Hine's taxidermist shop and there mounted, to be exhibited later at the Chicago World's Fair, and to be destroyed, alas! in the fire that reduced the Mulvey Grammar School to ashes in 1896.

* * *

It seems that Fiddler Paul, the handsome ne'er-do-well of the half-breed world, readier to hunt than to work, was prowling with his gun along the wooded banks of the Red River by Kildonan, one day in the June of 1880. He saw a Gray-wolf come out of a hole in a bank and fired a chance shot that killed it. Having made sure, by sending in his Dog, that no other large Wolf was there, he crawled into the den, and found, to his utter amazement and delight, eight young Wolves—nine bounties of ten dollars each. How much is that? A fortune surely. He used a stick vigorously, and with the assistance of the yellow Cur, all the little ones were killed but one. There is a superstition about the last of a brood—it is not lucky to kill it. So Paul set out for town with the scalp of the old Wolf, the scalps of the seven young, and the last Cub alive.

The saloon-keeper, who got the dollars for which the scalps were exchanged, soon got the living Cub. He grew up at the end of a chain, but developed a chest and jaws that no Hound in town could match. He was kept in the yard for the amusement of customers, and this amusement usually took the form of baiting the captive with Dogs. The young Wolf was bitten and mauled nearly to death on several occasions, but he recovered, and each month there were fewer Dogs willing to face him. His life was as hard as it could be. There was but

Surrounded by a score of dogs was a great gray-wolf

one gleam of gentleness in it all, and that was the friendship that grew up between himself and Little Jim, the son of the saloon-keeper.

Jim was a wilful little rascal with a mind of his own. He took to the Wolf because it had killed a Dog that had bitten him. He thenceforth fed the Wolf and made a pet of it, and the Wolf responded by allowing him to take liberties which no one else dared venture.

Jim's father was not a model parent. He usually spoiled his son, but a times would get in a rage and beat him cruelly for some trifle. The child was quick to learn that he was beaten, not because he had done wrong, but because he had made his father angry. If, therefore, he could keep out of the way until that anger had cooled, he had no further cause for worry. One day, seeking safety in flight with his father behind him, he dashed into the Wolf's kennel, and his grizzly chum thus unceremoniously awakened turned to the door, displayed a double row of ivories, and plainly said to the father: "Don't you dare to touch him."

If Hogan could have shot the Wolf then and there he would have done so, but the chances were about equal of killing his son, so he let them alone and, half an hour later, laughed at the whole affair. Thenceforth Little Jim made for the Wolf's den whenever he was in danger, and sometimes the only notice any one had that the boy had been in mischief was seeing him sneak in behind the savage captive.

Economy in hired help was a first principle with Hogan. Therefore his "barkeep" was a Chinaman. He was a timid, harmless creature, so Paul des Roches did not hesitate to bully him. One day, finding Hogan out, and the Chinaman alone in charge, Paul, already tipsy, demanded a drink on credit, and Tung Ling, acting on standing orders, refused. His artless explanation, "No good, neber pay," so far from clearing up the difficulty, brought Paul staggering back of the bar to avenge the insult. The Celestial might have suffered grievous bodily hurt, but that Little Jim was at hand and had a long stick, with which he adroitly tripped up the Fiddler and sent him sprawling. He staggered to his feet swearing he would have Jim's life. But the child was near the back door and soon found refuge in the Wolf's kennel.

Seeing that the boy had a protector, Paul got the long stick, and from a safe distance began to belabor the Wolf. The grizzly creature raged at the end of the chain, but, though he parried many cruel blows by seizing the stick in his teeth, he was suffering severely, when Paul realized that Jim, whose tongue had not been idle, was fumbling away with nervous fingers to set the Wolf loose, and soon would succeed. Indeed, it would have been done already but for the strain that the Wolf kept on the chain.

The thought of being in the yard at the mercy of the huge animal that he had so enraged, gave the brave Paul a thrill of terror.

Jim's wheedling voice was heard—"Hold on now, Wolfie; back up just a little, and you shall have him. No do; there's a good Wolfie"— that was enough; the Fiddler fled and carefully closed all doors behind him.

Thus the friendship between Jim and his pet grew stronger, and the Wolf, as he developed his splendid natural powers, gave daily evidence also of the mortal hatred he bore to men that smelt of whiskey and to all Dogs, the causes of his sufferings. This peculiarity, coupled with his love for the child—and all children seemed to be included to some extent—grew with his growth and seemed to prove the ruling force of his life.

* * *

At this time—that is, the fall of 1881—there were great complaints among the Qu'Appelle ranchmen that the Wolves were increasing in their country and committing great depredations among the stock. Poisoning and trapping had proved failures, and when a distinguished German visitor appeared at the Club in Winnipeg and announced that he was bringing some Dogs that could easily rid the country of Wolves, he was listened to with unusual interest. For the cattle-men are fond of sport, and the idea of helping their business by establishing a kennel of Wolfhounds was very alluring.

The German soon produced as samples of his Dogs, two magnificent Danes, one white, the other blue with black spots and a singular white eye that completed an expression of unusual ferocity. Each of these great creatures weighed nearly two hundred pounds. They were muscled like Tigers, and the German was readily believed when he claimed that these two alone were more than a match for the biggest Wolf. He thus described their method of hunting: "All you have to do is show them the trail and, even if it is a day old, away they go on it. They cannot be shaken off. They will soon find that Wolf, no matter how he doubles and hides. Then they close on him. He turns to run, the blue Dog takes him by the haunch and throws him like this," and the German jerked a roll of bread into the air; "then before he touches the ground the white Dog has his head, the other his tail, and they pull him apart like that."

It sounded all right; at any rate every one was eager to put it to the proof. Several of the residents said there was a fair chance of finding a Gray-wolf along the Assiniboine, so a hunt was orgainzed. But they searched in vain for three days and were giving it up when some one suggested that down at Hogan's saloon was a Wolf chained up, that they could get for the value of the bounty, and though little more than a year old he would serve to show what the Dogs could do.

The value of Hogan's Wolf went up at once when he knew the importance of the occasion; besides, "he had conscientious scruples." All his scruples vanished, however, when his views as to price were met. His first care was to get Little Jim out of the way by sending him on an errand to his grandma's; then the Wolf was driven into his box and nailed in. The box was put in a wagon and taken to the open prairie along the Portage trail.

The Dogs could scarcely be held back, they were so eager for the fray, as soon as they smelt the Wolf. But several strong men held their leash, the wagon was drawn half a mile farther, and the Wolf was turned out with some difficulty. At first he looked scared and sullen. He tried to get out of sight, but made no attempt to bite. However, on finding himself free, as well as hissed and hooted at, he started off at a slinking trot toward the south, where the land seemed broken. The Dogs were released at that moment, and, baying furiously, they bounded away after the young Wolf. The men cheered loudly and rode behind them. From the very first it was clear that he had no chance. The Dogs were much swifter; the white one could run like a Greyhound. The German was wildly enthusiastic as she flew across the prairie, gaining visibly on the Wolf at every second. Many bets were offered on the Dogs, but there were no takers. The only bets accepted were Dog against Dog. The young Wolf went at speed now, but within a mile the white Dog was right behind him—was closing in.

The German shouted: "Now watch and see that Wolf go up in the air."

In a moment the runners were together. Both recoiled, neither went up in the air, but the white Dog rolled over with a fearful gash in her shoulder—out of the fight, if not killed. Ten seconds later the Blue-spot arrived, open-mouthed. This meeting was as quick and almost as mysterious as the first. The animals barely touched each other. The gray one bounded aside, his head out of sight for a moment in the flash of quick movement. Spot reeled and showed a bleeding flank. Urged on by the men, he assaulted again, but only to get another wound that taught him to keep off.

Now came the keeper with four more huge Dogs. They turned these loose, and the men armed with clubs and lassos were closing to help in finishing the Wolf, when a small boy came charging over the plain on a Pony. He leaped to the ground and wriggling through the ring flung his arms around the Wolf's neck. He called him his "Wolfie pet," his "dear Wolfie"—the Wolf licked his face and wagged its tail—then the child turned on the crowd and through his streaming tears, he—Well! it would not do to print what he said. He was only nine, but he was very old-fashioned, as well as a rude little boy. He had been

His dear Wolfie

brought up in a low saloon, and had been an apt pupil at picking up the vile talk of the place. He cursed them one and all and for generations back; he did not spare even his own father.

If a man had used such shocking and insulting language he might have been lynched, but coming from a baby, the hunters did not know what to do, so finally did the best thing. They laughed aloud—not at themselves, that is not considered good form—but they all laughed at the German whose wonderful Dogs had been worsted by a half-grown Wolf.

Jimmie now thrust his dirty, tear-stained little fist down into his very-much-of-a-boy's pocket, and from among marbles and chewing-gum, as well as tobacco, matches, pistol cartridges, and other contra-band, he fished out a flimsy bit of grocer's twine and fastened it around the Wolf's neck. Then, still blubbering a little, he set out for home on the Pony, leading the Wolf and hurling a final threat and anathema at the German nobleman: "Fur two cents I'd sic him on *you*, gol darn ye."

* * *

Early that winter Jimmie was taken down with a fever. The Wolf howled miserably in the yard when he missed his little friend, and finally on the boy's demand was admitted to the sick-room, and there this great wild Dog—for that is all a Wolf is—continued faithfully watching by his friend's bedside.

The fever had seemed slight at first, so that every one was shocked when there came suddenly a turn for the worse, and three days before Christmas Jimmie died. He had no more sincere mourner than his "Wolfie." The great gray creature howled in miserable answer to the church-bell tolling when he followed the body on Christmas Eve to the graveyard at St. Boniface. He soon came back to the premises behind the saloon, but when an attempt was made to chain him again, he leaped a board fence and was finally lost sight of.

Later that same winter old Renaud, the trapper, with his pretty half-breed daughter, Ninette, came to live in a little log-cabin on the river bank. He knew nothing about Jimmie Hogan, and he was not a little puzzled to find Wolf tracks and signs along the river on both sides between St. Boniface and Fort Garry. He listened with interest and doubt to tales that the Hudson Bay Company's men told of a great Gray-wolf that had come to live in the region about, and even to enter the town at night, and that was in particular attached to the woods about St. Boniface Church.

On Christmas Eve of that year when the bell tolled again as it had done for Jimmie, a lone and melancholy howling from the woods almost convinced Renaud that the stories were true. He knew the wolf-cries—the howl for help, the love song, the lonely wail, and the sharp defiance of the Wolves. This was the lonely wail.

The trapper went to the riverside and gave an answering howl. A shadowy form left the far woods and crossed on the ice to where the man sat, log-still, on a log. It came up near him, circled past and sniffed, then its eye glowed; it growled like a Dog that is a little angry, and glided back into the night.

Thus Renaud knew, and before long many townfolk began to learn, that a huge Gray-wolf was living in their streets, "a Wolf three times as big as the one that used to be chained at Hogan's gin-mill." He was the terror of Dogs, killing them on all possible occasions, and some said, though it was never proven, that he had devoured more than one half-breed who was out on a spree.

And this was the Winnipeg Wolf that I had seen that day in the wintry woods. I had longed to go to his help, thinking the odds so hopelessly against him, but later knowledge changed the thought. I do not know how that fight ended, but I do know that he was seen many times afterward and some of the Dogs were not.

Thus his was the strangest life that ever his kind had known. Free of all the woods and plains, he elected rather to lead a life of daily hazard in the town—each week at least some close escape, and every day a day of daring deeds; finding momentary shelter at times under the very boardwalk crossings. Hating the men and despising the Dogs, he fought his daily way and held the hordes of Curs at bay or slew them when he found them few or single; harried the drunkard, evaded men with guns, learned traps—learned poison, too—just how, we cannot tell, but learn it he did, for he passed it again and again, or served it only with a Wolf's contempt.

Not a street in Winnipeg that he did not know; not a policeman in Winnipeg that had not seen his swift and shadowy form in the gray dawn as he passed where he would; not a Dog in Winnipeg that did not cower and bristle when the telltale wind brought proof that old Garou was crouching near. His only path was the warpath, and all the world his foes. But throughout this lurid, semi-mythic record there was one recurring pleasant thought—Garou never was known to harm a child.

* * *

Ninette was a desert-born beauty like her Indian mother, but gray-eyed like her Normandy father, a sweet girl of sixteen, the belle of her set. She might have married any one of the richest and steadiest young men of the country, but of course, in feminine perversity her heart was set on that ne'er-do-well, Paul des Roches. A handsome fellow, a good dancer and a fair violinist, Fiddler Paul was in demand at all festivities, but he was a shiftless drunkard and it was even whispered that he had a wife already in Lower Canada. Renaud very properly dismissed him when he came to urge his suit, but dismissed him in vain. Ninette, obedient in all else, would not give up her lover. The very day after her

father had ordered him away she promised to meet him in the woods just across the river. It was easy to arrange this, for she was a good Catholic, and across the ice to the Church was shorter than going around by the bridge. As she went through the snowy wood to the tryst she noticed that a large gray Dog was following. It seemed quite friendly, and the child (for she was still that) had no fear, but when she came to the place where Paul was waiting, the gray Dog went forward rumbling in its chest. Paul gave one look, knew it for a huge Wolf, then fled like the coward he was. He afterward said he ran for his gun. He must have forgotten where it was, as he climbed the nearest tree to find it. Meanwhile Ninette ran home across the ice to tell Paul's friends of his danger. Not finding any firearms up the tree, the valiant lover made a spear by fastening his knife to a branch and succeeded in giving Garou a painful wound on the head. The savage creature growled horribly but thenceforth kept at a safe distance, though plainly showing his intention to wait till the man came down. But the approach of a band of rescuers changed his mind, and he went away.

Fiddler Paul found it easier to explain matters to Ninette than he would to any one else. He still stood first in her affections, but so hopelessly ill with her father that they decided on an elopement, as soon as he should return from Fort Alexander, whither he was to go for the Company, as dog-driver. The Factor was very proud of his train Dogs—three great Huskies with curly, bushy tails, big and strong as Calves, but fierce and lawless as pirates. With these the Fiddler Paul was to drive to Fort Alexander from Fort Garry—the bearer of several important packets. He was an expert Dog-driver, which usually means relentlessly cruel. He set off blithely down the river in the morning, after the several necessary drinks of whiskey. He expected to be gone a week, and would then come back with twenty dollars in his pocket, and having thus provided the sinews of war, would carry out the plan of elopement. Away they went down the river on the ice. The big Dogs pulled swiftly but sulkily as he cracked the long whip and shouted, "*Allez, allez, marchez*." They passed at speed by Renaud's shanty on the bank, and Paul, cracking his whip and running behind the train, waved his hand to Ninette as she stood by the door. Speedily the cariole with the sulky Dogs and drunken driver disappeared around the bend—and that was the last ever seen of Fiddler Paul.

That evening the Huskies came back singly to Fort Garry. They were spattered with frozen blood, and were gashed in several places. But strange to tell they were quite "unhungry."

Runners went on the back trail and recovered the packages. They were lying on the ice unharmed. Fragments of the sled were strewn for a mile or more up the river; not far from the packages were shreds of clothing that had belonged to the Fiddler.

It was quite clear, the Dogs had murdered and eaten their driver.

The Factor was terribly wrought up over the matter. It might cost him his Dogs. He refused to believe the report and set off to sift the evidence for himself. Renaud was chosen to go with him, and before they were within three miles of the fatal place Renaud pointed to a very large track crossing from the east to the west bank of the river, just after the Dog sled. He ran it backward for a mile or more on the eastern bank, noted how it had walked when the Dogs walked and run when they ran, before he turned to the Factor and said: "A beeg Voolf—he come after ze cariole all ze time."

Now they followed the track where it had crossed to the west shore. Two miles above Kildonan woods the Wolf had stopped his gallop to walk over to the sled trail, had followed it a few yards, then had returned to the woods.

"Paul he drop somesin' here, ze packet maybe; ze Voolf he come for smell. He follow so—now he know zat eez ze drunken Paul vot slash heem on ze head."

A mile farther the Wolf track came galloping on the ice behind the cariole. The man track disappeared now, for the driver had leaped on the sled and lashed the Dogs. Here is where he cut adrift the bundles. That is why things were scattered over the ice. See how the Dogs were bounding under the lash. Here was the Fiddler's knife in the snow. He must have dropped it in trying to use it on the Wolf. And here—what! the Wolf track disappears, but the sled track speeds along. The Wolf has leaped on the sled. The Dogs, in terror, added to their speed; but on the sleigh behind them there is a deed of vengeance done. In a moment it is over; both roll off the sled; the Wolf track reappears on the east side to seek the woods. The sled swerves to the west bank, where, after half a mile, it is caught and wrecked on a root.

The snow also told Renaud how the Dogs, entangled in the harness, had fought with each other, had cut themselves loose, and trotting homeward by various ways up the river, had gathered at the body of their late tyrant and devoured him at a meal.

Bad enough for the Dogs, still they were cleared of the murder. That certainly was done by the Wolf, and Renaud, after the shock of

horror was past, gave a sigh of relief and added, "Eet is le Garou. He hab save my leel girl from zat Paul. He always was good to children."

* * *

This was the cause of the great final hunt that they fixed for Christmas Day just two years after the scene at the grave of Little Jim. It seemed as though all the Dogs in the country were brought together. The three Huskies were there—the Factor considered them essential—there were Danes and trailers and a rabble of farm Dogs and nondescripts. They spent the morning beating all the woods east of St. Boniface and had no success. But a telephone message came that the trail they sought had been seen near the Assiniboine woods west of the city, and an hour later the hunt was yelling on the hot scent of the Winnipeg Wolf.

Away they went, a rabble of Dogs, a motley rout of horsemen, a mob of men and boys on foot. Garou had no fear of the Dogs, but men he knew had guns and were dangerous. He led off for the dark timber line of the Assiniboine, but the horsemen had open country and they headed him back. He coursed along the Colony Creek hollow and so eluded the bullets already flying. He made for a barbwire fence, and passing that he got rid of the horsemen for a time, but still must keep the hollow that baffled the bullets. The Dogs were now closing on him. All he might have asked would probably have been to be left alone with them—forty or fifty to one as they were—he would have taken the odds. The Dogs were all around him now, but none dared to close in. A lanky Hound, trusting to his speed, ran alongside at length and got a side chop from Garou that laid him low. The horsemen were forced to take a distant way around, but now the chase was toward the town, and more men and Dogs came running out to join the fray.

The Wolf turned toward the slaughter-house, a familiar resort, and the shooting ceased on account of the houses, as well as the Dogs, being so near. These were indeed now close enough to encircle him and hinder all further flight. He looked for a place to guard his rear for a final stand, and seeing a wooden foot-bridge over a gutter he sprang in, there faced about and held the pack at bay. He leaped out, knowing now that he had to die, but ready, wishing only to make a worthy fight, and then for the first time in broad day view of all his foes he stood—

the shadowy Dog-killer, the disembodied voice of St. Boniface woods, the wonderful Winnipeg Wolf.

* * *

At last after three long years of fight he stood before them alone, confronting twoscore Dogs, and men with guns to back them—but facing them just as resolutely as I saw him that day in the wintry woods. The same old curl was on his lips—the hard-knit flanks heaved just a little, but his green and yellow eye glowed steadily. The Dogs closed in, led not by the huge Huskies from the woods—they evidently knew too much for that—but by a Bulldog from the town; there was scuffling of many feet; a low rumbling for a time replaced the yapping of the pack; a flashing of those red and grizzled jaws, a momentary hurl back of the onset, and again he stood alone and braced, the grim and grand old bandit that he was. Three times they tried and suffered. Their boldest were lying about him. The first to go down was the Bulldog. Learning wisdom now, the Dogs held back, less sure; but his square-built chest showed never a sign of weakness yet, and after waiting impatiently he advanced a few steps, and thus, alas! gave to the gunners their long-expected chance. Three rifles rang, and in the snow Garou went down at last, his life of combat done.

He had made his choice. His days were short and crammed with quick events. His tale of many peaceful years was spent in three of daily brunt. He picked his trail, a new trail, high and short. He chose to drink his cup at a single gulp, and break the glass—but he left a deathless name.

Who can look into the mind of the Wolf? Who can show us his wellspring of motive? Why should he still cling to a place of endless tribulation? It could not be because he knew no other country, for the region is limitless, food is everywhere, and he was known at least as far as Selkirk. Nor could his motive be revenge. No animal will give up its whole life to seeking revenge; that evil kind of mind is found in man alone. The brute creation seeks for peace.

There is then but one remaining bond to chain him, and that the strongest claim that anything can own—the mightiest force on earth.

The Wolf is gone. The last relic of him was lost in the burning Grammar School, but to this day the sexton of St. Boniface Church avers that the tolling bell on Christmas Eve never fails to provoke that weird and melancholy Wolf-cry from the wooded graveyard a hundred steps away, where they laid his Little Jim, the only being on earth that ever met him with the touch of love.

THE LEGEND OF THE WHITE REINDEER

Bleak, black, deep, and cold is Utrovand, a long pocket of glacial water, a crack in the globe, a wrinkle in the high Norwegian mountains, blocked with another mountain, and flooded with a frigid flood, three thousand feet above its Mother Sea, and yet no closer to its Father Sun. Around its cheerless shore is a belt of stunted trees, that sends a long tail up the high valley, till it dwindles away to sticks and moss, as it also does some half-way up the granite hills that rise a thousand feet, encompassing the lake. This is the limit of trees, the end of the growth of wood. The birch and willow are the last to drop out of the long fight with frost. Their miniature thickets are noisy with the cries of Fieldfare, Pipit, and Ptarmigan, but these are left behind on nearing the upper plateau, where shade of rock and sough of wind are all that take their place. The chilly Hoifjeld rolls away, a rugged, rocky plain, with great patches of snow in all the deeper hollows, and the distance blocked by snowy peaks that rise and roll and whiter gleam, till, dim and dazzling in the north, uplifts the Jötunheim, the home of spirits, of glaciers, and of the lasting snow.

The treeless stretch is one vast attest to the force of heat. Each failure of the sun by one degree is marked by a lower realm of life. The northern slope of each hollow is less boreal than its southern side. The pine and spruce have given out long ago; the mountain-ash went next; the birch and willow climbed up half the slope. Here, nothing grows but creeping plants and moss. The plain itself is pale grayish green, one vast expanse of reindeer-moss, but warmed at spots into orange by great beds of polytrichum, and, in sunnier nooks, deepened to a herbal green. The rocks that are scattered everywhere are of a delicate lilac, but each is variegated with spreading frill-edged plasters of gray-green lichen or orange powder-streaks and beauty-spots of black. These rocks have great power to hold the heat, so that each of them is surrounded by a little belt of heat-loving plants that could not otherwise live so high. Dwarfed representatives of the birch and willow both are here, hugging the genial rock, as an old French *habitant* hugs his stove in winter-time, spreading their branches over it, instead of in the frigid air. A foot away is seen a chillier belt of heath, and farther off, colder, where none else can grow, is the omni-present gray-green reindeer-moss that gives its color to the upland. The hollows are still filled with snow, though now it is June. But each of these white expanses is shrinking, spending itself in ice-cold streams that somehow reach the lake. These *snö-fläcks* show no sign of life, not even the 'red-snow' tinge, and around each is a belt of barren earth, to testify that life and warmth can never be divorced.

Birdless and lifeless, the gray-green snow-pied waste extends over all the stretch that is here between the timber-line and the snow-line, above which winter never quits its hold. Farther north both come lower, till the timber-line is at the level of the sea; and all the land is in that treeless belt called Tundra in the Old World, and Barrens in the New, and that everywhere is the Home of the Reindeer—the Realm of the Reindeer-moss.

* * *

In and out it flew, in and out, over the water and under, as the Varsimlé, the leader doe of the Reindeer herd, walked past on the vernal banks, and it sang:—

"*Skoal! Skoal! Gamle Norge Skoal!*" and more about "a White Reindeer and Norway's good luck," as though the singer were gifted with special insight.

When old Sveggum built the Vand-dam on the Lower Hoifjeld, just above the Utrovand, and set his *ribesten* a-going, he supposed that he was the owner of it all. But some one was there before him. And in and out of the spouting stream this some one dashed, and sang songs that he made up to fit the place and the time. He skipped from *skjæke* to *skjæke* of the wheel, and did many things which Sveggum could set down only to luck—whatever that is; and some said that Sveggum's luck was a Wheel-troll, a Water-fairy, with a brown coat and a white beard, one that lived on land or in water, as he pleased.

But most of Sveggum's neighbors saw only a Fossekal, the little Waterfall Bird that came each year and danced in the stream, or dived where the pool is deep. And maybe both were right, for some of the very oldest peasants will tell you that a Fairy-troll may take the form of a man or the form of a bird. Only this bird lived a life no bird can live, and sang songs that men never had sung in Norway. Wonderful vision had he, and sights he saw that man never saw. For the Fieldfare would build before him, and the Lemming fed its brood under his very eyes. Eyes were they to see; for the dark speck on Suletind that man could barely glimpse was a Reindeer, with half-shed coat, to him; and the green slime on the Vandren was beautiful green pasture with a banquet spread.

Oh, Man is so blind, and makes himself so hated! But Fossekal harmed none, so none were afraid of him. Only he sang, and his songs were sometimes mixed with fun and prophecy, or perhaps a little scorn.

From the top of the tassel-birch he could mark the course of the Vand-dam stream past the Nystuen hamlet to lose itself in the gloomy waters of Utrovand; or by a higher flight he could see across the barren upland that rolled to Jötunheim in the north.

The great awakening was on now. The springtime had already reached the woods; the valleys were a-throb with life; new birds coming from the south, winter sleepers reappearing, and the Reindeer that had wintered in the lower woods should soon again be seen on the uplands.

Not without a fight do the Frost Giants give up the place so long their own; a great battle was in progress; but the Sun was slowly, surely winning, and driving them back to their Jötunheim. At every hollow and shady place they made another stand, or sneaked back by night, only to suffer another defeat. Hard hitters these, as they are stubborn fighters; many a granite rock was split and shattered by their blows in reckless fight, so that its inner fleshy tints were shown and warmly gleamed among the gray-green rocks that dotted the plain, like the countless flocks of Thor. More or less of these may be found at every place of battle-brunt, and straggled along the slope of Suletind was a host that reached for half a mile. But stay! these moved. Not rocks were they, but living creatures.

They drifted along erratically, yet one way, all up the wind. They swept out of sight in a hollow, to reappear on a ridge much nearer, and serried there against the sky, we marked their branching horns, and knew them for the Reindeer in their home.

The band came drifting our way, feeding like Sheep, grunting like only themselves. Each one found a grazing-spot, stood there till it was cleared off, then trotted on crackling hoofs to the front in search of another. So the band was ever changing in rank and form. But one there was that was always at or near the van—a large and well-favored Simlé, or Hind. However much the band might change and spread, she was in the forefront, and the observant would soon have seen signs that she had an influence over the general movement—that she, indeed, was the leader. Even the big Bucks, in their huge velvet-clad antlers, admitted this untitular control; and if one, in a spirit of independence, evinced a disposition to lead elsewhere, he soon found himself uncomfortably alone.

The Varsimlé, or leading Hind, had kept the band hovering, for the last week or two, along the timber-line, going higher each day to the baring uplands, where the snow was clearing and the deer-flies were blown away. As the pasture zone had climbed she had followed in her daily foraging, returning to the sheltered woods at sundown, for the wild things fear the cold night wind even as man does. But now the deer-flies were rife in the woods, and the rocky hillside nooks warm enough for the nightly bivouac, so the woodland was deserted.

Probably the leader of a band of animals does not consciously pride itself on leadership, yet has an uncomfortable sensation when not followed. But there are times with all when solitude is sought. The Varsimlé had been fat and well through the winter, yet now was listless, and lingered with drooping head as the grazing herd moved past her.

Sometimes she stood gazing blankly while the unchewed bunch of moss hung from her mouth, then roused to go on to the front as before; but the spells of vacant stare and the hankering to be alone grew stronger. She turned downward to seek the birch woods, but the whole band turned with her. She stood stock-still, with head down. They grazed and grunted past, leaving her like a statue against the hillside. When all had gone on, she slunk quietly away; walked a few steps, looked about, made a pretense of grazing, snuffed the ground, looked after the herd, and scanned the hills; then downward fared toward the sheltering woods.

Once as she peered over a bank she sighted another Simlé, a doe Reindeer, uneasily wandering by itself. But the Varsimlé wished not for company. She did not know why, but she felt that she must hide away somewhere.

She stood still until the other had passed on, then turned aside, and went with faster steps and less wavering, till she came in view of Utrovand, away down by the little stream that turns old Sveggum's ribesten. Up above the dam she waded across the limpid stream, for deep-laid and sure is the instinct of a wild animal to put running water between itself and those it shuns. Then, on the farther bank, now bare and slightly green, she turned, and passing in and out among the twisted trunks, she left the noisy Vand-dam. On the higher ground beyond she paused, looked this way and that, went on a little, but returned; and here, completely shut in by softly painted rocks, and birches wearing little springtime hangers, she seemed inclined to rest; yet not to rest, for she stood uneasily this way and that, driving away the flies that settled on her legs, heeding not at all the growing grass, and thinking she was hid from all the world.

But nothing escapes the Fossekal. He had seen her leave the herd, and now he sat on a gorgeous rock that overhung, and sang as though he had waited for this and knew that the fate of the nation might turn on what passed in this far glen. He sang:

> Skoal! Skoal! For Norway Skoal!
> Sing ye the song of the Vand-dam troll.
> When I am hiding
> Norway's luck
> On a White Storbuk
> Comes riding, riding.

There are no Storks in Norway, and yet an hour later there was a wonderful little Reindeer lying beside the Varsimlé. She was brushing his coat, licking and mothering him, proud and happy as though this was the first little Renskalv ever born. There might be hundreds born in the herd that month, but probably no more like this one, for he was snowy white, and the song of the singer on the painted rock was about

> Good luck, good luck,
> And a White Storbuk,

as though he foresaw clearly the part that the White Calf was to play when he grew to be a Storbuk.

But another wonder now came to pass. Before an hour, there was a second little Calf—a brown one this time. Strange things happen, and hard things are done when they needs must. Two hours later, when the Varsimlé led the White Calf away from the place, there was no Brown Calf, only some flattened rags with calf-hair on them.

The mother was wise: better one strongling than two weaklings. Within a few days the Simlé once more led the band, and running by her side was the White Calf. The Varsimlé considered him in all things, so that he really set the pace for the band, which suited very well all the mothers that now had Calves with them. Big, strong, and wise was the Varsimlé, in the pride of her strength, and this White Calf was the flower of her prime. He often ran ahead of his mother as she led the herd, and Rol, coming on them one day, laughed aloud at the sight as they passed, old and young, fat Simlé and antlered Storbuk, a great brown herd, all led, as it seemed, by a little White Calf.

So they drifted away to the high mountains, to be gone all summer. "Gone to be taught by the spirits who dwell where the Black Loon laughs on the ice," said Lief of the Lower Dale; but Sveggum, who had always been among the Reindeer, said: "Their mothers are the teachers, even as ours are."

When the autumn came, old Sveggum saw a moving snö-fläck far off on the brown moorland; but the Troll saw a white yearling, a Nekbuk; and when they ranged alongside of Utrovand to drink, the still sheet seemed fully to reflect the White One, though it barely sketched in the others, with the dark hills behind.

Many a little Calf had come that spring, and had drifted away on the moss-barrens, to come back no more; for some were weaklings and some were fools; some fell by the way, for that is law; and some would not learn the rules, and so died. But the White Calf was strongest of them all, and he was wise, so he learned of his mother, who was wisest of them all. He learned that the grass on the sun side of a rock is sweet, and though it looks the same in the dark hollows, it is there worthless. He learned that when his mother's hoofs crackled he must be up and moving, and when all the herd's hoofs crackled there was danger, and he must keep by his mother's side. For this crackling is like the whistling of a Whistler Duck's wings: it is to keep the kinds together. He learned that where the little Bomuldblomster hangs its cotton tufts is dangerous bog; that the harsh cackle of the Ptarmigan means that close at hand are Eagles, as dangerous for Fawn as for Bird. He learned that the little troll-berries are deadly, that when the *verra*-flies come stinging he must take refuge on a snow-patch, and that of all animal smells only that of his mother was to be fully trusted. He learned that he was growing. His flat calf sides and big joints were changing to the full barrel and clean limbs of the Yearling, and the little bumps which began to show on his head when he was only a fortnight old were now sharp, hard spikes that could win in fight.

More than once they had smelt that dreaded destroyer of the north

that men call the Gjerv or Wolverene; and one day, as this danger-scent
came suddenly and in great strength, a huge blot of dark brown sprang
rumbling from a rocky ledge, and straight for the foremost—the White
Calf. His eye caught the flash of a whirling, shaggy mass, with
gleaming teeth and eyes, hot-breathed and ferocious. Blank horror set
his hair on end; his nostrils flared in fear: but before he fled there rose
within another feeling—one of anger at the breaker of his peace, a
sense that swept all fear away, braced his legs, and set his horns at
charge. The brown brute landed with a deep-chested growl, to be
received on the young one's spikes. They pierced him deeply, but the
shock was overmuch; it bore the White One down, and he might yet
have been killed but that his mother, alert and ever near, now charged
the attacking monster, and heavier, better armed, she hurled and
speared him to the ground. And the White Calf, with a very demon
glare in his once mild eyes, charged too; and even after the Wolverene
was a mere hairy mass, and his mother had retired to feed, he came,
snorting out his rage, to drive his spikes into the hateful thing, till his
snowy head was stained with his adversary's blood.

　　Thus he showed that below the ox-like calm exterior was the
fighting beast; that he was like the men of the north, rugged, square-
built, calm, slow to wrath, but when aroused "seeing red."

　　When they ranked together by the lake that fall, the Fossekal sang
his old song:

> When I am hiding
> Norway's luck
> On a White Storbuk
> Comes riding, riding,

as though this was something he had awaited, then disappeared no one
knew where. Old Sveggum had seen it flying through the stream, as
birds fly through the air, walking in the bottom of a deep pond as a
Ptarmigan walks on the rocks, living as no bird can live; and now the
old man said it had simply gone southward for the winter. But old
Sveggum could neither read nor write: how should he know?

* * *

Each springtime when the Reindeer passed over Sveggum's mill-run, as
they moved from the lowland woods to the bleaker shore of Utrovand,
the Fossekal was there to sing about the White Storbuk, which each
year became more truly the leader.

　　That first spring he stood little higher than a Hare. When he came
to drink in the autumn, his back was above the rock where Sveggum's
stream enters Utrovand. Next year he barely passed under the stunted
birch, and the third year the Fossekal on the painted rock was looking
up, not down, at him as he passed. This was the autumn when Rol and
Sveggum sought the Hoifjeld to round up their half-wild herd and
select some of the strongest for the sled. There was but one opinion
about the Storbuk. Higher than the others, heavier, white as snow,

The White Renskalv facing the wolverene

with a mane that swept the shallow drifts, breasted like a Horse and with horns like a storm-grown oak, he was king of the herd, and might easily be king of the road.

There are two kinds of deer-breakers, as there are two kinds of horse-breakers: one that tames and teaches the animal, and gets a spirited, friendly helper; one that aims to break its spirit, and gets only a sullen slave, ever ready to rebel and wreak its hate. Many a Lapp and many a Norsk has paid with his life for brutality to his Reindeer, and Rol's days were shortened by his own pulk-Ren. But Sveggum was of gentler sort. To him fell the training of the White Storbuk. It was slow, for the Buck resented all liberties from man, as he did from his brothers; but kindness, not fear, was the power that tamed him, and when he had learned to obey and glory in the sled race, it was a noble sight to see the great white mild-eyed beast striding down the long snow-stretch of Utrovand, the steam jetting from his nostrils, the snow swirling up before like the curling waves on a steamer's bow, sled, driver, and Deer all dim in flying white.

Then came the Yule-tide Fair, with the races on the ice, and Utrovand for once was gay. The sullen hills about reëchoed with merry shouting. The Reindeer races were first, with many a mad mischance for laughter. Rol himself was there with his swiftest sled Deer, a tall, dark, five-year-old, in his primest prime. But over-eager, over-brutal, he harried the sullen, splendid slave till in mid-race—just when in a way to win—it turned at a cruel blow, and Rol took refuge under the upturned sled until it had vented its rage against the wood; and so he lost the race, and the winner was the young White Storbuk. Then he won the five-mile race around the lake; and for each triumph Sveggum hung a little silver bell on his harness, so that now he ran and won to merry music.

Then came the Horse races,—running races these: the Reindeer only trots,—and when Balder, the victor Horse, received his ribbon and his owner the purse, came Sveggum with all his winnings in his hand, and said: "Ho, Lars, thine is a fine Horse, but mine is a better Storbuk; let us put our winnings together and race, each his beast, for all."

A Ren against a Race-horse—such a race was never seen till now. Off at the pistol-crack they flew. "Ho, Balder! (*cluck!*) Ho, hi, Balder!" Away shot the beautiful Racer, and the Storbuk, striding at a slower trot, was left behind.

"Ho, Balder!" "Hi, Storbuk!" How the people cheered as the Horse went bounding and gaining! But he had left the line at his top speed; the Storbuk's rose as he flew—faster—faster. The Pony ceased to gain. A mile whirled by; the gap began to close. The Pony had over-spurted at the start, but the Storbuk was warming to his work—striding evenly, swiftly, faster yet, as Sveggum cried in encouragement: "Ho Storbuk! good Storbuk!" or talked to him only with a gentle rein. At the turning-point the pair were neck and neck; then the Pony—though well driven and well shod—slipped on the ice, and thenceforth held back as though in fear, so the Storbuk steamed away. The Pony and his driver were far behind when a roar from every human throat in Filefjeld told that the

Storbuk had passed the wire and won the race. And yet all this was before the White Ren had reached the years of his full strength and speed.

Once that day Rol essayed to drive the Storbuk. They set off at a good pace, the White Buk ready, responsive to the single rein, and his mild eyes veiled by his drooping lashes. But, without any reason other than the habit of brutality, Rol struck him. In a moment there was a change. The Racer's speed was checked, all four legs braced forward till he stood; the drooping lids were raised, the eyes rolled—there was a green light in them now. Three puffs of steam were jetted from each nostril. Rol shouted, then, scenting danger, quickly upset the sled and hid beneath. The Storbuk turned to charge the sled, sniffing and tossing the snow with his foot; but little Knute, Sveggum's son, ran forward and put his arms around the Storbuk's neck; then the fierce look left the Reindeer's eye, and he suffered the child to lead him quietly back to the starting-point. Beware, O driver! the Reindeer, too, "sees red."

This was the coming of the White Storbuk for the folk of Filefjeld.

In the two years that followed he became famous throughout that country as Sveggum's Storbuk, and many a strange exploit was told of him. In twenty minutes he could carry old Sveggum round the six-mile rim of Utrovand. When the snow-slide buried all the village of Holaker, it was the Storbuk that brought the word for help to Opdalstole and returned again over the forty miles of deep snow in seven hours, to carry brandy, food, and promise of speedy aid.

When over-venturesome young Knute Sveggumsen broke through the new thin ice of Utrovand, his cry for help brought the Storbuk to the rescue; for he was the gentlest of his kind and always ready to come at call.

He brought the drowning boy in triumph to the shore, and as they crossed the Vand-dam stream, there was the Troll-bird to sing:

> Good luck, good luck,
> With the White Storbuk.

After which he disappeared for months—doubtless dived into some subaqueous cave to feast and revel all winter; although Sveggum did not believe it was so.

* * *

How often is the fate of kingdoms given into child hands, or even committed to the care of Bird or Beast! A She-wolf nursed the Roman Empire. A Wren pecking crumbs on a drum-head aroused the Orange army, it is said, and ended the Stuart reign in Britain. Little wonder, then, that to a noble Reindeer Buk should be committed the fate of Norway: that the Troll on the wheel should have reason in his rhyme.

These were troublous times in Scandinavia. Evil men, traitors at heart, were sowing dissension between the brothers Norway and Sweden. "Down with the Union!" was becoming the popular cry.

Oh, unwise peoples! If only you could have been by Sveggum's wheel to hear the Troll when he sang:

> The Raven and the Lion
> They held the Bear at bay;
> But he picked the bones of both
> When they quarrelled by the way.

Threats of civil war, of a fight for independence, were heard throughout Norway. Meetings were held more or less secretly, and at each of them was some one with well-filled pockets and glib tongue, to enlarge on the country's wrongs, and promise assistance from an outside irresistible power as soon as they showed that they meant to strike for freedom. No one openly named the power. That was not necessary; it was everywhere felt and understood. Men who were real patriots began to believe in it. Their country was wronged. Here was one to set her right. Men whose honor was beyond question became secret agents of this power. The state was honeycombed and mined;

society was a tangle of plots. The king was helpless, though his only wish was for the people's welfare. Honest and straightforward, what could he do against this far-reaching machination? The very advisers by his side were corrupted through mistaken patriotism. The idea that they were playing into the hands of the foreigner certainly never entered into the minds of these dupes—at least, not those of the rank and file. One or two, tried, selected, and bought by the arch-enemy, knew the real object in view, and the chief of these was Borgrevinck, a former lansman of Nordlands. A man of unusual gifts, a member of the Storthing, a born leader, he might have been prime minister long ago, but for the distrust inspired by several unprincipled dealings. Soured by what he considered want of appreciation, balked in his ambition, he was a ready tool when the foreign agent sounded him. At first his patriotism had to be sopped, but that necessity disappeared as the game went on, and perhaps he alone, of the whole far-reaching conspiracy, was prepared to strike at the Union for the benefit of the foreigner.

Plans were being perfected,—army officers being secretly misled and won over by the specious talk of "their country's wrongs," and each move made Borgrevinck more surely the head of it all,—when a quarrel between himself and the "deliverer" occurred over the question of recompense. Wealth untold they were willing to furnish; but regal power, never. The quarrel became more acute. Borgrevinck continued to attend all meetings, but was ever more careful to centre all power in himself, and even prepared to turn round to the king's party if necessary to further his ambition. The betrayal of his followers would purchase his own safety. But proofs he must have, and he set about getting signatures to a declaration of rights which was simply a veiled confession of treason. Many of the leaders he had deluded into signing this before the meeting at Laersdalsoren. Here they met in the early winter, some twenty of the patriots, some of them men of position, all of them men of brains and power. Here, in the close and stifling parlor,

they planned, discussed, and questioned. Great hopes were expressed, great deeds were forecast, in the stove-hot room.

Outside, against the fence, in the winter night, was a Great White Reindeer, harnessed to a sled, but lying down with his head doubled back on his side as he slept, calm, unthoughtful, ox-like. Which seemed likelier to decide the nation's fate, the earnest thinkers indoors, or the ox-like sleeper without? Which seemed more vital to Israel, the bearded council in King Saul's tent, or the light-hearted shepherd-boy hurling

stones across the brook at Bethlehem? At Laersdalsoren it was as
before: deluded by Borgrevinck's eloquent plausibility, all put their
heads in the noose, their lives and country in his hands, seeing in this
treacherous monster a very angel of self-sacrificing patriotism. All? No,
not all. Old Sveggum was there. He could neither read nor write. That
was his excuse for not signing. He could not read a letter in a book, but
he could read something of the hearts of men. As the meeting broke up
he whispered to Axel Tanberg: "Is his own name on that paper?" And
Axel, starting at the thought, said: "No." Then said Sveggum: "I don't
trust that man. They ought to know of this at Nystuen." For there was
to be the really important meeting. But how to let them know was the
riddle. Borgrevinck was going there at once with his fast Horses.

Sveggum's eye twinkled as he nodded toward the Storbuk,
standing tied to the fence. Borgrevinck leaped into his sleigh and went
off at speed, for he was a man of energy.

Sveggum took the bells from the harness, untied the Reindeer,
stepped into the pulk. He swung the single rein, clucked to the Storbuk,
and also turned his head toward Nystuen. The fast Horses had a long
start, but before they had climbed the eastward hill Sveggum needs
must slack, so as not to overtake them. He held back till they came to
the turn above the woods at Maristuen; then he quit the road, and up
the river flat he sped the Buk, a farther way, but the only way to bring
them there ahead.

Squeak, crack—squeak, crack—squeak, crack—at regular intervals
from the great spreading snow-shoes of the Storbuk, and the steady
sough of his breath was like the *Nordland* as she passes up the
Hardanger Fjord. High up, on the smooth road to the left, they could
hear the jingle of the horse-bells and the shouting of Borgrevinck's
driver, who, under orders, was speeding hard for Nystuen.

The highway was a short road and smooth, and the river·valley
was long and rough; but when, in four hours, Borgrevinck got to

Nystuen, there in the throng was a face that he had just left at Laersdalsoren. He appeared not to notice, though nothing ever escaped him.

At Nystuen none of the men would sign. Some one had warned them. This was serious; might be fatal at such a critical point. As he thought it over, his suspicions turned more and more to Sveggum, the old fool that could not write his name at Laersdalsoren. But how did he get there before himself with his speedy Horses?

There was a dance at Nystuen that night; the dance was necessary to mask the meeting; and during that Borgrevinck learned of the swift White Ren.

The Nystuen trip had failed, thanks to the speed of the White Buk. Borgrevinck must get to Bergen before word of this, or all would be lost. There was only one way, to be sure of getting there before any one else. Possibly word had already gone from Laersdalsoren. But even at that, Borgrevinck could get there and save himself, at the price of all Norway, if need be, provided he went with the White Storbuk. He would not be denied. He was not the man to give up a point, though it took all the influence he could bring to bear, this time, to get old Sveggum's leave.

The Storbuk was quietly sleeping in the corral when Sveggum came to bring him. He rose leisurely, hind legs first, stretched one, then the other, curling his tail tight on his back as he did so, shook the hay from the great antlers as though they were a bunch of twigs, and slowly followed Sveggum at the end of the tight halter. He was so sleepy and slow that Borgrevinck impatiently gave him a kick, and got for response a short snort from the Buk, and from Sveggum an earnest warning, both of which were somewhat scornfully received. The tinkling bells on the harness had been replaced, but Borgrevinck wanted them removed. He wished to go in silence. Sveggum would not be left behind when his favorite Ren went forth, so he was given a seat in the horse-sleigh which was to follow, and the driver thereof received from his master a secret hint to delay.

Then, with papers on his person to death-doom a multitude of misguided men, with fiendish intentions in his heart as well as the power to carry them out, and with the fate of Norway in his hands, Borgrevinck was made secure in the sled, behind the White Storbuk, and sped at dawn on his errand of desolation.

At the word from Sveggum the White Ren set off with a couple of bounds that threw Borgrevinck back in the pulk. This angered him, but he swallowed his wrath on seeing that it left the horse-sleigh behind. He shook the line, shouted, and the Buk settled down to a long, swinging trot. His broad hoofs clicked double at every stride. His nostrils, out level, puffed steady blasts of steam in the frosty morning as he settled to his pace. The pulk's prow cut two long shears of snow, that swirled up over man and sled till all were white. And the great ox-eyes of the King Ren blazed joyously in the delight of motion, and of conquest too, as the sound of the horse-bells faded far behind.

Even masterful Borgrevinck could not but mark with pleasure the noble creature that had balked him last night and now was lending its speed to his purpose; for it was his intention to arrive hours before the horse-sleigh, if possible.

Up the rising road they sped as though downhill, and the driver's spirits rose with the exhilarating speed. The snow groaned ceaselessly under the prow of the pulk, and the frosty creaking under the hoofs of the flying Ren was like the gritting of mighty teeth. Then came the level stretch from Nystuen's hill to Dalecarl's, and as they whirled by in the early day, little Carl chanced to peep from a window, and got sight of the Great White Ren in a white pulk with a white driver, just as it is in the stories of the Giants, and clapped his hands, and cried, "Good, good!"

But his grandfather, when *he* caught a glimpse of the white wonder that went without even sound of bells, felt a cold chill in his scalp, and went back to light a candle that he kept at the window till the sun was high, for surely this was the Storbuk of Jötunheim.

But the Ren whirled on, and the driver shook the reins and thought only of Bergen. He struck the White Steed with the loose end of the rope. The Buk gave three great snorts and three great bounds, then faster went, and as they passed by Dyrskaur, where the Giant sits on the edge, his head was muffled in scud, which means that a storm is coming. The Storbuk knew it. He sniffed, and eyed the sky with anxious look, and even slacked a little; but Borgrevinck yelled at the speeding beast, though going yet as none but he could go, and struck him once, twice, and thrice, and harder yet. So the pulk was whirled along like a skiff in a steamer's wake; but there was blood in the Storbuk's eye now; and Borgrevinck was hard put to balance the sled. The miles flashed by like roods till Sveggum's bridge appeared. The storm-wind now was blowing, but there was the Troll. Whence came he now, none knew, but there he was, hopping on the keystone and singing of

> Norway's fate and Norway's luck
> Of the hiding Troll and the riding Buk.

Down the winding highway they came, curving inward as they swung around the corner. At the voice on the bridge the Deer threw back his ears and slackened his pace. Borgrevinck, not knowing whence it came, struck savagely at the Ren. The red light gleamed in those ox-like eyes. He snorted in anger and shook the great horns, but he did not stop to avenge the blow. For him was a vaster vengeance still. He onward sped as before, but from that time Borgrevinck had lost all control. The one voice that the Ren would hear had been left behind. They whirled aside, off the road, before the bridge was reached. The pulk turned over, but righted itself, and Borgrevinck would have been thrown out and killed but for the straps. It was not to be so; it seemed rather as though the every curse of Norway had been gathered into the sled for a purpose. Bruised and battered, he reappeared. The Troll from the bridge leaped lightly to the Storbuk's head, and held on to the horns as he danced and sang his ancient song, and a new song, too:

> Ha! at last! Oh, lucky day,
> Norway's curse to wipe away!

Borgrevinck was terrified and furious. He struck harder at the Storbuk as he bounded over the rougher snow, and vainly tried to control him. He lost his head in fear. He got out his knife, at last, to strike at the wild Buk's hamstrings, but a blow from the hoof sent if flying from his hand. Their speed on the road was slow to that they now made: no longer striding at the trot, but bounding madly, great five-stride bounds, the wretched Borgrevinck strapped in the sled, alone and helpless through his own contriving, screaming, cursing, and praying. The Storbuk with bloodshot eyes, madly steaming, careered up the rugged ascent, up to the broken, stormy Hoifjeld; mounting the hills as a Petrel mounts the rollers, skimming the flats as a Fulmar skims the shore, he followed the trail where his mother had first led his tottering steps, up from the Vand-dam nook. He followed the old familiar route that he had followed for five years, where the white-winged Rype flies aside, where the black rock mountains, shining white, come near and block the sky, "where the Reindeer find their mysterie."

On like the little snow-wreath that the storm-wind sends dancing before the storm, on like a whirlwind over the shoulder of Suletind, over the knees of Torholmenbræ—the Giants that sit at the gateway. Faster than man or beast could follow, up—up—up—and on; and no one saw them go, but a Raven that swooped behind, and flew as Raven never flew, and the Troll, the same old Troll that sang by the Vand-dam, and now danced and sang between the antlers:

Good luck, good luck for Norway
With the White Storbuk comes riding.

Over Tvindehoug they faded like flying scud on the moorlands, on to the gloomy distance, away toward Jötunheim, the home of the Evil Spirits, the Land of the Lasting Snow. Their every sign and trail was wiped away by the drifting snow, and the end of them no man knows.

The Norse folk awoke as from a horrid nightmare. Their national ruin was averted; there were no deaths, for there were no proofs; and the talebearer's strife was ended.

The one earthly sign remaining from that drive is the string of silver bells that Sveggum had taken from the Storbuk's neck—the victory bells, each the record of a triumph won; and when the old man came to understand, he sighed, and hung to the string a final bell, the largest of them all.

Nothing more was ever seen or heard of the creature who so nearly sold his country, or of the White Storbuk who balked him. Yet those who live near Jötunheim say that on stormy nights, when the snow is flying and the wind is raving in the woods, there sometimes passes, at frightful speed, an enormous White Reindeer with fiery eyes, drawing a

The passing of the King Ren

snow-white pulk, in which is a screaming wretch in white, and on the head of the Deer, balancing by the horns, is a brown-clad, white-bearded Troll, bowing and grinning pleasantly at him, and singing

> Of Norway's luck
> And a White Storbuk—

the same, they say, as the one that with prophetic vision sang by Sveggum's Vand-dam on a bygone day when the birches wore their springtime hangers, and a great mild-eyed Varsimlé came alone, to go away with a little white Renskalv walking slowly, demurely, by her side.

MONARCH
THE
BIG BEAR

CONTENTS

MONARCH THE BIG BEAR

THE TWO SPRINGS

High above Sierra's peaks stands grim Mount Tallac. Ten thousand feet above the sea it rears its head to gaze out north to that vast and wonderful turquoise that men call Lake Tahoe, and north-west, across a piney sea, to its great white sister, Shasta of the Snows; wonderful colors and things on every side, mast-like pine trees strung with jewelry, streams that a Buddhist would have made sacred, hills that an Arab would have held holy. But Lan Kellyan's keen gray eyes were turned to other things. The childish delight in life and light for their own sakes had faded, as they must in one whose training had been to make him hold them very cheap. Why value grass? All the world is grass. Why value air, when it is everywhere in measureless immensity? Why value life, all alive, his living came from taking life? His senses were alert, not for the rainbow hills and the gem-bright lakes, but for the living things that he must meet in daily rivalry, each staking on the game, his life. Hunter was written on his leathern garb, on his tawny face, on his lithe and sinewy form, and shone in his clear gray eye.

The cloven granite peak might pass unmarked, but a faint dimple

403

The pony bounded in terror while the Grizzly ran almost alongside

in the sod did not. Calipers could not have told that it was widened at one end, but the hunter's eye did, and following, he looked for and found another, then smaller signs, and he knew that a big Bear and two little ones had passed and were still close at hand, for the grass in the marks was yet unbending. Lan rode his hunting pony on the trail. It sniffed and stepped nervously, for it knew as well as the rider that a Grizzly family was near. They came to a terrace leading to an open upland. Twenty feet on this side of it Lan slipped to the ground,

dropped the reins, the well-known sign to the pony that he must stand at that spot, then cocked his rifle and climbed the bank. At the top he went with yet greater caution, and soon saw an old Grizzly with her two cubs. She was lying down some fifty yards away and afforded a poor shot; he fired at what seemed to be the shoulder. The aim was true, but the Bear got only a flesh-wound. She sprang to her feet and made for the place where the puff of smoke arose. The Bear had fifty yards to cover, the man had fifteen, but she came racing down the bank before he was fairly on the horse, and for a hundred yards the pony bounded in terror while the old Grizzly ran almost alongside, striking at him and missing by a scant hair's-breadth each time. But the Grizzly rarely keeps up its great speed for many yards. The horse got under full headway, and the shaggy mother, falling behind, gave up the chase and returned to her cubs.

She was a singular old Bear. She had a large patch of white on her breast, white cheeks and shoulders, graded into the brown elsewhere, and Lan from this remembered her afterwards as the "Pinto." She had almost caught him that time, and the hunter was ready to believe that he owed her a grudge.

A week later his chance came. As he passed along the rim of Pocket Gulch, a small, deep valley with sides of sheer rock in most places, he saw afar the old Pinto Bear with her two little brown cubs. She was crossing from one side where the wall was low to another part easy to climb. As she stopped to drink at the clear stream Lan fired with his rifle. At the shot Pinto turned on her cubs, and slapping first one, then the other, she chased them up the tree. Now a second shot struck her and she charged fiercely up the sloping part of the wall, clearly recognizing the whole situation and determined to destroy that hunter. She came snorting up the steep acclivity wounded and raging, only to receive a final shot in the brain that sent her rolling back to lie

dead at the bottom of Pocket Gulch. The hunter, after waiting to make
sure, moved to the edge and fired another shot into the old one's body;
then reloading, he went cautiously down to the tree where still were
the cubs. They gazed at him with wild seriousness as he approached
them, and when he began to climb they scrambled up higher. Here one
set up a plaintive whining and the other an angry growling, their out-
cries increasing as he came nearer.

He took out a stout cord, and noosing them in turn, dragged them
to the ground. One rushed at him and, though little bigger than a cat,
would certainly have done him serious injury had he not held it off
with a forked stick. After tying them to a strong but swaying branch
he went to his horse, got a grain-bag, dropped them into that, and rode
with them to his shanty. He fastened each with a collar and chain to a
post, up which they climbed, and sitting on the top they whined and
growled, according to their humor. For the first few days there was
danger of the cubs strangling themselves or of starving to death, but at
length they were beguiled into drinking some milk most ungently
procured from a range cow that was lassoed for the purpose. In another
week they seemed somewhat reconciled to their lot, and thenceforth
plainly notified their captor whenever they wanted food or water.

And thus the two small rills ran on, a little farther down the mountain now, deeper and wider, keeping near each other; leaping bars,
rejoicing in the sunlight, held for a while by some trivial dam, but over-
leaping that and running on with pools and deeps that harbor bigger
things.

THE SPRINGS AND THE MINER'S DAM

Jack and Jill, the hunter named the cubs; and Jill, the little fury, did
nothing to change his early impression of her bad temper. When at

food-time the man came she would get as far as possible up the post and growl, or else sit in sulky fear and silence; Jack would scramble down and strain at his chain to meet his captor, whining softly, and gobbling his food at once with the greatest of gusto and worst of manners. He had many odd ways of his own, and he was a lasting rebuke to those who say an animal has no sense of humor. In a month he had grown so tame that he was allowed to run free. He followed his master like a dog, and his tricks and funny doings were a continual delight to Kellyan and the few friends he had in the mountains.

On the creek-bottom below the shack was a meadow where Lan cut enough hay each year to feed his two ponies through the winter. This year when hay-time came Jack was his daily companion, either following him about in dangerous nearness to the snorting scythe, or curling up an hour at a time on his coat to guard it assiduously from such aggressive monsters as Ground Squirrels and Chipmunks. An interesting variation of the day came about whenever the mower found a bumble-bees's nest. Jack loved honey, of course, and knew quite well what a bees' nest was, so the call, "Honey—Jacky—honey!" never failed to bring him in waddling haste to the spot. Jerking his nose up in token of pleasure, he would approach cautiously, for he knew that bees have stings. Watching his chance, he would dexterously slap at them with his paws till, one by one, they were knocked down and crushed; then sniffing hard for the latest information, he would stir up the nest gingerly till the very last was tempted forth to be killed. When the dozen or more that formed the swarm were thus got rid of, Jack would carefully dig out the nest and eat first the honey, next the grubs and wax, and last of all the bees he had killed, champing his jaws like a little Pig at a trough, while his long red, snaky tongue was ever busy lashing the stragglers into his greedy maw.

Lan's nearest neighbor was Lou Bonamy, an ex-cowboy and sheep-herder, now a prospecting miner. He lived, with his dog, in a shanty about a mile below Kellyan's shack. Bonamy had seen Jack "perform on a bee-crew." And one day, as he came to Kellyan's, he called out: "Lan, bring Jack here and we'll have some fun." He led the way down the stream into the woods. Kellyan followed him, and Jacky waddled at Kellyan's heels, sniffing once in a while to make sure he was not following the wrong pair of legs.

"There, Jacky, honey—honey!" and Bonamy pointed up a tree to an immense wasps' nest.

Jack cocked his head on one side and swung his nose on the other. Certainly those things buzzing about looked like bees, though he never before saw a bees' nest of that shape, or in such a place.

But he scrambled up the trunk. The men waited—Lan in doubt as to whether he should let his pet cub go into such danger, Bonamy insisting it would be a capital joke "to spring a surprise" on the little Bear. Jack reached the branch that held the big nest high over the deep water, but went with increasing caution. He had never seen a bees' nest like this; it did not have the right smell. Then he took another step forward on the branch—what an awful lot of bees; another step—still they were undoubtedly bees; he cautiously advanced a foot—and bees mean honey; a little farther—he was now within four feet of the great paper globe. The bees hummed angrily and Jack stepped back, in doubt. The men giggled; then Bonamy called softly and untruthfully: "Honey—Jacky—honey!"

"Honey—Jacky—honey"

Jack ate till his paunch looked like a rubber balloon

The little Bear, fortunately for himself, went slowly, since in doubt; he made no sudden move, and he waited a long time, though urged to go on, till the whole swarm of bees had reëntered their nest. Now Jacky jerked his nose up, hitched softly out a little farther till right over the fateful paper globe. He reached out, and by lucky chance put one horny little paw-pad over the hole; his other arm grasped the nest, and leaping from the branch he plunged headlong into the pool below, taking the whole thing with him. As soon as he reached the water his hind feet were seen tearing into the nest, kicking it to pieces; then he let it go and struck out for the shore, the nest floating in rags down-stream. He ran alongside till the comb lodged against a shallow place, then he plunged in again; the wasps were drowned or too wet to be dangerous, and he carried his prize to the bank in triumph. No honey; of course, that was a disappointment, but there were lots of fat white grubs—almost as good—and Jack ate till his paunch looked like a little rubber balloon.

"How is that?" chuckled Lan.

"The laugh is on us," answered Bonamy, with a grimace.

THE TROUT POOL

Jack was now growing into a sturdy cub, and he would follow Kellyan even as far as Bonamy's shack. One day, as they watched him rolling head over heels in riotous glee, Kellyan remarked to his friend: "I'm afraid some one will happen on him an' shoot him in the woods for a wild B'ar."

"Then why don't you ear-mark him with them thar new sheep-rings?" was the sheep-man's suggestion.

Thus it was that, much against his will, Jack's ears were punched and he was decorated with earrings like a prize ram. The intention was good, but they were neither ornamental nor comfortable. Jack fought them for days, and when at length he came home trailing a branch that was caught in the jewel of his left ear, Kellyan impatiently removed them.

At Bonamy's he formed two new acquaintances, a blustering, bullying old ram that was "in storage" for a sheep-herder acquaintance, and which inspired him with a lasting enmity for everything that smelt of sheep—and Bonamy's dog.

This latter was an active, yapping, unpleasant cur that seemed to think it rare fun to snap at Jacky's heels, then bound out of reach. A joke is a joke, but this horrid beast did not know where to stop, and Jack's first and second visits to the Bonamy hut were quite spoiled by the tyranny of the dog. If Jack could have got hold of him he might have settled the account to his own satisfaction, but he was not quick enough for that. His only refuge was up a tree. He soon discovered that he was happier away from Bonamy's, and thenceforth when he saw his protector take the turn that led to the miner's cabin, Jack said plainly with a look, "No, thank you," and turned back to amuse himself at home.

His enemy, however, often came with Bonamy to the hunter's cabin, and there resumed his amusement of teasing the little Bear. It proved so interesting a pursuit that the dog learned to come over on his own account whenever he felt like having some fun, until at length Jack was kept in continual terror of the yellow cur. But it all ended very suddenly.

One hot day, while the two men smoked in front of Kellyan's house, the dog chased Jack up a tree and then stretched himself out for a pleasant nap in the shade of its branches. Jack was forgotten as the dog slumbered. The little Bear kept very quiet for a while, then, as his twinkling brown eyes came back to that hateful dog, that he could neither catch nor get away from, an idea seemed to grow in his small brain. He began to move slowly and silently down the branch until he was over the foe, slumbering, twitching his limbs, and making little sounds that told of dreams of the chase, or, more likely, dreams of tormenting a helpless Bear cub. Of course, Jack knew nothing of that. His one thought, doubtless, was that he hated that cur and now he could vent hate. He came just over the tyrant, and taking careful aim, he jumped and landed squarely on the dog's ribs. It was a terribly rude awakening, but the dog gave no yelp, for the good reason that the breath was knocked out of his body. No bones were broken, though he was barely able to drag himself away in silent defeat, while Jacky played a lively tune on his rear with paws that were fringed with meat-hooks.

Evidently it was a most excellent plan; and when the dog came around after that, or when Jack went to Bonamy's with his master, as he soon again ventured to do, he would scheme with more or less success to "get the drop on the purp", as the men put it. The dog now rapidly lost interest in Bear-baiting, and in a short time it was a forgotten sport.

THE STREAM THAT SANK IN THE SAND

Jack was funny; Jill was sulky. Jack was petted and given freedom, so grew funnier; Jill was beaten and chained, so grew sulkier. She had a bad name and she was often punished for it; it is usually so.

One day, while Lan was away, Jill got free and joined her brother. They broke into the little storehouse and rioted among the provisions.

Jack . . . held up his sticky, greasy arms

They gorged themselves with the choicest sorts; and the common stuffs, like flour, butter, and baking-powder, brought fifty miles on horseback, were good enough only to be thrown about the ground or rolled in. Jack had just torn open the last bag of flour, and Jill was puzzling over a box of miner's dynamite, when the doorway darkened and there stood Kellyan, a picture of amazement and wrath. Little Bears do not know anything about pictures, but they have some aquaintance with wrath. They seemed to know that they were sinning, or at least in danger, and Jill sneaked, sulky and snuffy, into a dark corner, where she glared defiantly at the hunter. Jack put his head on one side, then, quite forgetful of all his misbehavior, he gave a delighted grunt, and scuttling toward the man, he whined, jerked his nose, and held up his sticky, greasy arms to be lifted and petted as though he were the best little Bear in the world.

Alas, how likely we are to be taken at our own estimate! The scowl faded from the hunter's brow as the cheeky and deplorable little Bear began to climb his leg. "You little divil," he growled, "I'll break your cussed neck"; but he did not. He lifted the nasty, sticky little beast and fondled him as usual, while Jill, no worse—even more excusable, because less trained—suffered all the terrors of his wrath and was double-chained to the post, so as to have no further chance of such ill-doing.

This was a day of bad luck for Kellyan. That morning he had fallen and broken his rifle. Now, on his return home, he found his provisions spoiled, and a new trial was before him.

A stranger with a small pack-train called at his place that evening and passed the night with him. Jack was in his most frolicsome mood and amused them both with tricks half-puppy and half-monkey like, and in the moorning, when the stranger was leaving, he said: "Say, pard, I'll give you twenty-five dollars for the pair." Lan hesitated, thought of the wasted provisions, his empty purse, his broken rifle, and answered: "Make it fifty and it's a go."

"Shake on it."

So the bargain was made, the money paid, and in fifteen minutes

the stranger was gone with a little Bear in each pannier of his horse.

Jill was surly and silent; Jack kept up a whining that smote on Lan's heart with a reproachful sound, but he braced himself with, "Guess they're better out of the way; couldn't afford another storeroom racket," and soon the pine forest had swallowed up the stranger, his three led horses, and the two little Bears.

"Well, I'm glad he's gone," said Lan, savagely, though he knew quite well that he was already scourged with repentance. He began to set his shanty in order. He went to the storehouse and gathered the remnants of the provisions. After all, there was a good deal left. He walked past the box where Jack used to sleep. How silent it was! He noted the place where Jack used to scratch the door to get into the cabin, and started at the thought that he should hear it no more, and told himself, with many cuss-words, that he was "mighty glad of it." He pottered about, doing—doing—oh, anything, for an hour or more; then suddenly he leaped on his pony and raced madly down the trail on the track of the stranger. He put the pony hard to it, and in two hours he overtook the train at the crossing of the river.

"Say, pard, I done wrong. I didn't orter sell them little B'ars, leastwise not Jacky. I—I—wall, now, I want to call it off. Here's yer yellow."

"I'm satisfied with my end of it," said the stranger, coldly.

"Well, I ain't," said Lan, with warmth, "an' I want it off."

"Ye're wastin' time if that's what ye come for," was the reply.

"We'll see about that," and Lan threw the gold pieces at the rider and walked over toward the pannier, where Jack was whining joyfully at the sound of the familiar voice.

"Hands up," said the stranger, with the short, sharp tone of one who had said it before, and Lan turned to find himself covered with a .45 navy Colt.

"Ye got the drop on me," he said; "I ain't got no gun; but look-a here, stranger, that there little B'ar is the only pard I got; he's my stiddy company an' we're almighty fond o' each other. I didn't know how much I was a-goin' to miss him. Now look-a here: take back yer fifty; ye give me Jack an' keep Jill."

"If ye got five hundred cold plunks in yaller ye kin get him; if not, you walk straight to that tree thar an' don't drop yer hands or turn or I'll fire. Now start."

Mountain etiquette is very strict, and Lan, being without weapons, must needs obey the rules. He marched to the distant tree under cover of the revolver. The wail of little Jack smote painfully on his ear, but he knew the ways of the mountaineers too well to turn or make another offer, and the stranger went on.

Many a man has spent a thousand dollars in efforts to capture some wild thing and felt it worth the cost—for a time. Then he is willing to sell it for half cost, then for quarter, and at length he ends by giving it away. The stranger was vastly pleased with his comical Bear cubs at first, and valued them proportionately; but each day they seemed more troublesome and less amusing, so that when, a week later, at the Bell-Cross Ranch, he was offered a horse for the pair, he readily closed, and their days of hamper-travel were over.

The owner of the ranch was neither mild, refined, nor patient. Jack, good-natured as he was, partly grasped these facts as he found himself taken from the pannier, but when it came to getting cranky little Jill out of the basket and into a collar, there ensued a scene so unpleasant that no collar was needed. The ranchman wore his hand in a sling for two weeks, and Jacky at his chain's end paced the ranch-yard alone.

THE RIVER HELD IN THE FOOTHILLS

There was little of pleasant interest in the next eighteen months of Jack's career. His share of the globe was a twenty-foot circle around a pole in the yard. The blue hills of the offing, the nearer pine grove, and even the ranch-house itself were fixed stars, far away and sending merely faint suggestions of their splendors to his not very bright eyes. Even the horses and men were outside his little sphere and related to him about as much as comets are to the earth. The very tricks that had made him valued were being forgotten as Jack grew up in chains.

At first a butter-firkin had made him an ample den, but he rapidly passed through the various stages—butter-firkin, nail-keg, flour-barrel, oil-barrel—and had now to be graded as a good average hogshead Bear, though he was far from filling that big round wooden cavern that formed his latest den.

The ranch hotel lay just where the foothills of the Sierras with their groves of live oaks were sloping into the golden plains of the Sacramento. Nature had showered on it every wonderful gift in her lap. A foreground rich with flowers, luxuriant in fruit, shade and sun, dry pastures, rushing rivers, and murmuring rills, were here. Great trees were variants of the view, and the high Sierras to the east overtopped the wondrous plumy forests of their pines with blocks of sculptured blue. Back of the house was a noble river of water from the hills, fouled and chained by sluice and dam, but still a noble stream whose earliest parent rill had gushed from grim old Tallac's slope.

Things of beauty, life, and color were on every side, and yet most sordid of the human race were the folk about the ranch hotel. To see them in this setting might well raise doubt that any "rise from Nature up to Nature's God." No city slum has ever shown a more ignoble crew, and Jack, if his mind were capable of such things, must have graded the two-legged ones lower in proportion as he knew them better.

Cruelty was his lot, and hate was his response. Almost the only amusing trick he now did was helping himself to a drink of beer. He was very fond of beer, and the loafers about the tavern often gave him a bottle to see how dexterously he would twist off the wire and work out the cork. As soon as it popped, he would turn it up between his paws and drink to the last drop.

The monotony of his life was occasionally varied with a dog fight. His tormentors would bring their Bear dogs "to try them on the cub." It seemed to be very pleasant sport to men and dogs, till Jack learned how to receive them. At first he used to rush furiously at the nearest tormentor until brought up with a jerk at the end of his chain and completely exposed to attack behind from another dog. A month or two entirely changed his method. He learned to sit against the hogshead and quietly watch the noisy dogs around him, with much show of inattention, making no move, no matter how near they were, until they "bunched," that is, gathered in one place. Then he charged. It was inevitable that the hind dogs would be the last to jump, and so hindered the front ones; thus Jack would "get" one or more of them, and the game became unpopular.

When about eighteen months old, and half grown, an incident took place which defied all explanation. Jack had won the name of being dangerous, for he had crippled one man with a blow and nearly killed a tipsy fool who volunteered to fight him. A harmless but good-for-nothing sheep-herder who loafed about the place got very drunk one night and offended some fire-eaters. They decided that, as he had no gun, it would be the proper thing to club him to their hearts' content instead of shooting him full of holes, in the manner usually prescribed by their code. Faco Tampico made for the door and staggered out into the darkness. His pursuers were even more drunk, but, bent on mischief, they gave chase, and Faco dodged back of the house and into the yard. The mountaineers had just wit enough to keep out of reach of the Grizzly as they searched about for their victim, but they did not find him. Then they got torches, and making sure that he was not in the yard, were satisfied that he had fallen into the river behind the barn and doubtless was drowned. A few rude jokes, and they returned to the house. As they passed the Grizzly's den their lanterns awoke in his eyes a glint of fire. In the morning the cook, beginning his day, heard strange sounds in the yard. They came from the Grizzly's den: "Hyar, you, lay over dahr," in sleepy tones; then a deep, querulous grunting.

The cook went as close as he dared and peeped in. Said the same voice in sleepy tones: "Who are ye crowdin' caramba!" and a human elbow was seen jerking and pounding; and again impatient growling in bear-like tones was the response.

The sun came up and the astonished loafers found it was the missing sheep-herder that was in the Bear's den, calmly sleeping off his debauch in the very cave of death. The men tried to get him out, but the Grizzly plainly showed that they could do so only over his dead body. He charged with vindictive fury at any who ventured near, and when they gave up the attempt he lay down at the door of the den on guard. At length the sheep-herder came to himself, rose up on his elbows, and realizing that he was in the power of the young Grizzly, he stepped gingerly over his guardian's back and ran off without even saying "Thank you."

The Fourth of July was at hand now, and the owner of the tavern, growing weary of the huge captive in the yard, announced that he would celebrate Independence Day with a grand fight between a "picked and fighting range bull and a ferocious Californian Grizzly." The news was spread far and wide by the "Grapevine Telegraph." The roof of the stable was covered with seats at fifty cents each. The hay-wagon was half loaded and drawn alongside the corral; seats here gave a perfect view and were sold at a dollar apiece. The old corral was repaired, new posts put in where needed, and the first thing in the morning a vicious old bull was herded in and tormented till he was "snuffy" and extremely dangerous.

Jack meanwhile had been roped, "choked down," and nailed up in his hogshead. His chain and collar were permanently riveted together, so the collar was taken off, as "it would be easy to rope him, *if need be, after the bull was through with him.*"

The hogshead was rolled over to the corral gate and all was ready.

The cowboys came from far and near in their most gorgeous trappings, and the California cowboy is the peacock of his race. Their best girls were with them, and farmers and ranchmen came for fifty miles to enjoy the Bull-and-Bear fight. Miners from the hills were there, Mexican sheep-herders, store-keepers from Placerville, strangers from Sacramento; town and county, mountain and plain, were represented. The hay-wagon went so well that another was brought into market. The barn roof was sold out. An ominous crack of the timbers somewhat shook the prices, but a couple of strong uprights below restored the market, and all "The Corners" was ready and eager for the great fight. Men who had been raised among cattle were betting on the bull.

"I tell you, there ain't nothing on earth kin face a big range bull that hez good use of hisself."

But the hillman were backing the Bear. "Pooh, what's a bull to a Grizzly? I tell you, I seen a Grizzly send a horse clean over the Hetch-Hetchy with one clip of his left. Bull! I'll bet he'll never show up in the second round."

So they wrangled and bet, while burly women, trying to look fetching, gave themselves a variety of airs, were "scared at the whole thing, nervous about the uproar, afraid it would be shocking," but really were as keenly interested as the men.

All was ready, and the boss of "The Corners" shouted: "Let her go, boys; house is full an' time's up!"

Faco Tampico had managed to tie a bundle of chaparral thorn to the bull's tail, so that the huge creature had literally lashed himself into a frenzy.

Jack's hogshead meanwhile had been rolled around till he was raging with disgust, and Faco, at the word of command, began to pry open the door. The end of the barrel was close to the fence, the door cleared away; now there was nothing for Jack to do but go forth and claw the bull to pieces. But he did not go. The noise, the uproar, the strangeness of the crowd affected him so that he decided to stay where he was, and the bullbackers raised a derisive cry. Their champion came forward bellowing and sniffing, pausing often to paw the dust. He held his head very high and approached slowly until he came within ten feet of the Grizzly's den; then, giving a snort, he turned and ran to the other end of the corral. Now it was the Bear-backers' turn to shout.

But the crowd wanted a fight, and Faco, forgetful of his debt to Grizzly Jack, dropped a bundle of Fourth of July crackers into the hogshead by way of the bung. "Crack!" and Jack jumped up. "Fizz—crack— c-r-r-r-a-a-c-k, cr-k-crk-ck!" and Jack in surprise rushed from his den into the arena. The bull was standing in a magnificent attitude there in the middle, but when he saw the Bear spring toward him, he gave two mighty snorts and retreated as far as he could, amid cheers and hisses.

Perhaps the two main characteristics of the Grizzly are the quickness with which he makes a plan and the vigor with which he follows it up. Before the bull had reached the far side of the corral Jack seemed to know the wisest of courses. His pig-like eyes swept the fence in a flash—took in the most climbable part, a place where a cross-piece was nailed on in the middle. In three seconds he was there, in two seconds he was over, and in one second he dashed through the running, scattering mob and was making for the hills as fast as his strong and supple legs could carry him. Women screamed, men yelled, and dogs barked; there was a wild dash for the horses tied far from the scene of the fight, to spare their nerves, but the Grizzly had three hundred yards' start, five hundred yards even, and before the gala mob gave out a long and flying column of reckless, riotous riders, the Grizzly had plunged into the river, a flood no dog cared to face, and had reached the chaparral and the broken ground in line for the piney hills. In an hour the ranch hotel, with its galling chain, its cruelties, and its brutal human beings, was a thing of the past, shut out by the hills of his youth, cut off by the river of his cubhood, the river grown from the rill born in this birthplace away in Tallac's pines. That Fourth of July was a glorious Fourth—it was Independence Day for Grizzly Jack.

THE BROKEN DAM

A wounded deer usually works downhill, a hunted Grizzly climbs. Jack knew nothing of the country, but he did know that he wanted to get away from that mob, so he sought the roughest ground, and climbed and climbed.

He had been alone for hours, traveling up and on. The plain was lost to view. He was among the granite rocks, the pine trees, and the berries now, and he gathered in food from the low bushes with dexterous paws and tongue as he traveled, but stopped not at all until among the tumbled rock, where the sun heat of the afternoon seemed to command rather than invite him to rest.

The night was black when he awoke, but Bears are not afraid of the dark—they rather fear the day—and he swung along, led, as before, by the impulse to get up above the danger; and thus at last he reached the highest range, the region of his native Tallac.

He had but little of the usual training of a young Bear, but he had a few instincts, his birthright, that stood him well in all the main issues, and his nose was an excellent guide. Thus he managed to live, and wild-life experiences coming fast gave his mind the chance to grow.

Jack's memory for faces and facts was not at all good, but his memory for smells was imperishable. He had forgotten Bonamy's cur, but the smell of Bonamy's cur would instantly have thrilled him with the old feelings. He had forgotten the cross ram, but the smell of "Old Woolly Whiskers" would have inspired him at once with anger and hate; and one evening when the wind came richly laden with ram smell it was like a bygone life returned. He had been living on roots and berries for weeks and now began to experience that hankering for flesh that comes on every candid vegetarian with dangerous force from time to time. The ram smell seemed an answer to it. So down he went by night (no sensible Bear travels by day), and the smell brought him from the pines on the hillside to an open rocky dale.

Long before he got there a curious light shone up. He knew what that was; he had seen the two-legged ones make it near the ranch of evil smells and memories, so feared it not. He swung along from ledge to ledge in silence and in haste, for the smell of sheep grew stronger at every stride, and when he reached a place above the fire he blinked his eyes to find the sheep. The smell was strong now; it was rank, but no sheep to be seen. Instead he saw in the valley a stretch of gray water that seemed to reflect the stars, and yet they neither twinkled nor rippled; there was a murmuring sound from the sheet, but it seemed not at all like that of the lakes around.

The stars were clustered chiefly near the fire, and were less like stars than spots of the phosphorescent wood that are scattered on the ground when one knocks a rotten stump about to lick up its swarms of wood-ants. So Jack came closer, and at last so close that even his dull eyes could see. The great gray lake was a flock of sheep and the phosphorescent specks were their eyes. Close by the fire was a log or a low rough bank—that turned out to be the shepherd and his dog. Both were objectionable features, but the sheep extended far from them. Jack knew that his business was with the flock.

He came very close to the edge and found them surrounded by a low hedge of chaparral; but what little things they were compared with that great and terrible ram that he dimly remembered! The blood-thirst came on him. He swept the low hedge aside, charged into the mass of sheep that surged away from him with rushing sounds of feet and murmuring groans, struck down one, seized it, and turning away, he scrambled back up the mountains.

The sheep-herder leaped to his feet, fired his gun, and the dog came running over the solid mass of sheep, barking loudly. But Jack was gone. The sheep-herder contented himself with making two or three fires, shooting off his gun, and telling his beads.

That was Jack's first mutton, but it was not the last. Thenceforth when he wanted a sheep—and it became a regular need—he knew he had merely to walk along the ridge till his nose said, "Turn, and go so," for smelling is believing in Bear life.

THE FRESHET

Pedro Tamico and his brother Faco were not in the sheep business for any maudlin sentiment. They did not march ahead of their beloveds waving a crook as wand of office or appealing to the esthetic sides of their ideal followers with a tabret and pipe. Far from leading the flock with symbol, they drove them with an armful of ever-ready rocks and clubs. They were not shepherds; they were sheep-herders. They did not view their charges as loved and loving followers, but as four-legged cash; each sheep was worth a dollar bill. They were cared for only as a man cares for his money, and counted after each alarm or day of travel. It is not easy for any one to count three thousand sheep, and for a Mexican sheep-herder it is an impossibility. But he has a simple device which answers the purpose. In an ordinary flock about one sheep in a hundred is a black one. If a portion of the flock has gone astray, there is likely to be a black one in it. So by counting his thirty black sheep each day Tampico kept rough count of his entire flock.

Grizzly Jack had killed but one sheep that first night. On his next visit he killed two, and on the next but one, yet that last one happened to be black, and when Tampico found but twenty-nine of its kind remaining he safely reasoned that he was losing sheep—according to the index a hundred were gone.

"If the land is unhealthy move out" is ancient wisdom. Tampico filled his pocket with stones, and reviling his charges in all their walks in life and history, he drove them from the country that was evidently the range of a sheep-eater. At night he found a walled-in cañon, a natural corral, and the woolly scattering swarm, condensed into a solid fleece, went pouring into the gap, urged intelligently by the dog and idiotically by the man. At one side of the entrance Tampico made his fire. Some thirty feet away was a sheer wall of rock.

Ten miles may be a long day's travel for a wretched wool-plant, but it is little more than two hours for a Grizzly. It is farther than eyesight, but it is well within nosesight, and Jack, feeling mutton-hungry, had not the least difficulty in following his prey. His supper was a little later than usual, but his appetite was the better for that. There was no alarm in camp, so Tampico had fallen asleep. A growl from the dog awakened him. He started up to behold the most appalling creature

The thirty-foot bear

that he had ever seen or imagined, a monster Bear standing on his hind legs, and thirty feet high at least. The dog fled in terror, but was valor itself compared with Pedro. He was so frightened that he could not express the prayer that was in his breast: "Blessed saints, let him have every sin-blackened sheep in the band, but spare your poor worshiper," and he hid his head; so never learned that he saw, not a thirty-foot Bear thirty feet away, but a seven-foot Bear not far from the fire and casting a black thirty-foot shadow on the smooth rock behind. And, helpless with fear, poor Pedro groveled in the dust.

When he looked up the giant Bear was gone. There was a rushing of the sheep. A small body of them scurried out of the cañon into the night, and after them went an ordinary-sized Bear, undoubtedly a cub of the monster.

Pedro had been neglecting his prayers for some months back, but he afterward assured his father confessor that on this night he caught up on all arrears and had a goodly surplus before morning. At sunrise he left his dog in charge of the flock and set out to seek the runaways, knowing, first, that there was little danger in the day-time, second, that some would escape. The missing ones were a considerable number, raised to the second power indeed, for two more black ones were gone. Strange to tell, they had not scattered, and Pedro trailed them a mile or more in the wilderness till he reached another very small box cañon. Here he found the missing flock perched in various places on boulders and rocky pinnacles as high up as they could get. He was delighted and worked for half a minute on his bank surplus of prayers, but was sadly upset to find that nothing would induce the sheep to come down from the rocks or leave that cañon. One or two that he manoeuvered as far as the outlet sprang back in fear from *something on the ground*, which, on examination, he found—yes, he swears to this—to be the deep-worn, fresh-worn pathway of a Grizzly from one wall across to the other. All the sheep were now back again beyond his reach. Pedro began to fear for himself, so hastily returned to the main flock. He was worse off than ever now. The other Grizzly was a Bear of ordinary size and ate a sheep each night, but the new one, into whose range he entered, was a monster, a Bear mountain, requiring forty or fifty sheep to a meal. The sooner he was out of this the better.

It was now late, too late, and the sheep were too tired to travel, so Pedro made unusual preparations for the night: two big fires at the entrance to the cañon, and a platform fifteen feet up in a tree for his own bed. The dog could look out for himself.

ROARING IN THE CAÑON

Pedro knew that the big Bear was coming; for the fifty sheep in the little cañon were not more than an appetizer for such a creature. He loaded his gun carefully as a matter of habit and went up-stairs to bed. Whatever defects his dormitory had the ventilation was good, and Pedro was soon a-shiver. He looked down in envy at his dog curled up by the fire; then he prayed that the saints might intervene and direct the steps of the Bear toward the flock of some neighbour, and carefully specified the neighbor to avoid mistakes. He tried to pray himself to sleep. It had never failed in church when he was at the mission, so why now? But for once it did not succeed. The fearsome hour of midnight passed, then the gray dawn, the hour of dull despair, was near. Tampico felt it, and a long groan vibrated through his chattering teeth. His dog leaped up, barked savagely, the sheep began to stir, then went backing into the gloom; there was a rushing of stampeding sheep and a huge, dark form loomed up. Tampico grasped his gun and would have fired, when it dawned on him with sickening horror that the Bear was thirty feet high, his platform was only fifteen, just a convenient height for the monster. None but a madman would invite the Bear to eat by shooting at him now. So Pedro flattened himself face down-ward on the platform, and, with his mouth to a crack, he poured forth prayers to his representative in the sky, regretting his unconventional attitude and profoundly hoping that it would be overlooked as unavoidable, and that somehow the petitions would get the right direction after leaving the under side of the platform.

In the morning he had proof that his prayers had been favorably received. There was a Bear-track, indeed, but the number of black sheep was unchanged, so Pedro filled his pocket with stones and began his usual torrent of remarks as he drove the flock.

"Hyah, Capitan—you huajalote," as the dog paused to drink. "Bring back those ill-descended sons of perdition," and a stone gave force to the order, which the dog promptly obeyed. Hovering about the great host of grumbling hoofy locusts, he kept them together and on the move, while Pedro played the part of a big, noisy, and troublesome second.

As they journeyed through the open country the sheep-herder's eye fell on a human figure, a man sitting on a rock above them to the left. Pedro gazed inquiringly; the man saluted and beckoned. This meant "friend"; had he motioned him to pass on it might have meant, "Keep away or I shoot." Pedro walked toward him a little way and sat down. The man came forward. It was Lan Kellyan, the hunter.

Each was glad of a chance to "talk with a human" and to get the news. The latest concerning the price of wool, the Bull-and-Bear fiasco, and, above all, the monster Bear that had killed Tampico's sheep, afforded topics of talk. "Ah, a Bear devill—de hellbrute—a Gringo Bear—pardon, my amigo, I mean a very terroar."

As the sheep-herder enlarged on the marvelous cunning of the Bear that had a private sheep corral of his own, and the size of the monster, forty or fifty feet high now—for such Bears are of rapid and continuous growth—Kellyan's eye twinkled and he said:

"Say, Pedro, I believe you once lived pretty nigh the Hassayampa, did n't you?"

This does not mean that that is a country of great Bears, but was an allusion to the popular belief that any one who tastes a single drop of the Hassayampa River can never afterward tell the truth. Some scientists who have looked into the matter aver that this wonderful property is common to the Rio Grande as well as the Hassayampa, and, indeed, all the rivers of Mexico, as well as their branches, and the springs, wells, ponds, lakes, and irrigation ditches. However that may be, the Hassayampa is the best-known stream of this remarkable peculiarity. The higher one goes, the greater its potency, and Pedro was from the

head-waters. But he protested by all the saints that his story was true. He pulled out a little bottle of garnets, got by glancing over the rubbish laid about their hills by the desert ants; he thrust it back into his wallet and produced another bottle with a small quantity of gold-dust, also gathered at the rare times when he was not sleepy, and the sheep did not need driving, watering, stoning, or reviling.

"Here, I bet dat it ees so."

Gold is a loud talker.

Kellyan paused. "I can't cover your bet, Pedro, but I'll kill your Bear for what's in the bottle."

"I take you," said the sheep-herder, "eef you breeng back dose sheep dat are now starving up on de rocks of de cañon of Baxstaire's."

The Mexican's eyes twinkled as the white man closed on the offer. The gold in the bottle, ten or fifteen dollars, was a trifle, and yet enough to send the hunter on the quest—enough to lure him into the enterprise, and that was all that was needed. Pedro knew his man: get him going and profit would count for nothing; having put his hand to the plow Lan Kellyan would finish the furrow at any cost; he was incapable of turning back. And again he took up the trail of Grizzly Jack, his one-time "pard," now grown beyond his ken.

The hunter went straight to Baxter's cañon and found the sheep highperched upon the rocks. By the entrance he found the remains of two of them recently devoured, and about them the tracks of a medium-sized Bear. He saw nothing of the pathway—the dead-line—made by the Grizzly to keep the sheep prisoners till he should need them. But the sheep were standing in stupid terror on various high places, apparently willing to starve rather than come down.

Lan dragged one down; at once it climbed up again. He now realised the situation, so made a small pen of chaparral outside the cañon, and dragging the dull creatures down one at a time, he carried them—except one—out of the prison of death and into the pen. Next he made a hasty fence across the cañon's mouth, and turning the sheep out of the pen, he drove them by slow stages toward the rest of the flock.

Only six or seven miles across country, but it was late night when Lan arrived.

Tampico gladly turned over half of the promised dust. That night they camped together, and, of course, no Bear appeared.

In the morning Lan went back to the cañon and found, as expected, that the Bear had returned and killed the remaining sheep.

The hunter piled the rest of the carcasses in an open place, lightly sprinkled the Grizzly's trail with some very dry brush, then making a platform some fifteen feet from the ground in a tree, he rolled up in his blanket there and slept.

An old Bear will rarely visit a place three nights in succession; a cunning Bear will avoid a trail that has been changed overnight; a skilful Bear goes in absolute silence. But Jack was neither old, cunning, nor skilful. He came for the fourth time to the cañon of the sheep. He followed his old trail straight to the delicious mutton bones. He found the human trail, but there was something about it that rather attracted him. He strode along on the dry boughs. "Crack!" went one; "crack-crack!" went another; and Kellyan arose on the platform and strained his eyes in the gloom till a dark form moved into the opening by the bones of the sheep. The hunter's rifle cracked, the Bear snorted, wheeled into the bushes, and, crashing away, was gone.

FIRE AND WATER

That was Jack's baptism of fire, for the rifle had cut a deep flesh-wound in his back. Snorting with pain and rage, he tore through the bushes and traveled on for an hour or more, then lay down and tried to lick the wound, but it was beyond reach. He could only rub it against a log. He continued his journey back toward Tallac, and there, in a cave that was formed of tumbled rocks, he lay down to rest. He was still rolling about in pain when the sun was high and a strange smell of fire came searching through the cave; it increased, and volumes of blinding smoke were

about him. It grew so choking that he was forced to move, but it followed him till he could bear it no longer, and he dashed out of another of the ways that led into the cavern. As he went he caught a distant glimpse of a man throwing wood on the fire by the in-way, and the whiff that the wind brought him said: "This is the man that was last night watching the sheep." Strange as it may seem, the woods were clear of smoke except for a trifling belt that floated in the trees, and Jack went striding away in peace. He passed over the ridge, and finding berries, ate the first meal he had known since killing his last sheep. He had wandered on, gathering fruit and digging roots, for an hour or two, when the smoke grew blacker, the smell of fire stronger. He worked away from it, but in no haste. The birds, deer, and wood hares were now seen scurrying past him. There was a roaring in the air. It grew louder, was coming nearer, and Jack turned to stride after the wood things that fled.

The whole forest was ablaze; the wind was rising, and the flames, gaining and spreading, were flying now like wild horses. Jack had no place in his brain for such a thing; but his instinct warned him to shun that coming roaring that sent above dark clouds and flying fire-flakes, and messengers of heat below, so he fled before it, as the forest host was doing. Fast as he went, and few animals can outrun a Grizzly in rough country, the hot hurricane was gaining on him. His sense of danger had grown almost to terror, terror of a kind that he had never known before, for here there was nothing he could fight; nothing that he could resist. The flames were all around him now; birds without number, hares, and deer had gone down before the red horror. He was plunging wildly on through chaparral and manzanita thickets that held all feebler things until the fury seized them; his hair was scorching, his wound was forgotten, and he thought only of escape when the brush ahead opened, and the Grizzly, smoke-blinded, half roasted, plunged down a bank and into a small clear pool. The fur on his back said "hiss," for it was sizzling-hot. Down below he went, gulping the cool drink, wallowing in safety and unheat. Down below the surface he crouched as long as his lungs would bear the strain, then slowly and cautiously he raised his head. The sky above was one great sheet of flame. Sticks aflame and flying embers came in hissing showers on the water. The air was hot, but breathable at times, and he filled his lungs till he had difficulty in keeping his body down below. Other creatures there were in the pool, some burnt, some dead, some small and in the margin, some bigger in the deeper places, and one of them was close beside him. Oh, he knew that smell; fire—all Sierra's woods ablaze—could not disguise the hunter who had shot at him from the platform, and, though he did not know this, the hunter really who had followed him all day, and who had tried to smoke him out of his den and thereby set the woods ablaze.

Here they were, face to face, in the deepest end of the little pool; they were only ten feet apart and could not get more than twenty feet apart. The flames grew unbearable. The Bear and man each took a hasty breath and bobbed below the surface, each wondering, according to his intelligence, what the other would do. In half a minute both came up again, each relieved to find the other no nearer. Each tried to keep his nose and one eye above the water. But the fire was raging hot; they had to dip under and stay as long as possible.

The roaring of the flame was like a hurricane. A huge pine tree came crashing down across the pool; it barely missed the man. The splash of water quenched the blazes for the most part, but it gave off such a heat that he had to move—a little nearer to the Bear. Another fell at an angle, killing a coyote, and crossing the first tree. They blazed fiercely at their junction, and the Bear edged from it a little nearer the man. Now they were within touching distance. His useless gun was lying in shallow water near shore, but the man had his knife ready, ready for self-defense. It was not needed; the fiery power had proclaimed a peace. Bobbing up and dodging under, keeping a nose in the air and an eye on his foe, each spent an hour or more. The red hurricane passed on. The smoke was bad in the woods, but no longer intolerable, and as the Bear straightened up in the pool to move away into shallower water and off into the woods, the man got a glimpse of red blood streaming from the shaggy back and dyeing the pool. The blood on the trail had not escaped him. He knew that this was the Bear of Baxter's cañon, this was the Gringo Bear, but he did not know that this was also his old-time Grizzly Jack. He scrambled out of the pond, on the other side from that taken by the Grizzly, and, hunter and hunted, they went their diverse ways.

THE EDDY

All the west slopes of Tallac were swept by the fire, and Kellyan moved to a new hut on the east side, where still were green patches; so did the

grouse and the rabbit and coyote, and so did Grizzly Jack. His wound healed quickly, but his memory of the rifle smell continued; it was a dangerous smell, a new and horrible kind of smoke—one he was destined to know too well; one, indeed, he was soon to meet again. Jack was wandering down the side of Tallac, following a sweet odor that called up memories of former joys—the smell of honey, though he did not know it. A flock of grouse got leisurely out of his way and flew to a low tree, when he caught a whiff of man smell, then heard a crack like that which had stung him in the sheep-corral, and down fell one of the grouse close beside him. He stepped forward to sniff just as a man also stepped forward from the opposite bushes. They were within ten feet of each other, and they recognized each other, for the hunter saw that it was a singed Bear with a wounded side, and the Bear smelt the rifle-smoke and the leather clothes. Quick as a Grizzly—that is, quicker than a flash—the Bear reared. The man sprang backward, tripped and fell, and the Grizzly was upon him. Face to earth the hunter lay like dead, but, ere he struck, Jack caught a scent that made him pause. He smelt his victim, and the smell was the rolling back of curtains or the conjuring up of a past. The days in the hunter's shanty were forgotten, but the feelings of those days were ready to take command at the bidding of the nose. His nose drank deep of a draft that quelled all rage. The Grizzly's humor changed. He turned and left the hunter quite unharmed.

Oh, blind one with the gun! All he could find in explanation was: "You kin never tell what a Grizzly will do, but it's good play to lay low when he has you cornered." It never came into his mind to credit the shaggy brute with an impulse born of good, and when he told the sheep-herder of his adventure in the pool, of his hitting high on the body and of losing the trail in the forest fire—"down by the shack, when he turned up sudden and had me I thought my last day was come. Why he didn't swat me, I don't know. But I tell you this, Pedro: the B'ar what killed your sheep on the upper pasture and in the sheep cañon is the same. No two B'ars has hind feet alike when you get a clear-cut track, and this holds out even right along."

"What about the fifty-foot B'ar I saw wit' mine own eyes, caramba?"

That must have been the night you were working a kill-care with your sheep-herder's delight. But don't worry; I'll get him yet."

So Kellyan set out on a long hunt, and put in practice every trick he knew for the circumventing of a Bear. Lou Bonamy was invited to join with him, for his yellow cur was a trailer. They packed four horses with stuff and led them over the ridge to the east side of Tallac, and down away from Jack's Peak, that Kellyan had named in honor of his Bear cub, toward Fallen Leaf Lake. The hunter believed that here he would meet not only the Gringo Bear that he was after, but would also stand a chance of finding others, for the place had escaped the fire.

They quickly camped, setting up their canvas sheet for shade more than against rain, and, after picketing their horses in a meadow, went out to hunt. By circling around Leaf Lake they got a good idea of the wild population: plenty of deer, some Black Bear, and one or two Cinnamon and Grizzly, and one track along the shore that Kellyan pointed to, briefly saying: "That's him."

"Ye mean old Pedro's Gringo?"

"Yep. That's the fifty-foot Grizzly. I suppose he stands maybe seven foot high in daylight, but,'course, B'ars pulls out long at night."

So the yellow cur was put on the track, and led away with funny little yelps, while the two hunters came stumbling along behind him as fast as they could, calling, at times, to the dog not to go so fast, and thus making a good deal of noise, which Gringo Jack heard a mile away as he ambled along the mountain-side above them. He was following his nose to many good and eatable things, and therefore going up-wind. This noise behind was so peculiar that he wanted to smell it, and to do that he swung along back over the clamor, then descended to the down-wind side, and thus he came on the trail of the hunters and their dog.

His nose informed him at once. Here was the hunter he once felt kindly toward and two other smells of far-back—both hateful; all three were now the smell-marks of foes, and a rumbling "woof" was the expressive sound that came from his throat.

That dog-smell in particular roused him, though it is very sure he had forgotten all about the dog, and Gringo's feet went swiftly and silently, yes, with marvelous silence, along the tracks of the enemy.

On rough, rocky ground a dog is scarcely quicker than a Bear, and since the dog was constantly held back by the hunters the Bear had no difficulty in overtaking them. Only a hundred yards or so behind he continued, partly in curiosity, pursuing the dog that was pursuing him, till a shift of a wind brought the dog a smell-call from the Bear behind. He wheeled—of course you never follow trail smell when you can find body smell—and came galloping back with a different yapping and a bristling in his mane.

"Don't understand that," whispered Bonamy.

"It's B'ar, all right," was the answer; and the dog, bounding high, went straight toward the foe.

Jack heard him coming, smelt him coming, and at length saw him coming; but it was the smell that roused him—the full scent of the bully of his youth. The anger of those days came on him, and cunning enough to make him lurk in ambush: he backed to one side of the trail where it passed under a root, and, as the little yellow tyrant came, Jack hit him once, hit him as he had done some years before, but now with the power of a grown Grizzly. No yelp escaped the dog, no second blow was needed. The hunters searched in silence for half an hour before they found the place and learned the tale from many silent tongues.

"I'll get even with him," muttered Bonamy, for he loved that contemptible little yap-cur.

"That's Pedro's Gringo, all right. He's sure cunning to run his own back track. But we'll fix him yet," and they vowed to kill that Bear or "get done up" themselves.

Without a dog, they must make a new plan of hunting. They picked out two or three good places for pen-traps, where trees stood in pairs to make the pillars of the den. Then Kellyan returned to camp for the ax while Bonamy prepared the ground.

As Kellyan came near their open camping-place, he stopped from habit and peeped ahead for a minute. He was about to go down when a movement caught his eye. There, on his haunches, sat a Grizzly, looking down on the camp. The singed brown of his head and neck, and the white spot on each side of his back, left no doubt that Kellyan and Pedro's Gringo were again face to face. It was a long shot, but the rifle went up, and as he was about to fire, the Bear suddenly bent his head down, and lifting his hind paw, began to lick at a little cut. This brought the head and chest nearly in line with Kellyan—a sure shot; so sure that he fired hastily. He missed the head and the shoulder, but, strange to say, he hit the Bear in the mouth and in the hind toe, carrying away one of his teeth and the side of one toe. The Grizzly sprang up with a snort, and came tearing down the hill toward the hunter. Kellyan climbed a tree and got ready, but the camp lay just between them, and the Bear charged on that instead. One sweep of his paw and the canvas tent was down and torn. Whack! and tins went flying this way. Whisk! and flour-sacks went that. Rip! and the flour went off like smoke. Slap—crack! and a boxful of odds and ends was scattered into the fire. Whack! and a bagful of cartridges was tumbled after it. Whang! and the water-pail was crushed. Pat-pat-pat! and all the cups were in useless bits.

Kellyan, safe up the tree, got no fair view to shoot—could only wait till the storm-center cleared a little. The Bear chanced on a bottle of something with a cork loosely in it. He seized it adroitly in his paws, twisted out the cork, and held the bottle up to his mouth with a comical dexterity that told of previous experience. But, whatever it was, it did not please the invader; he spat and spilled it out, and flung the bottle down as Kellyan gazed, astonished. A remarkable "crack! crack! crack!" from the fire was heard now, and the cartridges began to go off in ones, twos, fours, and numbers unknown. Gringo whirled about; he had smashed everything in view. He did not like that Fourth of July sound,

so, springing to a bank, he went bumping and heaving down to the meadow and had just stampeded the horses when, for the first time, Gringo exposed himself to the hunter's aim. His flank was grazed by another leaden stinger, and Gringo, wheeling, went off into the woods.

The hunters were badly defeated. It was fully a week before they had repaired all the damage done by their shaggy visitor and were once more at Fallen Leaf Lake with a new store of ammunition and provisions, their camp outfit complete. They said little about their vow to kill that Bear. Both took for granted that it was a fight to the finish. They never said, "*If* we get him," but, "*When* we get him."

THE FORD

Gringo, savage, but still discreet, scaled the long mountain-side when he left the ruined camp, and afar on the southern slope he sought a quiet bed in a manzanita thicket, there to lie down and nurse his wounds and ease his head so sorely aching with the jar of his shattered tooth. There he lay for a day and a night, sometimes in great pain, and

at no time inclined to stir. But, driven forth by hunger on the second day, he quit his couch and, making for the nearest ridge, he followed that and searched the wind with his nose. The smell of a mountain hunter reached him. Not knowing just what to do he sat down and did nothing. The smell grew stronger, he heard sounds of trampling; closer they came, then the brush parted and a man on horseback appeared. The horse snorted and tried to wheel, but the ridge was narrow and one false step might have been serious. The cowboy held his horse in hand and, although he had a gun, he made no attempt to shoot at the surly animal blinking at him and barring his path. He was an old mountaineer, and he now used a trick that had long been practised by the Indians, from whom, indeed, he learned it. He began "making medicine with his voice."

"See here now, B'ar," he called aloud, "I ain't doing nothing to you. I ain't got no grudge ag'in' you, an' you ain't got no right to a grudge ag'in' me."

"Gro-o-o-h," said Gringo, deep and low.

"Now, I don't want no scrap with you, though I have my scrap-iron right handy, an' what I want you to do is just step aside an' let me pass that narrer trail an' go about my business."

"Grow-woo-oo-wow," grumbled Gringo.

"I'm honest about it, pard. You let me alone, and I'll let you alone; all I want is right of way for five minutes."

"Grow-grow-wow-oo-umph," was the answer.

"Ye see, thar's no way round an' on'y one way through, an' you happen to be settin' in it. I got to take it, for I can't turn back. Come, now, is it a bargain—hands off and no scrap?"

It is very sure that Gringo could see in this nothing but a human making queer, unmenacing, monotonous sounds, so giving a final "Gr-u-ph," the Bear blinked his eyes, rose to his feet and strode down the bank, and the cowboy forced his unwilling horse to and past the place.

"Wall, wall," he chuckled, "I never knowed it to fail. Thar's whar most B'ars is alike."

If Gringo had been able to think clearly, he might have said: "This surely is a new kind of man."

SWIRL AND POOL AND GROWING FLOOD

Gringo wandered on with nose alert, passing countless odors of berries, roots, grouse, deer, till a new and pleasing smell came with especial force.

"Now, B'ar, I don't want no scrap with you"

It was not sheep, or game, or a dead thing. It was a smell of living meat. He followed the guide to a little meadow, and there he found it. There were five of them, red, or red and white—great things as big as himself; but he had no fear of them. The hunter instinct came on him, and the hunter's audacity and love of achievement. He sneaked toward them upwind in order that he might still smell them, and it also kept them from smelling him. He reached the edge of the wood. Here he must stop or be seen. There was a watering-place close by. He silently drank, then lay down in a thicket where he could watch. An hour passed thus. The sun went down and the cattle arose to graze. One of them, a small one, wandered nearer, then, acting suddenly with purpose, walked to the water-hole. Gringo watched his chance, and as she floundered in the mud and stooped he reared and struck with all his force. Square at her skull he aimed, and the blow went straight. But Gringo knew nothing of horns. The young, sharp horn, upcurling, hit his foot and was broken off; the blow lost half its power. The beef went down, but Gringo had to follow up the blow, then raged and tore in anger for his wounded paw. The other cattle fled from the scene. The Grizzly took the heifer in his jaws, then climbed the hill to his lair, and with this store of food he again lay down to nurse his wounds. Though painful, they were not serious, and within a week or so Grizzly Jack was as well as ever and roaming the woods about Fallen Leaf Lake and farther south and east, for he was extending his range as he grew—the king was coming to his kingdom. In time he met others of his kind and matched his strength with theirs. Sometimes he won and sometimes lost, but he kept on growing and learning and adding to his power.

Kellyan had kept track of him and knew at least the main facts of his life, because he had one or two marks that always served to distinguish him. A study of the tracks had told of the round wound in the front foot and the wound in the hind foot. But there was another: the hunter had picked up the splinters of bone at the camp where he had fired at the Bear, and, after long doubt, he guessed that he had broken a tusk. He hesitated to tell the story of hitting a tooth and hind toe at the same shot till, later, he had clearer proof of its truth.

No two animals are alike. Kinds which herd have more sameness than those that do not, and the Grizzly, being a solitary kind, shows great individuality. Most Grizzlies mark their length on the trees by rubbing their backs, and some will turn on the tree and claw it with their fore paws; others hug the tree with fore paws and rake it with their hind claws. Gringo's peculiarity of marking was to rub first, then turn and tear the trunk with his teeth.

It was on examining one of the Bear trees one day that Kellyan discovered the facts. He had been tracking the Bear all morning, had a fine set of tracks in the dusty trail, and thus learned that the rifle-wound was a toe-shot in the hind foot, but his fore foot of the same side had a large round wound, the one really made by the cow's horn. When he came to the Bear tree where Gringo had carved his initials, the marks were clearly made by the Bear's teeth, and one of the upper tusks was broken off, so the evidence of identity was complete.

"It's the same old B'ar," said Lan to his pard.

They failed to get sight of him in all this time, so the partners set to work at a series of Bear-traps. These are made of heavy logs and have a sliding door of hewn planks. The bait is on a trigger at the far end; a tug on this lets the door drop. It was a week's hard work to make four of these traps. They did not set them at once, for no Bear will go near a thing so suspiciously new-looking. Some Bears will not approach one till it is weather-beaten and gray. But they removed all chips and covered the newly cut wood with mud, then rubbed the inside with stale meat, and hung a lump of ancient venison on the trigger of each trap.

They did not go around for three days, knowing that the human smell must first be dissipated, and then they found but one trap sprung—the door down. Bonamy became greatly excited, for they had crossed the Grizzly's track close by. But Kellyan had been studying the dust and suddenly laughed aloud.

"Look at that,"—he pointed to a thing like a Bear-track, but scarcely two inches long. "There's the B'ar we'll find in that; that's a bushy-tailed B'ar," and Bonamy joined in the laugh when he realized that the victim in the big trap was nothing but a little skunk.

"Next time we'll set the bait higher and not set the trigger so fine."

They rubbed their boots with stale meat when they went the rounds, then left the traps for a week.

There are Bears that eat little but roots and berries; there are Bears that love best the great salmon they hook out of the pools when the long "run" is on; and there are Bears that have a special fondness for flesh. These are rare; they are apt to develop unusual ferocity and meet an early death. Gringo was one of them, and he grew like the brawny, meat-fed gladiators of old—bigger, stronger, and fiercer than his fruit- and root-fed kin. In contrast with this was his love of honey. The hunter on his trail learned that he never failed to dig out any bees' nest he could find, or, finding none, he would eat the little honey-flowers that hung like sleigh-bells on the heather. Kellyan was quick to mark the signs. "Say, Bonamy, we've got to find some honey."

It is not easy to find a bee tree without honey to fill your bee-guides; so Bonamy rode down the mountain to the nearest camp, the Tampico sheep camp, and got not honey but some sugar of which they made syrup. They caught bees at three or four different places, tagged them with cotton, filled them with syrup and let them fly, watching till the cotton tufts were lost to view, and by going on the lines till they met they found the hive. A piece of gunny-sack filled with comb was put on each trigger, and that night, as Gringo strode with that long, untiring swing that eats up miles like stream-wheels, his sentinel nose reported the delicious smell, the one that above the rest meant joy. So  Gringo Jack followed fast and far, for the place was a mile away, and reaching the curious log cavern, he halted and sniffed. There were hunters' smells; yes, but, above all, that smell of joy. He walked around to be sure, and knew it was inside; then cautiously he entered. Some wood-mice scurried by. He sniffed the bait, licked it, mumbled it, slobbered it, reveled in it, tugged to increase the flow, when "bang!" went the great door behind and Jack was caught. He backed up with a rush, bumped into the door, and had a sense, at least, of peril. He turned over with an effort and attacked the door, but it was strong. He examined the pen; went all around the logs where their rounded sides seemed easiest to tear at with his teeth. But they yielded nothing. He tried them all; he tore at the roof, the floor; but all were heavy, hard logs, spiked and pinned as one.

The sun came up as he raged, and shone through the little cracks of the door, and so he turned all his power on that. The door was flat, gave little hold, but he battered with his paws and tore with his teeth till plank after plank gave way. With a final crash he drove the wreck before him and Jack was free again.

The men read the story as though in print; yes, better, for bits of plank can tell no lies, and the track to the pen and from the pen was the track of a big Bear with a cut on the hind foot and curious round peg-like scar on the front paw, while the logs inside, where little torn, gave proof of a broken tooth.

"We had him that time, but he knew too much for us. Never mind, we'll see."

So they kept on and caught him again, for honey he could not resist. But the wreckage of the trap was all they found in the morning.

Pedro's brother knew a man who had trapped Bears, and the sheep-herder remembered that it is necessary to have the door quite *light-tight* rather than very strong, so they battened all with tar-paper outside. But Gringo was learning "pen-traps." He did not break the door that he did not see through, but he put one paw under and heaved it up when he had finished the bait. Thus he baffled them and sported with the traps, till Kellyan made the door drop into the deep groove so that the Bear could put no claw beneath it. But it was cold weather now. There was deepening snow on the Sierras. The Bear sign disappeared. The hunters knew that Gringo was sleeping his winter's sleep.

THE DEEPENING CHANNEL

April was bidding high Sierra snows go back to Mother Sea. The California woodwales screamed in clamorous joy. They thought it was about a few acorns left in storage in the Live Oak bark, but it really was joy of being alive. This outcry was to them what music is to the thrush, what joy-bells are to us—a great noise to tell how glad they were. The deer were bounding, grouse were booming, rills were rushing—all things were full of noisy gladness.

Kellyan and Bonamy were back on the Grizzly quest. "Time he was out again, and good trailing to get him, with lots of snow in the hollows." They had come prepared for a long hunt. Honey for bait, great steel traps with crocodilian jaws, and guns there were in the out-fit. The pen-trap, the better for the aging, was repaired and rebaited, and several Black Bears were taken. But Gringo, if about, had learned to shun it.

He was about, and the men soon learned that. His winter sleep was over. They found the peg-print in the snow, but with it, or just ahead, was another, the tracks of a smaller Bear.

"See that," and Kellyan pointed to the smaller mark. "This is mating-time; this is Gringo's honeymoon," and he followed the trail for a while, not expecting to find them, but simply to know their movements. He followed several times and for miles, and the trail told him many things. Here was the track of a third Bear joining. Here were marks of a combat, and a rival driven away was written there, and then the pair went on. Down from the rugged hills it took him once to where a love-feast had been set by the bigger Bear; for the carcass of a steer lay half devoured, and the telltale ground said much of the struggle that foreran the feast. As though to show his power, the Bear had seized the steer by the nose and held him for a while—so said the trampled earth for rods—struggling, bellowing, no doubt, music for my lady's ears, till Gringo judged it time to strike him down with paws of steel

Once only the hunters saw the pair—a momentary glimpse of a Bear so huge they half believed Tampico's tale, and a Bear of lesser size in fur that rolled and rippled in the sun with brown and silver lights.

"Oh, ain't that just the beautifulest thing that ever walked!" and both the hunters gazed as she strode from view in the chaparral. It was only a neck of the thicket; they both must reappear in a minute at the other side, and the men prepared to fire; but for some incomprehensible reason the two did not appear again. They never quit the cover, and had wandered far away before the hunters knew it, and were seen of them no more.

But Faco Tampico saw them. He was visiting his brother with the sheep, and hunting in the foot-hills to the east-ward, in hopes of getting a deer, his small black eyes fell on a pair of Bears, still love-bound, roaming in the woods. They were far below him. He was safe, and he sent a ball that laid the she-Bear low; her back was broken. She fell with a cry of pain and vainly tried to rise. Then Gringo rushed around, sniffed the wind for the foe, and Faco fired again. The sound and the smoke-puff told Gringo where the man lay hid. He raged up the cliff, but Faco climbed a tree, and Gringo went back to his mate. Faco fired again; Gringo made still another effort to reach him, but could not find him now, so returned to his "Silver-brown."

Whether it was chance or choice can never be known, but when Faco fired once more, Gringo Jack was between, and the ball struck him. It was the last in Faco's pouch, and the Grizzly, charging as before, found not a trace of the foe. He was gone—had swung across a place no Bear could cross and soon was a mile away. The big Bear limped back to his mate, but she no longer responded to his touch. He watched about for a time, but no one came. The silvery hide was never touched by man, and when the semblance of his mate was gone, Gringo quit the place.

The world was full of hunters, traps, and guns. He turned toward the lower hills where the sheep grazed, where once he had raided Pedro's flocks, limping along, for now he had another flesh-wound. He found the scent of the foe that killed his "Silver-brown," and would have followed, but it ceased at a place where a horse-track joined. Yet he found it again that night, mixed with the sheep smell so familiar once. He followed this, sore and savage. It led him to a settler's flimsy shack, the house of Tampico's parents, and as the big Bear reached it two human beings scrambled out of the rear door.

"My husband," shrieked the woman, "Pray! Let us pray to the saints for help!"

"Where is my pistol?" cried the husband.

"Trust in the saints," said the frightened woman.

"Yes, if I had a cannon, or if this was a cat; but with only a pepper-box pistol to meet a Bear mountain it is better to trust to a tree," and old Tampico scrambled up a pine.

The Grizzly looked into the shack, then passed to the pig-pen, killed the largest there, for this was a new kind of meat, and carrying it off, he made his evening meal.

He came again and again to that pig-pen. he found his food there till his wound was healed. Once he met with a spring-gun, but it was set too high. Six feet up, the sheep-folk judged, would be just about right for such a Bear; the charge went over his head, and so he passed unharmed—a clear proof that he was a devil. He was learning this: the human smell in any form is a smell of danger. He quit the little valley of the shack, wandering downward toward the plains. He passed a house one night, and walking up, he discovered a hollow thing with a delicious smell. It was a ten-gallon keg that had been used for sugar, some of which was still in the bottom, and thrusting in his huge head, the keg-rim, bristling with nails, stuck to him. He raged about, clawing at it wildly and roaring in it until a charge of shot from the upper windows stirred him to such effort that the keg was smashed to bits and his blinders removed.

Thus the idea was slowly borne in on him: going near a man-den is sure to bring trouble. Thenceforth he sought his prey in the woods or on the plains. He one day found the man scent that enraged him the day he lost his "Silver-brown." He took the trail, and passing in silence incredible for such a bulk, he threaded chaparral and manzanita on and down through tulé-beds till the level plain was reached. The scent led on, was fresher now. Far out were white specks—moving things. They meant nothing to Gringo, for he had never smelt wild geese, had scarcely seen them, but the trail he was hunting went on. He swiftly followed till the tulé ahead rustled gently, and the scent was *body scent*. A ponderous rush, a single blow—and the goose-hunt was ended ere well begun, and Faco's sheep became the brother's heritage.

THE CATARACT

Just as fads will for a time sway human life, so crazes may run through all animals of a given kind. This was the year when a beef-eating craze seemed to possess every able-bodied Grizzly of the Sierras. They had long been known as a root-eating, berry-picking, inoffensive race when let alone, but now they seemed to descend on the cattle-range in a body and make their diet wholly of flesh.

One cattle outfit after another was attacked, and the whole country seemed divided up among Bears of incredible size, cunning, and destructiveness. The cattlemen offered bounties—good bounties, growing bounties, very large bounties at last—but still the Bears kept on. Very few were killed, and it became a kind of rude jest to call each section of the range, not by the cattle brand, but by the Grizzly that was quartered on its stock.

Wonderful tales were told of these various Bears of the new breed. The swiftest was Reelfoot, the Placerville cattle-killer that could charge from a thicket thirty yards away and certainly catch a steer before it could turn and run, and that could even catch ponies in the open when they were poor. The most cunning of all was Brin, the Mokelumne Grizzly that killed by preference blooded stock, would pick out a Merino ram or a white-faced Hereford from among fifty grades; that killed a new beef every night; that never again returned to it, or gave the chance for traps or poisoning.

The Pegtrack Grizzly of Feather River was rarely seen by any. He was enveloped in mysterious terror. He moved and killed by night. Pigs were his favorite food, and he had also killed a number of men.

But Pedro's Grizzly was the most marvelous. "Hassayampa," as the sheep-herder was dubbed, came one night to Kellyan's hut.

"I tell you he's still dere. He has keel me a t'ousand sheep. You telled me you keel heem; you haff not. He is beegare as dat tree. He eat only sheep—much sheep. I tell you he ees Gringo devil—he ees devil Bear. I haff three cows, two fat, one theen. He catch and keel de fat; de lean run off. He roll een dust—make great dust. Cow come for see what make dust; he catch her an' keel. My fader got bees. De devil Bear chaw pine; I know he by hees broke toof. He gum hees face and nose wit' pine gum so bees no sting, then eat all bees. He devil all time. He get much rotten manzanita and eat till drunk—locoed—then go crazy and keel sheep just for fun. He get beeg bull by nose and drag like rat for fun. He keel cow, sheep, and keel Faco, too, for fun. He devil. You promise me you keel heem; you nevaire keel."

This is a condensation of Pedro's excited account.

And there was yet one more—the big Bear that owned the range from the Stanislaus to the Merced, the "Monarch of the Range" he had been styled. He was believed—yes known to be—the biggest Bear alive, a creature of supernatural intelligence. He killed cows for food, and scattered sheep or conquered bulls for pleasure. It was even said that the appearance of an unusually big bull anywhere was a guaranty that Monarch would be there for the joy of combat with a worthy foe. A destroyer of cattle, sheep, pigs and horses, and yet a creature known only by his track. He was never seen, and his nightly raids seemed planned with consummate skill to avoid all kinds of snares.

The cattlemen clubbed together and offered an enormous bounty for every Grizzly killed in the range. Bear-trappers came and caught some Bears, Brown and Cinnamon, but the cattle-killing went on. They set out better traps of massive steel and iron bars, and at length they caught a killer, the Mokelumne Grizzly; yes, and read in the dust how he had come at last and made the fateful step; but steel will break and iron will bend. The great Bear-trail was there to tell the tale: for a while he had raged and chafed at the hard black reptile biting into his paw; then, seeking a boulder, he had released the paw by smashing the trap to pieces on it. Thenceforth each year he grew more cunning, huge, and destructive.

Kellyan and Bonamy came down from the mountains now, tempted by the offered rewards. They saw the huge tracks; they learned that cattle were not killed in all places at once. They studied and

hunted. They got at length in the dust the full impressions of the feet of the various monsters in regions wide apart, and they saw that all the cattle were killed in the same way—their muzzles torn, their necks broken; and last, the marks on the trees where the Bears had reared and rubbed, then scored them with a broken tusk, the same all through the wide range; and Kellyan told them with calm certainty: "Pedro's Gringo, Old Pegtrack, the Placerville Grizzly, and the Monarch of the Range *are one and the same Bear.*"

The little man from the mountains and the big man from the hills set about the task of hunting him down with an intensity of purpose which, like the river that is dammed, grew more fierce from being balked.

All manner of traps had failed for him. Steel traps he could smash, no log trap was strong enough to hold this furry elephant; he would not come to a bait; he never fed twice from the same kill.

Two reckless boys once trailed him to a rocky glen. The horses would not enter; the boys went in afoot, and were never seen again. The Mexicans held him in superstitious terror, believing that he could not be killed; and he passed another year in the cattle-land, known and feared now as the "Monarch of the Range," killing in the open by night, and retiring by day to his fastness in the near hills, where horsemen could not follow.

Bonamy had been called away; but all that summer, and winter, too,—for the Grizzly no longer "denned up,"—Kellyan rode and rode, each time too late or too soon to meet the Monarch. He was almost giving up, not in despair, but for lack of means, when a message came from a rich man, a city journalist, offering to multiply the reward by ten if, instead of killing the Monarch, he would bring him in alive.

Kellyan sent for his old partner, and when word came that the previous night three cows were killed in the familiar way near the Bell-Dash pasture, they spared neither horse nor man to reach the spot. A ten-hour ride by night meant worn-out horses, but the men were iron, and new horses with scarcely a minute's delay were brought them. Here were the newly killed beeves, there the mighty foot-prints with the scars that spelled his name. No hound could have tracked him better than Kellyan did. Five miles away from the foot of the hills was an impenetrable thicket of chaparral. The great tracks went in, did not come out, so Bonamy sat sentinel while Kellyan rode back with the news. "Saddle up the best we got!" was the order. Rifles were taken down and cartridge-belts being swung when Kellyan called a halt.

"Say, boys, we've got him safe enough. He won't try to leave the chaparral till night. If we shoot him we get the cattlemen's bounty; if we take him alive—an' it's easy in the open—we get the newspaper bounty, ten times as big. Let's leave all guns behind; lariats are enough."

"Why not have the guns along to be handy?"

"'Cause I know the crowd too well; they could n't resist the chance to let him have it; so no guns at all. It's ten to one on the riata."

Nevertheless three of them brought their heavy revolvers. Seven gallant riders on seven fine horses, they rode out that day to meet the Monarch of the Range. He was still in the thicket, for it was yet morning. They threw stones in and shouted to drive him out, without effect,

till the noon breeze of the plains arose—the down-current of air from the hills. Then they fired the grass in several places, and it sent a rolling sheet of flame and smoke into the thicket. There was a crackling louder than the fire, a smashing of brush, and from the farther side out hurled the Monarch Bear, the Gringo, Grizzly Jack. Horsemen were all about him now, armed not with guns but with the rawhide snakes whose loops in air spell bonds or death. The men were calm, but the horses were snorting and plunging in fear. This way and that the Grizzly looked up at the horsemen—a little bit; scarcely up at the horses; then turning without haste, he strode toward the friendly hills.

"Look out, now, Bill! Manuel! It's up to you."

Oh, noble horses, nervy men! oh, grand of Grizzly, how I see you now! Cattle-keepers and cattle-killer face to face!.

Three riders of the range that horse had never thrown were sailing, swooping, like falcons; their lariats swung, sang—sang higher—and Monarch, much perplexed, but scarcely angered yet, rose to his hind legs, then from his towering height looked down on horse and man. If, as they say, the vanquished prowess goes into the victor, then surely in that mighty chest, those arms like necks of bulls, was the power of the thousand cattle he had downed in fight.

"Caramba! what a Bear! Pedro was not so far astray."

"Sing—sing—sing!" the lariats flew. "Swish—pat!" one, two, three, they fell. These were not men to miss. Three ropes, three horses, leaping away to bear on the great beast's neck. But swifter than thought the supple paws went up. The ropes were slipped, and the spurred cow-

ponies, ready for the shock, went, shockless, bounding—loose ropes trailing afar.

"Hi—Ha! Ho—Lan! Head him!" as the Grizzly, liking not the unequal fight, made for the hills. But a deft Mexican in silver gear sent his hide riata whistling, then haunched his horse as the certain coil sank in the Grizzly's hock, and checked the Monarch with a heavy jar. Uttering one great snort of rage, he turned; his huge jaws crossed the rope, back nearly to his ears it went, and he ground it as a dog might grind a twig, so the straining pony bounded free.

Round and round him now the riders swooped, waiting their chance. More than once his neck was caught, but he slipped the noose as though it were all play. Again he was caught by a foot and wrenched, almost thrown, by the weight of two strong steeds, and now he foamed in rage. Memories of olden days, or more likely the habit of olden days, came on him—days when he learned to strike the yelping pack that dodged his blows. He was far from the burnt thicket, but a single bush was near, and setting his broad back to that, he waited for the circling foe. Nearer and nearer they urged the frightened steeds, and Monarch watched—waited, as of old, for the dogs till they were almost touching each other, then he sprang like an avalanche of rock. What can elude a Grizzly's dash? The earth shivered as he launched himself, and trembled when he struck. Three men, three horses, in each other's way. The dust was thick; they only knew he struck—struck—struck! The horses never rose.

"Santa Maria!" came a cry of death, and hovering riders dashed to draw the Bear away. Three horses dead, one man dead, one nearly so, and only one escaped.

"Crack! crack! crack!" went the pistols now as the Bear went rock-

ing his huge form in rapid charge for the friendly hills; and the four
riders, urged by Kellyan, followed fast. They passed him, wheeled,
faced him. The pistols had wounded him in many places.

"Don't shoot—don't shoot, but tire him out," the hunter urged.

"Tire him out? Look at Carlos and Manuel back there. How many
minutes will it be before the rest are down with them?" So the infuriat-
ing pistols popped till all their shots were gone, and Monarch foamed
with slobbering jaws of rage.

"Keep on! keep cool," cried Kellyan.

His lariat flew as the cattle-killing paw lifted for an instant. The
lasso bound his wrist. "Sing! Sing!" went two, and caught him by the neck.
A bull with his great club-foot in a noose is surely caught, but the

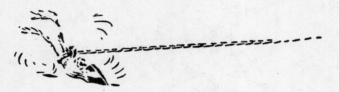

Grizzly raised his supple, hand-like, tapering paw and gave one jerk
that freed it. Now the two on his neck were tight; he could not slip
them. The horses at the ends—they were dragging, choking him; men
were shouting, hovering, watching for a new chance, when Monarch,
firmly planting both paws, braced, bent those mighty shoulders, and,
spite of shortening breath, leaned back on those two ropes as Samson
did on pillars of the house of Baal, and straining horses with their riders
were dragged forward more and more, long grooves being plowed
behind; dragging them, he backed faster and faster still. His eyes were
starting, his tongue lolling out.

"Keep on! hold tight!" was the cry, till the ropers swung together,
the better to resist; and Monarch, big and strong with frenzied hate,
seeing now his turn, sprang forward like a shot. The horses leaped and
escaped—almost; the last was one small inch too slow. The awful paw
with jags of steel just grazed his flank. How slight it sounds! But what
it really means is better not writ down.

The riders had slipped their ropes in fear, and the Monarch, rumbling, snorting, bounding, trailed them to the hills, there to bite them off
in peace, while the remnant of the gallant crew went, sadly muttering,
back.

Bitter words went round. Kellyan was cursed.

"His fault. Why didn't we have the guns?"

"We were all in it," was the answer, and more hard words, till
Kellyan flushed, forgot his calm, and drew a pistol hitherto concealed,
and the other "took it back."

Rumbling and snorting, he made for the friendly hills

THE FOAMING FLOOD

"What is next, Lan?" said Lou, as they sat dispirited by the fire that night.

Kellyan was silent for a time, then said slowly and earnestly, with a gleam in his eye: "Lou, that 's the greatest Bear alive. When I seen him set up there like a butte and swat horses like they was flies, I jest loved him. He's the greatest thing God has turned loose in these yer hills. Before to-day, I sure wanted to get him; now, Lou, I'm a-going to get him, an' get him alive, if it takes all my natural days. I think I kin do it alone, but I know I kin do it with you," and deep in Kellyan's eyes there glowed a little spark of something not yet rightly named.

They were camped in the hills, being no longer welcome at the ranch; the ranchers thought their price too high. Some even decided

that the Monarch, being a terror to sheep, was not an undesirable neighbor. The cattle bounty was withdrawn, but the newspaper bounty was not.

"I want you to bring in that Bear," was the brief but pregnant message from the rich newsman when he heard of the fight with the riders.

"How are you going about it, Lan?"

Every bridge has its rotten plank, every fence its flimsy rail, every great one his weakness, and Kellyan, as he pondered, knew how mad it was to meet this one of brawn with mere brute force.

"Steel traps are no good; he smashes them. Lariats won't do, and he knows all about log traps. But I have a scheme. First, we must follow him up and learn his range. I reckon that'll take three months."

So the two kept on. They took up that Bear-trail next day; they found the lariats chewed off. They followed day after day. They learned what they could from rancher and sheep-herder, and much more was told them than they could believe.

Three months, Lan said, but it took six months to carry out his plan; meanwhile Monarch killed and killed.

In each section of his range they made one or two cage- or pen-traps of bolted logs. At the back end of each they put a small grating of heavy steel bars. The door was carefully made and fitted into grooves. It was of double plank, with tar-paper between to make it surely light-tight. It was sheeted with iron on the inside, and when it dropped it went into an iron-bound groove in the floor.

They left these traps open and unset till they were grayed with age and smelt no more of man. Then the two hunters prepared for the final play. They baited all without setting them—baited them with honey, the lure that Monarch never had refused—and when at length they found the honey baits were gone, they came where he now was taking toll and laid the long-planned snare. Every trap was set, and baited as before with a mass of honey—but *honey now mixed with a potent sleeping draft.*

LANDLOCKED

That night the great Bear left his lair, one of his many lairs, and, cured of all his wounds, rejoicing in the fullness of his mighty strength, he strode toward the plains. His nose, ever alert, reported—sheep, a deer, a grouse; men—more sheep, some cows, and some calves; a bull—fighting bull—and Monarch wheeled in big, rude, Bearish joy at the coming battle brunt; but as he hugely hulked from hill to hill a different message came, so soft and low, so different from the smell of beefish brutes, one might well wonder he could sense it, but like a tiny ringing bell when thunder booms it came, and Monarch wheeled at once. Oh, it cast a potent spell! It stood for something very near to ecstasy with him, and down the hill and through the pines he went, on and on faster yet, abandoned to its sorcery. Here to its home he traced it, a long, low cavern. He had seen such many times before, had been held in them more than once, but had learned to spurn them. For weeks he had been robbing them of their treasures, and its odor, like a calling voice, was still his guide. Into the cavern he passed and it reeked with the smell of joy. There was the luscious mass, and Monarch, with all caution lulled now, licked and licked, then seized to tear the bag for more, when down went the door with a low "bang!" The Monarch started, but all was still and there was no smell of danger. He had forced such doors before. His palate craved the honey still, and he licked and licked, greedily at first, then calmly, then slowly, then drowsily—then at last stopped. His eyes were closing, and he sank slowly down on the earth and slept a heavy sleep.

Calm, but white-faced, were they—the men—when in the dawn they came. There were the huge scarred tracks in-leading; there was the door down; there dimly they could see a mass of fur that filled the pen, that heaved in deepest sleep.

Strong ropes, strong chains and bands of steel were at hand, with chloroform, lest he should revive too soon. Through holes in the roof with infinite toil they chained him, bound him—his paws to his neck, his neck and breast and hind legs to a bolted beam. Then raising the door, they dragged him out, not with horses—none would go near—but with a windlass to a tree; and fearing the sleep of death, they let him now revive.

Chained and double chained, frenzied, foaming, and impotent, what words can tell the state of the fallen Monarch? They put him on a sled, and six horses with a long chain drew it by stages to the plain, to the railway. They fed him enough to save his life. A great steam-derrick lifted Bear and beam and chain on to a flat-car, a tarpaulin was spread above his helpless form; the engine puffed, pulled out; and the Grizzly King was gone from his ancient hills.

So they brought him to the great city, the Monarch born, in chains. They put him in a cage not merely strong enough for a lion, but thrice as strong, and once a rope gave way as the huge one strained his bonds. "He is loose," went the cry, and an army of onlookers and keepers fled; only the small man with the calm eye and the big man of the hills were stanch, so the Monarch was still held.

Free in the cage, he swung round, looked this way and that, then heaved his powers against the triple angling steel and wrenched the cage so not a part of it was square. In time he clearly would break out. They dragged the prisoner to another that an elephant could not break down, but it stood on the ground, and in an hour the great beast had a cavern into the earth and was sinking out of sight, till a stream of water sent after him filled the hole and forced him again to view. They moved him to a new cage made for him since he came—a hard rock floor, great bars of nearly two-inch steel that reached up nine feet and then projected in for five. The Monarch wheeled once around, then, rearing, raised his ponderous bulk, wrenched those bars, unbreakable, and bent and turned them in their sockets with one heave till the five-foot spears were pointed out, and then sprang to climb. Nothing but spikes and blazing brands in a dozen ruthless hands could hold him back. The keepers watched him night and day till a stronger cage was made, impregnable with a steel above and rocks below.

The Untamed One passed swiftly around, tried every bar, examined every corner, sought for a crack in the rocky floor, and found at last the place where was a six-inch timber beam—the only piece of wood in its frame. It was sheathed in iron, but exposed for an inch its whole length. One claw could reach the wood, and here he lay on his side and raked—raked all day till a great pile of shavings was lying by it and the beam sawn in two; but the cross-bolts remained, and when Monarch put his vast shoulder to the place it yielded not a whit. That was his last hope; now it was gone; and the huge Bear sank down in the cage with his nose in his paws and sobbed—long, heavy sobs, animal sounds indeed, but telling just as truly as in man of the broken spirit—the hope and the life gone out. The keepers came with food at the appointed time, but the Bear moved not. They set it down, but in the morning it was still untouched. The Bear was lying as before, his ponderous form in the pose he had first taken. The sobbing was replaced by a low moan at intervals.

Two days went by. The food, untouched, was corrupting in the sun. The third day, and Monarch still lay on his breast, his huge muzzle under his huger paw. His eyes were hidden; only a slight heaving of his broad chest was now seen.

"He is dying," said one keeper. "He can't live overnight."

"Send for Kellyan," said another.

So Kellyan came, slight and thin. There was the beast that he had chained, pining, dying. He had sobbed his life out in his last hope's death, and a thrill of pity came over the hunter, for men of grit and power love grit and power. He put his arm through the cage bars and

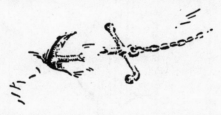

stroked him, but Monarch made no sign. His body was cold. At length a little moan was sign of life, and Kellyan said, "Here, let me go in to him."

"You are mad," said the keepers, and they would not open the cage. But Kellyan persisted till they put in a cross-grating in front of the Bear. Then, with this between, he approached. His hand was on the shaggy head, but Monarch lay as before. The hunter stroked his victim and spoke to him. His hand went to the big round ears, small above the head. They were rough to his touch. He looked again, then started. What! is it true? Yes, the stranger's tale was true, for both ears were pierced with a round hole—one torn large—and Kellyan knew that once again he had met his little Jack.

"Why, Jacky, I did n't know it was you. I never would have done it if I had known it was you. Jacky, old pard, don't you know me?"

But Jack stirred not, and Kellyan got up quickly. Back to the hotel he flew; there he put on his hunter's suit, smoky and smelling of pine gum and grease, and returned with a mass of honeycomb to reënter the cage.

"Jacky, Jacky!" he cried, "honey, honey!" and he held the tempting comb before him. But Monarch lay as one dead now.

"Jacky, Jacky! don't you know me?" He dropped the honey and laid his hands on the great muzzle.

The voice was forgotten. The old-time invitation, "Honey, Jacky— honey," had lost its power, but the *smell* of the honey, the coat, the hands that he had fondled, had together a hidden potency.

There is a time when the dying of our race forget their life, but clearly remember the scenes of childhood; these only are real and return with master power. And why not with a Bear? The power of scent was there to call them back again, and Jacky, the Grizzly Monarch, raised his head a liitle—just a little; the eyes were nearly closed, but the big brown nose was jerked up feebly two or three times—the sign of interest that Jacky used to give in days of old. Now it was Kellyan that broke down even as the Bear had done.

"I did n't know it was you, Jacky, or I never would have done it. Oh, Jacky, forgive me!" He rose and fled from the cage.

The keepers were there. They scarcely understood the scene, but one of them, acting on the hint, pushed the honeycomb nearer and cried, "Honey, Jacky—honey!"

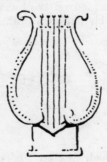

Filled by despair, he had lain down to die, but here was a new-born hope, not clear, not exact as words might put it, but his conqueror had shown himself a friend; this seemed a new hope, and the keeper, taking up the old call, "Honey, Jacky—honey!" pushed the comb till it touched his muzzle. The smell was wafted to his sense, its message reached his brain; hope honored, it must wake response. The great tongue licked the comb, appetite revived, and thus in newborn Hope began the chapter of his gloom.

Skilful keepers were there with plans to meet the Monarch's every want. Delicate foods were offered and every shift was tried to tempt him back to strength and prison life.

He ate and—lived.

And still he lives, but pacing—pacing—pacing—you may see him, scanning not the crowds, but something beyond the crowds, breaking down at times into petulant rages, but recovering anon his ponderous dignity, looking—waiting—watching—held ever by that Hope, that unknown Hope, that came. Kellyan has been to him since, but Monarch knows him not. Over his head, beyond him, was the great Bear's gaze, far away toward Tallac or far away on the sea, we knowing not which or why, but pacing—pacing—pacing—held like the storied Wandering One to a life of ceaseless journey—a journey aimless, endless, and sad.

The wound-spots long ago have left his shaggy coat, but the earmarks still are there, the ponderous strength, the elephantine dignity. His eyes are dull,—never were bright,—but they seem not vacant, and most often fixed on the Golden Gate where the river seeks the sea.

The river, born in high Sierra's flank, that lived and rolled and grew, through mountain pines, o'erleaping man-made barriers, then to reach with growing power the plains and bring its mighty flood at last to the Bay of Bays, a prisoner there to lie, the prisoner of the Golden Gate, seeking forever Freedom's Blue, seeking and raging—raging and seeking —back and forth, forever—in vain.

Monarch